VOYAGER IN TIME AND SPACE

The Life of John Couch Adams
Cambridge Astronomer

St. John's College, Cambridge portrait of John Couch Adams. Reproduced by permission of the Master and Fellows of St. John's College, Cambridge.

VOYAGER IN TIME AND SPACE

The Life of John Couch Adams

Cambridge Astronomer

H. M. Harrison

The Book Guild Ltd
Sussex, England

"After all I have only been like a little child, picking up a few pebbles on the seashore of the great ocean of Truth."
– Isaac Newton, 1642–1727

The Book Guild Ltd.
25 High Street,
Lewes, Sussex

First published 1994

Set in Palatino
Typesetting by Acorn Bookwork, Salisbury

Printed in Great Britain by
Antony Rowe Ltd.
Chippenham, Wiltshire.

A catalogue record for this book is available from the British Library

ISBN 0 86332 918 7

CONTENTS

PREFACE

Professor W. M. Smart, M.A., D.Sc., Regius Professor of Astronomy in the University of Glasgow, in his Addresses in August 1947, to the Royal Astronomical Society, entitled 'John Couch Adams, and the Discovery of Neptune' on the occasion of the Centenary Celebrations for the Discovery of Neptune, stated:

> As you are no doubt aware, a full-length biography of Adams has never been written; many of you, however, will be familiar with the excellent memoir of Adams by Dr. J. W. L. Glaisher, forming the Introduction to Adams's *Collected Scientific Papers*, published in two volumes (edited by Professor W. Grylls Adams, and Professor R. A. Sampson) by the Cambridge University Press in 1896 and 1900.
>
> Adams's letters, papers and diaries were carefully preserved and the late Sir Donald MacAlister Bart. – once a pupil, and later a close personal friend of Adams – undertook to transform the mass of ancient papers into a living biography of one of Cambridge's most famous sons. Before his death in 1892 Adams stipulated that his biography should be held back for a few years until the last vestiges of controversy had disappeared. So when MacAlister was appointed Principal of Glasgow

> University in 1907 the Adams' papers migrated with him across the Tweed. Unfortunately, the new Principal's multifarious duties allowed him little leisure for his pious task and, on his retiral to Cambridge in 1929, the Adams' papers crossed the border once more. As the first John Couch Adams Astronomer of the University of Cambridge, I was entrusted by Lady MacAlister on her husband's death in 1934 with the custody of the papers, which, on my appointment in 1937 to the Regius Chair of Astronomy in the University of Glasgow, crossed the border for the third time. My new duties and the almost immediate incidence of the World War prevented me, until recently, from making a systematic study of the papers. A scientist has rarely the opportunity and the privilege of seeing, in the day-to-day records of the past, the pages of history being unfolded; however imperfect the sequel may be I feel I must place on record the enthralling interest which the study of the papers had for me.

Since these words were written the Adams' papers and diaries once more crossed the Tweed to be lodged in the safe keeping of St. John's College, Cambridge, on the death of Professor Smart, and the biography of John Couch Adams still remains unwritten.

Dr. J. W. L. Glaisher in his Obituary Notice on Adams in *The Observatory*, No. 187, April 1892 (also in the monthly notices of the Royal Astronomical Society, Vol. LIII No. 4) shows the status of Adams as an Astronomer in his opening paragraph of the Monthly Notices, which acts as a prelude to the Obituary.

> By the death of Professor Adams, England has lost the greatest mathematical astronomer she has ever produced, Newton alone excepted. The analytical mechanism required to trace the consequences of

the Newtonian law has been devised and developed almost exclusively upon the Continent, and Newton's own countrymen have had but little share in carrying on his work. The names of Clairaut, Euler, Lagrange, Laplace, and Gauss, follow in natural sequence upon that of their great master; but till we come to Adams, there is no Englishman who can claim a place in the illustrious succession. His discovery of the planet Neptune by mathematical calculations, his memoir upon the secular acceleration of the Moon's mean motion, and his determination of the orbit of the November meteors, already take their place in the history of astronomy. He was a consummate master of all the refined and delicate methods with which the genius of the greatest mathematicians has endowed the subject of celestial mechanics, as well as of the detailed processes by which theory and observation are connected. No mathematician of our time has shown greater power or versatility in the treatment of the many difficult problems presented to us by the lunar and planetary theories, and it may safely be said that no mathematical astronomer was ever more sure of arriving at accurate conclusions by methods of such complication and difficulty.

The following chapters are an attempt at the first 'full-length biography' of this eminent astronomer, who died just over a hundred years ago, who voyaged in Time and Space, but who was also a very real human being, living through most of the nineteenth century (1819–92) in Victorian England. I have had access to his diaries and papers at St. John's College, Cambridge, and to his library, which he bequeathed to the University of Cambridge Library, as well as family letters; and I am familiar with his background in Cornwall and Cambridge as I am privileged as a great-great-niece to know and to belong to both areas of his life. I would like to dedicate this biography to my grandmother, Maria French Adams (1849–1907) who was his eldest niece, the eldest daughter of his brother Thomas.

H. M. Harrison, Cambridge
February 1993

ACKNOWLEDGEMENTS

I would like to acknowledge the help and encouragement given to me by the Librarian (Mr Guy Lee) of St John's College, and his friendly staff, especially Mr N. C. Buck, during the time I spent reading through the diaries and letters stored in the College Library in the innumerable boxes, which constantly crossed the Scottish border when in the possession of Professor Smart and Sir Donald MacAlister, during their abortive attempts at writing the official biography of John Couch Adams. I am also grateful to Ethel Roseveare of Saltash, a great-niece of Professor Adams, for the loan of many family letters, and for her knowledge of the Adams family; also to Dr Nigel Roseveare, son of Tom Roseveare and great-grandson of Mary Ann Adams, the younger sister of John Couch Adams, who lent me the R.A.S. *Bulletin*, Vol VII, 13 November 1846, containing the controversial correspondence referring to the disagreements over the discovery of Neptune; to Sir Harold and Lady Jeffreys, of Cambridge University, for drawing my attention to Dr Allen Chapman's lecture in Cambridge in 1979 based on his researches on Airy, and to Mr P. N. Harvey of Cambridge for lending me *The Strand Magazine* of August 1896. Finally I am most grateful to Cheryl Brook for her friendly co-operation and courageous attack on typing the book, and also to Jackie Wheddon (née Pond) for her equally courageous attack on the original preliminary script, and to Arthur Valle for discovering that Bray, Co. Wicklow, was where John Couch Adams was married, and to Frank Wright of Therfield, for checking calculations of RAS Bulletin Vol VII 13 Nov 1846.

1

Early Days: 1819–39

John Couch Adams was a modest man. This was part of his charm, and at times his misfortune. He soared above his fellow men in the realms of mathematical thought, and has been regarded as the greatest successor to Newton in his power of mathematical calculation. In fact, it was John Couch Adams who was entrusted with editing the works of Newton, when they were bequeathed to the University of Cambridge in the nineteenth century. Yet Adams's reserved nature and inability at times to reveal his genius fully when necessary, nearly lost him the recognition of his discovery of the planet Neptune, and as a result England would not have shared with France the fame of discovering the existence of one more planet in space. His innate modesty might have prevented the name of Adams gaining national recognition among the astronomers of his day. In fact his name even yet tends to get forgotten. This is an attempt to show some of his achievements as an astronomer, and to retrieve from oblivion something of the man, and his family, and his times. It traces his history from a quiet, somewhat remote, Cornish farm to the academic world of Cambridge and many realms beyond.

The Adams family of Cornwall were basically tenant farmers. It was from this background that John Couch Adams, the astronomer and discoverer of the planet Neptune, sprang. Their lives spanned the whole of the Victorian age. In a remote Cornish farm, Lidcott, on Laneast Down, seven children were born: four boys and three girls. Some rarely left the area all their lives while others scattered. The eldest, John Couch, eventually spent most of his life in Cambridge, in the realms of mathematics and outer space, where by his calculations he discovered the planet Neptune when he was twenty-seven years old. The second son, Thomas, explored spiritual regions as a missionary in the South Seas translating the Bible into Tonganuese, quelling tribal wars in the southern hemisphere, and bringing up a family of eight among the natives of Tonga and other Friendly Islands, whose inhabitants were only one generation removed from cannibals; he arrived there only seventy years after Captain Cook, in similar sailing ships. The third son, George, remained a farmer on Celtic soil. The youngest son, William Grylls, eventually became a Professor of Natural Sciences at King's College, London University, after an early teaching post at Marlborough College. The elder girl, Grace Couch, never married, but was an invaluable aunt for the next generation of motherless children. Elizabeth Grylls, the second girl, died when sixteen years of age; and the youngest girl, Mary Ann, married a Cornish farmer Henry Roseveare, and was the mother of six children; two of her daughters went to Newnham College, Cambridge, and of the three sons one became a headmaster and two became Civil Servants in Whitehall. The descendants from the family born at Lidcott Farm in early Victorian times have multiplied and spread their influence in many directions and professions throughout the world – some developed their mathematical potential, some the educational and administrative potential, and some the navigating and exploring of genes, which had led John Couch to explore the ocean of truth in outer space in the 1840s, as his brother did in the South Seas.

Though in many ways they were creatures of their time, there is a sense in which the members of the Adams family echo the universal quest of the human spirit to reach beyond itself to something larger than life, the great unknown of human knowledge and achievement. As with Ulysses when recreated once more by Tennyson in his poem of the same name, they were always:

> yearning in desire
> To follow knowledge like a sinking star
> Beyond the utmost bound of human thought.

The Celtic clan of Adams were also a part of all that they had met.

> Yet all experience is an arch wherethro' Gleams that untravell'd world, whose margin fades For ever and forever when I move, as Ulysses discovered.

Kierkegaard said, 'History is lived forward, but is understood backward'. So it is with the backward look we begin, and by exploring the past we realize that we can better interpret the present, when echoes from the past reverberate in present events. Most new discoveries emerge from previous research. So it was with John Couch Adams when exploring planets. Though much of his life and work are now forgotten in the twentieth century, he would bear no grudge as Achilles of old had done: 'What are my deeds forgot?' His was a modest and retiring nature – a characteristic that nearly lost him the race for Neptune because for him 'the Ocean of Truth', as Newton called it, was of greater importance than the achievements of any single human being. It was Adams who was eventually to edit the works of Newton. This was the world in which he was at home, and which had meaning; an area of far greater importance than any recorded achievements of his own.

The first half of the nineteenth century was a time of enlightenment in spite of the wars and the lack of freedom that predominated for many. In the year after Thomas Adams Senior's birth the Bastille fell in France giving new hopes for Liberty, Equality and Fraternity. More tightening of the despotic noose was to follow before further revolutions succeeded in producing those freedoms. England was at war with France and Napoleon was the terror of Europe until 1815, when Wellington's victory at Waterloo removed the menace. There had been fears of invasion along the English coast for some years and even babies had been punished by the threat of 'Boney' getting them. Nor was all peaceful in England, as Luddite riots broke out between 1811–18 as the Industrial Revolution was underway and machines were reducing manpower. These riots were mainly in the Midlands and Yorkshire, and Cornwall was only affected by the Agrarian Revolution in its use of land and stock-breeding.

Apart from wars and riots in the early decades of the century, new ideas were emerging. Tabitha Knill Grylls was born in 1796, two years before Wordsworth and Coleridge's 'Lyrical Ballads' were published in an attempt to bring back poetry to the people, and when 'emotion was to be recollected in Tranquility'. The Age of Romanticism had once more dawned to supersede the eighteenth-century Age of Reason. The slave trade was rampant until 1807 when Wilberforce, after twenty years of campaigning, eventually got his Bill through Parliament to emancipate the slaves. The Reform Bill of 1832 began a Reform of Parliament, though much more was to be achieved later in the fulfilment of a wider-based democracy. Nelson had died at Trafalgar in 1805, but the naval tradition was established, and England prided herself on her sea-going tradition dating from Elizabethan times – colonisation was a creed, and white domination a belief. The English took up the white man's burden as the

'Saviours of the Heathen', and were becoming richer by trade as the 'master race'. Heaven and Hell were realities and men had to be saved from Hell. The nineteenth century saw the growth of the Missionary Societies.

John Couch Adams was born in 1819, Karl Marx in 1818. A different age dawned from 1820–60. The railway era was dawning from 1819 onwards, when George Stephenson laid down a short railway, having designed and successfully tried his locomotive in 1814. Transport speeded up, and man was no longer so dependent on the horse. An efficient network of railways had developed over England, Scotland and Wales by the end of the century, altering the face of the British Isles.

It was to be a great literary age, as well as of great scientific advance by the latter decades of the century. 'Bliss was it in that dawn to be alive' Wordsworth had sung in the *Prelude,* when writing about his early life at the time of the French Revolution in France. He was to change his mind later, though 1830 and 1848 were to come as years of Revolution, when ideas were sweeping through Europe and toppling kings. The writers of the day were formidable. Novels were long, some the result of serialization. Many revealed social conditions and problems of the day. Thackeray and Dickens were born in 1811 and 1812 respectively – eight and seven years before John Couch Adams, though Thackeray's *Vanity Fair* was published in 1848, two years after the discovery of the planet Neptune. The Brontës were almost identical in age with the Adams family, and similar in background to some extent, as the mother and aunt of the Brontës were Branwells of Cornwall, with a Wesleyan background. Charlotte was born 1816, Branwell 1817, Emily in 1818 and Anne in 1820. Their mother died in 1821, and Aunt Branwell was summoned from Cornwall to look after the young family in Haworth Parsonage, as Aunt Grace Couch Adams was summoned from Cornwall forty years later to look after Thomas Adams' motherless six on their return from the Friendly Islands to manses in Chippenham, Wigan and Newark from 1860 onwards. Keats was dead in 1821, Shelley in 1822, Blake in 1827, but they had spread their idealism, and had seen visions of beauty, truth, justice and social righteousness, as well as glimpses of Jerusalem built in 'England's green and pleasant land', in spite of the establishment expressed in the dark satanic mills. Tolstoy, Hardy and Chekhov were producing novels and plays by the end of the century – *War and Peace* came in the 1860s, Hardy's novels in the 1880s, as also Chekhov's plays. All works were more realistic and gloomy in ideas than those being produced when the century had begun. How much was this change due to industrial progress, social change, or the arrival of Darwin with his *Origin of Species* in 1859, when he managed to rock the boat of a faith which previously had made man the god-like master of his destiny and the superior of the species with no suspicions of his evolution from lower forms of life? Genesis had declared man a separate and greater creation than the beasts, and who was Darwin to suggest otherwise?

The Communist Manifesto of Karl Marx appeared in 1848 and his *Das Kapital* in 1867, which stressed the evils of capitalism – an evil that the working classes must unite to suppress if their individual status and liberty were to emerge in capitalist-dominated states. The class struggle had openly begun towards the end of Victoria's reign, fairly soon after Darwin's unsettling of former religious confidence. The arrival of Sigmund Freud, born in 1856, ushered in the brave new world of psychoanalysis, when man was enabled to know himself in a way hitherto unexplained to him. The Adams family members were probably unaffected by some of these new ideas, though John Couch when at Cambridge was invited to be president of the Cambridge Psychical Research Society in 1887, an office he refused, though remained an interested member of the Society which was exploring mesmerism and the world of spirits.

England in 1819, when John Couch was born, was recovering from the ravages of the Napoleonic Wars, as well as living through the aftermath of the Methodist revival. According to the historian Lecky, it was this revival that saved England from a Revolution such as the French suffered. John Wesley had died in 1791 at the age of ninety, after travelling the length and breadth of the British Isles proclaiming salvation for *all* – not merely the elect or the select few of the Calvinistic creed. Cornwall was a county where Methodism 'took', and the Adams family inherited the legacy. Marx and Freud passed them by. It was Methodism which was to take them from their 'quiet homes and first beginnings', to Cambridge and discoveries in the Universe, and to the South Seas and discoveries in the hearts of men. It was to turn their world upside down, and God coupled with the eternal search for truth, were to be an even more revolutionary force for them than Marxism was to be for others of their time; their religion provided their catharsis. It was to bring them joy and sorrow, but the fabric of their life maintained its texture whatever new ideas were rampant, though warp and weft at times were sorely stretched. The missionary brother, Thomas, was to teach the natives of Tonga how to calculate eclipses by mathematics from 1846–60. He had learnt the method from John Couch who, among other things, was also investigating the moon motions by means of mathematics. So knowledge spreads and grows by means of the human links exploring the depths of truth. Here the link was a family one, from a humble and remote home, near Laneast Down, Cornwall.

The ethos of the family can best be gathered from the following account written in 1892 by the third son George looking back on his early family memories. The beginning of it all is here; from this seed the plant grew and developed. George Adams, in his direct style, shows the early origins in the following account. While his elder brothers, John Couch and Thomas were exploring space and the South Seas respectively, and enlarging the bounds of mind and spirit of mankind, George remained faithful to the farming origins of the family, expressing through bodily toil on Cornish soil all his life, something of the wonders of the co-operation of the divine and the human when harnessed in harmony.

The Anglican and Wesleyan strand is a recurring fact in the Adams family. Starting as tenant farmers, some eventually graduating to yeomen farmers, they were hard-working, patriotic and pious. They inherited their world view from Laneast Down by way of their religion; as followers of Wesley the world became their parish. It was no narrow sectarian creed which governed the household, though spiritual disciplines were maintained. They were curious about life, knowledge and truth, but always under the auspices of the rule and law of love. At times, in spite of shrewd commonsense and balanced judgement, they seemed to be innocents at large and at the mercy of the cruel and the calculating. In their humility they trusted people and suffered for it; but grievances did not rankle and life was larger than disappointments.

THE ADAMS FAMILY: 'REMINISCENCES OF OUR FAMILY' BY GEORGE ADAMS 1892

My father's ancestors were farmers residing at Trespearne in the parish of Laneast, in which parish they took a leading part in the management of the parish business and in the parish vestry, where the affairs of the parish were settled. From Trespearne they removed to a farm at Tregeare in the parish of Egloskerry, adjoining the parish of Laneast, where they rented a farm under their former landlord Jasper Baron Esq., the Lord of the Manor. Mr. Baron took a lively interest in the spiritual welfare of his tenantry, and those that were under him, and appropriated a coach house in the village of Tregeare, which was enlarged and fitted up for a Wesleyan Chapel, which became a centre of Christian work in the village and neighbourhood, and where the gospel was faithfully preached. Mr. Baron attended those services with his tenants and workmen. In the village my father, Thomas Adams, grew up, and with an elder brother, William, when young, became members of the Wesleyan Society, and assisted in its services.

My father's brother, who became helpful in the services of the chapel, died a young man much beloved by those who knew him. His end was blessed. Thomas, my father, greatly missed him as did his family and the Wesleyan Society in the village. My mother's family, who were also farmers, resided, when my mother was born on the 24th August 1796 at Maraborough, in the parish of Stoke Climsland by Callington. My mother, Tabitha Knill Grylls, daughter of John and Elizabeth Grylls, when eight years of age had a painful, and most trying affliction, which settled in one of her legs just above the ankle. Her suffering was extreme, and a piece of bone over 4" long worked its way out of her leg. On one occasion when lanced the matter from the leg flew up to the covering on top of the bed. She, although so young, would attend to and dress the wound. When recovering from the illness she went on a visit to her uncle and aunt, John and Grace Couch, her father's sister, at Badharlick, in the parish of Egloskerry. They, from that time, took her as their adopted child, and she never after returned to her father's house to reside. She assisted the woman servant as she was able in the housework, and was companion for her aunt. When at Badharlick young Susan, the servant, was her only companion except when with her uncle and aunt. This servant married, and on her marriage Aunt Couch gave her a piece of land in the village, on which her husband, George Holman, built a cottage with a garden attached. After her marriage she still assisted with the housework, and my mother could visit her in her cottage. Her husband was a steady man, and became a leader in the services at Tregeare. Besides these my mother had no companions. She had but little intercourse with any of her own age. Her Uncle Couch gave her lessons, and taught her to read and write a little, with the first rules of Arithmetic. She was never sent to school, and her education was but little. While my mother was thus growing up her father and family removed from Stoke Climsland to a farm called Trehare in Davidstow for a short time and after this to Badharlick to the small farm, of which Aunt Couch was owner – Uncle and Aunt Couch and my mother living in the old house, or old mansion, and the family in the house hard by on the farm. This estate was given to Aunt Couch by Miss Trewbody (now called Ann Trewbody's Badharlick), and with whom Aunt Couch had lived for many years as a confidential servant and companion.

My mother's life was uneventful and quiet as she was growing up, mostly living with older people, and when young her Uncle Couch died.

It was a great comfort to my mother that now she had the company of her father and mother and family living so near in the farmhouse, where they continued to reside until after the death of her parents, and where my mother could often see them.

After the death of Uncle Couch my mother became more the companion of her aunt, and so all went on for some time when her aunt became desirous that she should marry my father, who lived at Tregeare, in the neighbourhood, was well-known to her, and Aunt Couch proposed, and was accepted. They were married on the 20th May 1818 (Rev. John Oliver Vicar at Egloskerry). My father's family in addition to the farm they held at Tregeare also for eight

Note: Ann Trewbody was born Saturday, 14th January 1709 about three o'clock am. Baptized Friday, February 3rd 1709–Died Tuesday, August 25th 1795. Buried Saturday, August 29th 10 am. So ends the family.
Note: John Couch Junior of Egloskerry died on Monday, November 13th half past eight in the morning, and was buried November 15th, 1815 at Egloskerry, aged 63 years 6 months and 12 days.
Note: In the handwriting of my mother April 16th, 1820, John Grylls departed this life one Sunday, about 10 o'clock in the morning aged 69 years and 9 months, buried Wednesday 19th at Egloskerry. Elizabeth Grylls, wife of John Grylls, died May 13th, 1833 aged 74 years (my mother's parents).

years before the marriage of my father farmed Lidcott, in Laneast. This farm was handed over to my father and mother, and they went there to reside. Aunt Couch also gave up her house at Badharlick, and went to reside with them, where she remained to the time of her death at the age of 91 years, having been blind for many years. On her decease she gave the estate of Badharlick to my mother, who had been as her adopted child during her life, and to her children after her. My father continued at Lidcott until his death 28th March 1859, aged 71 years. Buried at Tregeare. The following year the farm was given up, and my mother returned to her former home at Badharlick, after a residence at Lidcott of 42 years, where she spent a busy life in the cares of a large family, and a husband. Lidcott Farm is situated adjoining Laneast Down, a bleak open moor, from which eminence may be seen the sea from Boscastle to Hartland Point, with Lundy Island in the distance, the Dartmoor Hills, and all surrounding country. The farm was a plain one, and required hard work to make a living out of it, and when my father took it prices were high in consequence of the French War but in about a year after they had bought their stock prices greatly went down, and in a year in consequence of the peace was not worth much more than half what it cost, which was a great loss and trial when money was scarce.

My father was almost yearly at this time laid up with fever, and my mother had a trying time. Fortunately my father found some manganese slorodes on the farm, and took them to Capt. Prout, who, at once, took a mining set and found a rich mine of manganese, and in reward gave my father the team work on the mine at a fair price, which was most useful, and this continued for several years.

On the 5th June 1819	John Couch Adams was born
On the 28th April 1821	Thomas Adams was born
On the 5th November 1823	George Adams was born
On the 1st September 1828	Grace Couch Adams was born
On the 3rd November 1831	Elizabeth Grylls Adams was born

On the 16th February 1836	Wiliam Grylls Adams was born
On the 28th April 1839	Mary Ann Adams was born

As there was 5 years between the youngest of the three boys and a sister they were close companions for some time in all their childish play, and going to their earliest school at Laneast going over the Down.

My father was one of the leading members of the Society at Tregeare, where he took his family to worship, and we were all baptised there by the Wesleyan ministers. On the Feast Days of the Church, as Easter and Christmas, my father would attend the Parish Church, and occasionally on other times with his children and my mother, and assisted the clergyman in the parish as Church Warden, and took an active part in Parish business, but chiefly worshipped in the Chapel at Tregeare, where he was a Prayer leader, and assisted in conducting Prayer Meetings. My father's house was a House of Prayer and family worship, reading of the Scriptures with prayer was conducted mornings and evenings, with all the family and servants, and in his chamber prayed three times a day.

One of my earliest recollections was my brother John taking his stand in the stairs with my brother Thomas and I as audience, when he would give out a hymn from his little hymn book and sing, after which we knelt down in silent prayer, hands before our faces in worship. My mother's family were musical [Stoke Climsland was famous for Psalm-singing, as is noted in the Church Porch], and on her family coming to reside at Badharlick she and her brothers joined for a time the Church Choir at Egloskerry, which was a large one, and where musical instruments were used. Frequently Psalms and hymns were sung. My mother, who had a good voice, enjoyed this in her otherwise rather close confinement. In after years John and my brother William would ask her to sing those Old Psalms and Anthems and old tunes and write them from her mouth with all their parts, and thus get them reproduced for our happy Christmas parties in the holidays when my mother's family would come to us. In this way my brother John was delighted to join when home from school, and all occasions for years he and my dear mother would sing together constantly those old tunes.

My brother John's first school was in the village of Laneast with Mrs. Ann Dawe, a most kind and truly affectionate person, who kept a small school for young children in a farmhouse, her husband being hired for the owner of the estate, who also farmed it. She was always fond of her pupil, and my brother in after years would frequently visit her, and always greatly respected her as also her husband, John Dawe. The distance to school was about a mile and a half over the Laneast Down. Frequently Father would carry his boy on the pony a considerable part of the way. Later on a Mr. Sleep established a school of greater pretensions at Laneast, and there we three brothers went together when I was *very young*, and suppose was sent mostly to be out of the way. My mother's was a busy life with her family and the farm work and she could have no time for teaching, and my father's was a busy life working on the farm, and with small means and an increasing family, who was almost yearly laid up with fever, and sometimes a long illness which greatly added to my mother's care.

John continued at school with Mr. Sleep a considerable time and was a great favourite with his master and school fellows, and a leader in the games. He made great progress in his school work in Arithmetic, and began Algebra. In his arithmetic he was always most proficient, working both at school and at home and generally self-taught, working from the rules before being advanced to them by his master, and this continued through all his school course. He was pre-eminently self-taught in Mathematics, and only required books to enable him to understand the work.

Those days at school at Laneast were happy days. Frequently Aunt Couch would walk over Laneast Down with our dinners, and we would sit and eat them by the hedge with her. She was fond of her boys, as she would call them.

At other times we took our dinners with us, and spent the hour in play and games, in those *John would lead the way*. On one occasion my brother Thomas complained to mother that his shoulder was sore, she examined it, and found it burnt with the sun, said nothing as to the cause, but sent a note to the master, when the dinner hour came the boys went as usual to the river at Laneast Bridge to bathe, and shortly after Mr. Sleep, the master, appeared cane in hand. There was a general scamper to dress and run towards the school. John, who it was always considered was generally in favour with the master was equal to the occasion. When the run commenced from the river up the hill to the school, with the master after, he quietly knelt down on one knee to properly tie his shoes, was left behind and he and I quietly walked on to school. I was too young to enter into the water, or to run and this ended the going to the river for bathing, and the shoulders were never after burnt in this way. My brother John was always pleased to go to school. It was a delight to him, and he was always fond of books. He did not take interest in the farm or farm work. My mother was always firm in discipline, and required her children to obey but ruled pre-eminently by *love*. A word of hers was enough–a more loving, tender, and kind mother I believe there never was and all her children were most devoted to her, and united as a family. She would never allow a child to come to the farm and go away empty without something to eat, and all the farm servants would do whatever they could for her. She was not only respected but loved by all.

Father, whose chief work was the Bible; daily morning and evenings read to the family, and held family prayers, and regularly took us to worship as a united family at Chapel and Church. Our farm being situated away from any other dwelling we were mostly alone, and John would lead in our boyish games and play, both at school and at the farm. I remember well those happy days, and our childish play. John was our leader, and would always enter into our play heartily, as well as with his books, which occupied all his time. He was constantly at his books, and in his early years Old Moore's Almanack was to him a source of great delight. He always treasured these up. Mr. Sleep knew something of Algebra, and although so young John began it also, but was in this I believe almost self-taught. John was sent, after leaving this school at Laneast, to school, for a short time, at Callington, and while there lodged with a sister of my father's. It was but a short time, and was uneventful.

My father took John for a visit to Hatherleigh, in Devon, to see some friends, and while there met Mr. Pearse of Launceston, who was also on a visit to his friends the Pearses of Hatherleigh, who were also related to my father's family, and who had a son at school there who was doing algebra. The boys were set to work, and John distinguished himself. Our friend, Mr. Pearse of Launceston, asked my father to allow John to remain with him for a short time that he might be tested as to his ability by the school master there, and offered to bring him back to Launceston after a few days as my father had to return, and this was done. John again distinguished himself, and not only gave a proof of his proficiency beyond that of his rival Pearse, but the master also, who set an equation that he himself could not solve, but John did so, to the astonishment of his friends.

On Mr. Pearse returning with John to Launceston he saw my father, and told him what John had done and said: 'If he was my boy, I would sell my hat off my head rather than not send him to college.' Father and Mother from that time resolved to send John off to school, and he was sent to Devonport with a cousin of my mother's, the Rev. John Couch Grylls, I believe in 1831, being then about 12 years old. For a short time my brother lodged with my mother's sister, Mrs. Smith, for a year, or a little more, and went to school as a day scholar. On the cholera making its trouble ravages in Devonport in 1832 my father took John home until it had passed away, and on his again returning to school he went as a boarder with Mr. Grylls, where he continued for many years, the rest of his school life. Mr. Grylls moved his school from Devonport to Church House, Saltash, where he was Chaplain to the Corporation. He was elected an Alderman of the Borough and Mayor – (School at Saltash 1834–35). From Saltash he removed to Landulph 1835, and again to Devonport, and John continued with him as he was growing up. In addition to his work he helped somewhat in the school up to 1838. The journeys from school to home would be on the pony chiefly, and often have I walked as a lad to St. Mellion, or Carkell 20 miles to take back the horse, and John would ride as far as that, and then walk the remainder to Saltash (the luggage being sent on by Ham, a regrator from Trespearne, who took weekly farm produce to the school, and bring back letters or a message from John, and so he would return from school – the pony being taken on, and left for him, and I have been caught up by him sometimes when nearly home. The carrier Ham would travel through the night, and bring letters and empties weekly, or a message from John. Mr. Grylls gave up the school, and went to Australia in 1840. John worked in classics with Mr. Grylls, and did his mathematics chiefly from books, and partly assisted in the school. At this time he found the Mechanics Institute at Devonport a great advantage, where he could often get the books he wanted. On one occasion he took a mathematical work, and a gentleman noticing which book it was, said, 'I don't think, my lad, you will find that book much use to you.' It was just the book he wanted. In this he was self-taught. About the last vacation before leaving school he remained at Devonport for part of the holidays as private tutor to the two sons of Admiral Hornby, who were preparing for an examination. He had then a week at home at the beginning and end of his holidays. He came home from, and went to, St. Mellion on the pony, which was sent there to meet him, and walked home, and in the return to Devonport I walked to St. Mellion to take back the pony. I remember those journeys well, and the pleasure it gave to do anything for John. Thomas and I used to hand to him our little savings, which he would spend on books for us, and he would bring us little books as presents as his spare money would allow. Before leaving home he would be busy, and most careful in putting away in a drawer appropriate to him his papers that he had worked at while at home, with his small maps of the stars, in such nice order, and thus the time would slip by before he was ready to mount the pony for the journey. I have walked as far as Carkeel, 20 miles, within 2 miles of Saltash, and there waited for him to take home the pony, and Thomas would do this before I was able. It was an event in the family John going off to school, and we were, as a family greatly attached to each other.

On one occasion when John was leaving, I was a little fellow. I had in the morning to go into the fields, leading horses to the plough. I felt this terribly, not being able to stay and say goodbye at his going, and my heart was almost bursting. I rushed away, jumped on one of the plough horses, and could not say goodbye and show my tears at his going, and my heart was almost bursting. I was working just a mile from the house. Before John left he enquired 'Where is George?' My mother, who had noticed my grief in part at being sent to work, told him. He ran to the field where I was, to say goodbye before leaving, as a most kind and dear brother. I shall never forget that 'Goodbye George'. I thought it so good and kind of him. We all honoured our brother John, he was so clever as well as good. His schooldays with Mr. Grylls were comfortable, and he was in a great measure associated with the family, who were some of them about his age.

Mr. Grylls with his family going to Australia, my brother left school, and for a short time went as tutor to the sons of Mr. Foot at Pillaton in Linkinghorne, to teach them land surveying. Mr. Foot with his family were going to Australia, and John remained with them up to the time of their leaving. Now the question arose as to John's future course. *Should he go to college*, or what turn should he take. *This question had to be fully considered*. The costs would be heavy, and in case John took an ordinary degree, taking into account the position and means of the family could not be easily borne. The family he was then with were willing and anxious he should go with them, and Mrs. Foot said she would do for him what she would do for her own sons, and suggested that he would do well in Australia. I believe John was seriously considering the matter, rather inclined to go. He knew that there would be great difficulty from the resources of the farm to pay his college bills. Mr. Letherbridge, our landlord, did not look upon this outlay with favour, and said education was getting more prevalent, and not well paid. It was a time for grave deliberation. Mother and Father were most anxious that he should go to Cambridge, and the younger members of the family also joined in that desire. We all agreed that he must not go to Australia but to College. At that time I was sent with a message to him, and Mr. and Mrs. Foot, saying he must not go with them but that he should go to the University. I did not see John on that occasion, who had with the two sons and Miss Foot gone to a party at Launceston, but told Mrs. Foot, who was sorry at the decision that John was not going with them.

As it was now settled that John should go to Cambridge and the Rev. Mr. Cowlard, Vicar of Lamerton, who was a relation of Mr. Letherbirdge, having just taken a curate (Mr. Martyn, afterwards Dr. Martyn, vicar of St. Brecnard, Cornwall) who had just taken his degree at Cambridge, it was arranged that John should go with him for some months to prepare for his first examinations. Consequently he went to Lamerton, and the following October entered at St. John's College, Cambridge.

His journey to Cambridge was a most tiresome one. We, his family, went with him to see him on the coach, in the middle of the night on Laneast Down. Anxious prayers were offered up for his safety, and protection. He had never before gone so far as Exeter, and was a young traveller. To make sure that he should go on right he booked through the journey, and was sent on by a slow coach 'The Traveller'. It took him two days and a night or more to do the journey. On his arrival at St. John's College he went in for a scholarship examination, and won it. At the close of the examination the examiner said to him 'If you work, the highest honours are in your reach'. He did work and that statement was fulfilled. In his college from the beginning he took the 1st place, and in the end of his college course was Senior Wrangler, and 1st Smith's Prizeman. By taking an exhibition, and gaining prizes during his college course, and by using every economy his expenses were kept as moderate as could be, and all energy was used on the farm to raise money to pay his bills. This sometimes was difficult, but always done by the united family cheerfully. During the last year, and when taking his degree these expenses could not be met but by borrowing money, which was done. This, John, as soon as he was able, repaid, and also assisted in the education of the younger members of our family. While the last examination was going on at the University our anxiety was great, and the pleasure and delight in proportion when we knew the result. Father and Mother with my brother Thomas and I, who were working on the farm with all our family, and the neighbourhood rejoiced, and felt so proud of his great success. The news was brought to us on a Saturday afternoon. Mr. Letherbridge, our landlord, was at Launceston market. He returned an hour earlier than usual, and sent a message to the farm to inform the family of the result. He, on entering his yard on horseback took off his hat and shouted 'Adams for ever', and at once sent the messenger with the joyful news. My father was also at Launceston, and he hastened home, overwhelmed with joy and thanksgiving. Thomas and I were, when the news came, to Tregeare, working on land we held there, cutting wood. We soon heard the news, gave up work at once, and hastened home to join in congratulations together at John's success, and also thankfulness that we all had helped to produce such results. We had worked and now were fully rewarded. At home, much of John's time during vacation was occupied in his calculations. In the family he was always most cheerful and happy and thoroughly enjoyed the country life. He was, during his college course, invited to the houses of the clergy around Tregeare by our landlord, and at Penhale, Mr. Simcoe taking a great interest in him, and his success. He was never idle, and did a large part of the work connected with the great problem of the discovery of the planet Neptune in vacation time at home. Frequently, night after night, I have sat up with him in our little parlour at Lidcott when all else had gone to bed looking over his shoulder seeing that he copied, added and subtracted his figures correctly to save his doing it twice over. On those occasions dear Mother, who would be exhausted with her heavy work, before going to bed would prepare the milk and bread for us for supper before retiring. This I should warm when required and we take together. This was usually done. Often have I been tired, and said 'It's time to go to bed, John'. His reply would be, 'In a minute,' and go on almost unconscious of anything but his calculations. In his walks on those occasions on Laneast Down, often with me, his mind would be fully occupied in his work. I might call his attention to some object, and get a reply, but he would again relapse into his calculations. He *completed* this great work during his vacation at home, and took it with him on his way to Cambridge to the Astronomer Royal at Greenwich early in October. He left the results of his calculations, not seeing the Astronomer Royal, unfortunately behind him, and the result is well known. *They were neglected*. John was terribly disappointed and annoyed, for which he had great reason. Later from calculations made by M. Le Verrier the Planet was discovered. Now Professor Airy was called to Account. At a meeting of the Royal Astronomical Society in London (see Account on p 43), at which John, my brother Thomas and I were present, he read the correspondence on the matter, showing that the work had been done by John so many months before that by Mr. Le Verrier, and gave his reasons for not acting on John's calculations. This is a matter of history.

Soon after my brother John took his degree, my brother Thomas was accepted as a candidate for a Wesleyan missionary and went to the Wesleyan Theological Institution at Richmond. While there, going through his three years course, John and he often met as brothers. Thomas was appointed a missionary to the Friendly Islands, South Seas, where he did a great and important work for many years, and on the death of his wife returned to circuit work in England, which ended by his death at Chatteris, October 24th 1885 in the 41st year of his ministry. His death was sudden, aged 64 years. He was interred at Chatteris.

My sister, Elizabeth Grylls Adams died at Lidcott 29th May 1848 aged 16 years, and was buried at Tregeare. She was of a most amiable disposition, and died just as she was leaving school, and coming home to reside. She was becoming a great help to her mother. She had for some time been a member of the Wesleyan Society, and in her last sickness bore her sufferings with great fortitude and resignation. Her dear mother, and her brother George were constantly with her in her sickness, and she had her dear mother's disposition remarkably displayed. A more lovely girl it would be hard to find. Her friends greatly missed her, and especially her dear mother. My mother, who left Lidcott at Lady day 1860 went to her former home which had been partially rebuilt and put in order for her by my brother John, who paid for the work at Badharlick, which was her home up to her death, the 17th May 1866, aged 69 years. She died while on a visit to me at my farm Trewen, St. Tudy with all her children about her, who loved her well. Her children, who were so dearly attached to her, missed her greatly. Her life had been a trying one, in her farm work, in which she was always engaged, and the watching over the interests of her family. Her constitution was not strong, but she was kept up by her great spirit and energy. Her leg was always a source of care, and often a cause of pain, but she went on her course cheerfully, and full of life and brightness. It was her great delight to see her family happy, and enjoying themselves, and she always did what she could to promote their pleasure. She made our home most happy, and promoted the comfort of all about her. Her kindness to all *knew no bounds*, and she shared the affection of all who knew her. She was a good housekeeper, and did what she could to train her family in the right way. A more loving mother never lived, or a kinder neighbour and friend. She was interred at Tregeare.

My sister, Mary Ann, went with my mother to reside at Badharlick after leaving Lidcott. She married Henry Roseveare of Wivilscombe, where she resided up to the time of her death on 26th February 1888, in the 49th year of her life. She left a family of six children to mourn the loss of a dear mother. She was of a strong constitution, and worked hard in her calling in the farmhouse, caught a cold, and in a week passed away. Her disposition was that of her dear mother, she ruled her family by love. She was buried at St. Stephen's by Saltash March 1st. 1888.

My sister Grace, during her young days, helped her mother at Lidcott, went with her to Badharlick for a short time. When my brother Thomas returned from the Friendly Islands with his family she went with him for some years to look after his house and family in several circuits until they were grown up, and on our dear mother's death had a home with my sister Mary Ann at Wivilscombe for some years, and on her sudden death managed the house, and took charge of the family for three years to the time of her death 21st. July 1891, aged 62 years. She was interred at Tregeare. She died suddenly, with her Bible spread before her in her bedroom, we believe saying her prayers. She was constant in her devotions, and made the Bible her chief book. My brother John died at the Observatory, Cambridge on 21st. January 1892. Thus in 4 years, three of our family passed away. Thus only my brother William and I remain of a family of seven brothers and sisters. May we be ready, as they were, when the call shall come.

So ends the brief contemporary account of the early life of the family of John Couch Adams of Cornwall, and later of Cambridge. His brother George, who continued farming in Cornwall, was eventually also Mayor of Saltash for a time, contributing to the civic life of his day. He married twice, but had no children. Only Thomas, William and Mary Ann had offspring: Thomas had six surviving out of eight (two boys and four girls), William three (two boys and a girl), and Mary Ann (later Roseveare) six (three boys and three girls). The name of Adams only survives today through William's line.

2

Cambridge 1839–54: The Discovery of the Planet Neptune

The Adams family had determined, whatever the cost, that the eldest boy, John Couch, should go to Cambridge. His fortunes might have been different if those who had advised Australia as his destination had prevailed. Eventually, however, it was to Cambridge that he went; and it was in Cambridge that he stayed for the greater part of his life. His mathematical genius, which had been spotted in the west of England when a schoolboy, was to blossom in Cambridge, and enable him to discover the as-yet-unknown planet Neptune, by observing the erratic movements of the known planet Uranus.

John Couch Adams entered St. John's College, Cambridge, in October 1839. He was twenty years old – probably a year older than his contemporaries. He graduated Senior Wrangler in 1843, gaining more than double the marks awarded to the Second Wrangler in that year. Two years previous to this achievement, according to a note found among his papers at Cambridge, dated 3 July 1841, he had already

> formed a design, at the beginning of this week, of investigating, as soon as possible, after taking my

> degree, the irregularities in the motion of Uranus, which are yet unaccounted for, in order to find whether they may be attributed to the action of an undiscovered planet beyond it; and if possible then to determine approximately the elements of its orbit etc., which would probably lead to its discovery.

Further notes show the progress made on this project:

> September 1845–Papers forwarded to Professor Challis of Cambridge.
> October 1845–Copy left with Airy at Greenwich.
> November 1845–Le Verrier *begins* his calculations – nearly a month *after* Adams completed his calculations. [Could Airy leak information to Le Verrier? If any proof of a liaison between Greenwich and France could be proved there would be an end to the controversy.]
> 12 and 20 August 1846–Challis saw the Planet in Cambridge without recognizing it.
> 18 September 1846–Planet discovered in Berlin by Galle on Le Verrier's calculations. Le Verrier noted that he 'discovered the matter had been fully dealt with by a young man called Adams of Cambridge in June 1846.'

Judging by his brother George's account of the Cambridge bungling of Adam's discovery (given in Chapter 1), John Couch was bitterly disappointed about it, though this he never showed to his Cambridge contemporaries. Finally, after much bitter controversy between France and England over the issue, Adams and Le Verrier were both allowed to share the honour of the planet's discovery. The muddles and frustrations, and the element of 'a near miss' in winning the race, owing to human vacillations and delays, turned the story into a popular legend of Victorian times – a legend almost forgotten today. An article in *The Strand Magazine* of August 1896, fifty years after the event, shows the nature of the popular appeal of the story. Sir Robert Ball, Adams's successor at Cambridge Observatory in 1892, in a series called 'Through the Telescope' in that magazine, chose to tell the story of 'The Discovery of Neptune'. He was well-known as a writer who was able to make science popular for all. The following account, which he gave of the dramatic discovery, reveals some of the Victorian's enthusiasm, and exaggeration, as well as giving an accurate scientific account of a somewhat complicated story.

In the course of the present year (1896) we have to celebrate the fiftieth anniversary of one of the most famous astronomical discoveries of modern times; indeed, it may truly be said, of one of the most famous discoveries ever made in the whole annals of astronomy. There is no chapter in the history of science which contains incidents of a more dramatic character than those which are described in the narrative of the discovery of the planet Neptune.

The human element is present in a memorable controversy, the smouldering embers of which still occasionally burst into flame, with respect to the discoverer of the remotest planet in our system.

The older planets, Jupiter, Saturn, Mercury, Venus, and Mars, had been known to observers of the heavens, prior to the very earliest ages of which we have any record. No fresh additions had been made to the slender list of five, until William Herschel, then organist at the Octagon Chapel at Bath, suddenly sprang into fame by the announcement that, with a home-made telescope, he had, on the night of the 13th March, 1781 discovered the vast orb, which presently received the name of 'Uranus'. An immense enlargement was given to the dimensions of the planetary system as previously understood. It was later found that the planet required a period of about 81 years for the accomplishment of a complete revolution around the sun. As the years passed by, observations were accumulated showing the several positions which the planet occupied in the different stages of its circuit. At last the astronomers could track the great highway of Uranus; it was found that, like the orbits of the other great planets, the highway of Uranus was not exactly a circle, but an oval, or more accurately an ellipse. Once the track of Uranus was determined it was possible to find with some approximation the position which the planet occupied at any particular date, even though that date were antecedent to its discovery. In fact a timetable was formed from which the reality of the planet, not only for each year but even for each day, could be ascertained for any past epoch extending, if necessary, to centuries before Herschel lived. When the highway which Uranus was following at the time of its discovery, and for years subsequent thereto, was compared with the trace which the same planet was pursuing in those earlier years before Herschel's time, when it was unwittingly observed by preceding astronomers, it was found that the two tracks did not agree. It was therefore clear that there must be some other influence upon the planet Uranus besides that which was due to the supreme controlling attraction of the sun. It was known that the movements of Earth were affected by Jupiter, and Mars by the attraction of Earth. The effects which Jupiter could produce upon Uranus admitted of being estimated, and so also the disturbing influence of Saturn, as well as of the other planets, could be certainly ascertained. After due allowance had been made for all known sources of disturbance it was, however, found that there were still certain discrepancies outstanding between the places actually occupied by the planet discovered by Herschel and the places in which calculation seemed to locate it. The belief in the universal validity of the laws of gravitation is so well founded that it suggested the possibility that the perturbations of Uranus, which could not be otherwise accounted for, must be due to the attraction of some other planet which was quite unknown to astronomers. This gave rise to one of the grandest intellectual problems which the mind of man has ever undertaken to solve. Accordingly two accomplished mathematicians, Le Verrier in France, and Adams in England, undertook, unknowingly to each other, to investigate the whereabouts of a conceivable planet which could produce these disturbances in the motion of Uranus, which had been observed. First, some well-considered guess had to be hazarded as to the distance from the sun at which the hypothetical planet might be likely to revolve. Its orbit should certainly be presumed to lie outside that of Uranus, and from a certain curious law which governed with some regularity the distances of the other planets from the sun, it was possible to anticipate what the distance from the sun of an additional planet revolving outside Uranus might be reasonably expected to amount to. Its weight could only be estimated vaguely, but it was hoped, if such a body existed, its effects on Uranus could be calculated. By making successive trials on its possible varying distances from the sun and different magnitudes a solution was near.

Two astronomers, Le Verrier and Adams, pursuing their researches independently, both came to the same conclusions as to where the as yet unknown planet could be found. Le Verrier had ascertained the track in which the planet moved, and the mass of that body, so that he knew its place among the stars, which it occupied day by day. With this confidence in his calculations he wrote to Dr. Galle at the Berlin Observatory on 18th September 1846 to direct his telescope to a carefully selected spot in the sky 'and you will see a planet which I have not seen, and which no human eye has ever seen, but which nevertheless must be in that spot, because calculations have pointed out the necessity for its existence.' This astonishing prediction was literally fulfilled on the very evening Le Verrier's letter was received in Berlin. Dr. Galle's search was greatly facilitated by a new and accurate chart of the skies. Most of the stars in the sky could be verified on the chart that night. There was, however, one starlike object in the field of the telescope not represented by any point on the chart. It was clear to the observer in Berlin that night that the orb he was now looking at could not have been visible to the painstaking astronomer who had prepared the chart. This could mean one of two possibilities, i.e. that the new object was a star that had sprung into visibility subsequent to observations made for the map, or it was a planet, i.e. a wanderer of the heavens, which had been at some other part of the sky when the chart was made, but which had since moved into the position where it was found in September 1846. It was found to be in motion; it was therefore, indeed a planet. No amount of magnifying power will ever exhibit a single star other than as a brilliant point of light, whereas a planet may frequently be observed to show a distinctly marked disc. This test was applied; the new object in the sky possessed the planetary figure.

The circumstances under which this planet was brought to light marked an epoch in the history of the human intellect. Here was a superb planet, eighty times larger than earth, discovered, not by a mere accidental survey, but in consequence of refined mathematical anticipations, which illustrated in the most emphatic manner the truth of the law of universal gravitation. The name of Le Verrier was immediately elevated to a pinnacle of renown transcending that which had been attained by any mathematical astronomer since the days of Newton. It presently appeared, however, that the fame of the discovery of Neptune was not to be solely the property of Le Verrier, but that it would have to be shared with a young English mathematician.

Mr. J. C. Adams, who had recently taken an exceptionally brilliant degree at Cambridge, had also, as we have said, discovered the calculation ere it had ever been telescopically seen. Adams had also, like Le Verrier, provided instructions for the practical astronomer by which the telescope search for the planet might be undertaken.

Professor Challis, of Cambridge, commenced to search for the planet in accordance with the calculations of Adams, but he was, unfortunately not provided with that special appliance for faciliating such a research, which was available to Dr. Galle at Berlin. The Cambridge observer had not yet received a copy of that star-chart without which the task of discriminating the planet from among the hundred of adjacent stars involved an arduous and tedious piece of work. Professor Challis did, however, manfully commence the laborious duty of instituting a careful survey of the region. We now know that in the course of his work he had, on more than one occasion, unwittingly observed the planet Neptune, so that there cannot be the least doubt that the process which he was pursuing must necessarily in due time have resulted in complete success. But while Challis was engaged in the laborious work, news reached Cambridge of the discovery of the planet which had already been effected at Berlin. A considerable controversy thereupon ensued. The French nation claimed for Le Verrier the credit of the discovery of Neptune and were at first inclined to deny to Adams any share whatever in the immortal achievement. They urged that Le Verrier, quite unconscious of the labours of Adams, had completely worked out the position of the planet, and in consequence of that work, and solely in consequence of it, the planet had been telescopically discovered at Berlin. Those who put forward the claims of the English mathematician urged the undoubted fact that the calculations of Adams were really prior to those of Le Verrier, though it was admitted that the optical discovery by Dr. Galle anticipated the discovery, which certainly would have been made by Challis when he had completed and compared his observation at Cambridge. The English claim demanded that the fame of the discovery of Neptune by mathematical research should be equally shared between Le Verrier and Adams.

Gradually this claim has come to be almost universally recognised as a just one. It is true that certain French writers occasionally speak of the discovery of Neptune as simply due to Le Verrier, but impartial judges generally refer to it as the joint result of the concurrent labours of the French and English astronomers.

There can be no doubt that Neptune would, in the course of time, have been discovered by simple survey work of the chart makers, when a new 'star' was noticed on their maps. Indeed, as a matter of fact, Neptune had once been very nearly discovered in what may be described as an accidental manner before Adams or Le Varrier were born. Astronomer Lalande records in his great celestial catalogue a certain 'star' in a certain place on the 10th May 1795. Subsequent inquiries instituted by Adams showed that this object was not a star as Lalande thought, but that it was really the planet Neptune. A reference to the original manuscript observations of Lalande brought to light circumstances of much interest. It appears that the astronomer had observed this object on 8th May, as well as on 10th May, but as his observations showed a different position on the 10th from that which he had set down on the 8th, Lalande concluded that the latter was erroneous. We now know that the discrepancy in the two positions was simply due to the movement of the planet in the interval. Little did Lalande dream that a superb discovery had lain so nearly in his grasp, but we cannot regret that he did not make it. Had he done so, we should have been deprived of the most glorious illustration science has yet given of the principles of theoretical astronomy. (Sir Robert Ball, *The Strand Magazine,* August 1896)

This account is more fulsome than would ever have flowed from the pen of the modest, and self-effacing Adams, but it shows how the discovery was still regarded in the contemporary scientific world, fifty years after the discovery. It has also been recently stated that had Adams and Le Verrier not searched when they did in 1846 they might not have succeeded in finding Neptune, as at certain times in its orbit it is invisible to earth once more. It would still make sensational reading today if a link could be found in the correspondence of Airy and Le Verrier, or other French astronomers, during the time Adams's calculations were left at Greenwich, namely October 1845 and 18 September 1846, when the planet was sighted in Berlin. Adams began calculating in 1841; Le

Verrier in 1845. It is a strange coincidence that both men were calculating simultaneously in France and Cambridge.

A few more details from Cambridge sources may be added to this popular account of Sir Robert Ball. In 1843 Adams's friend, Earnshaw, had urged Adams to disclose his findings to the Cambridge Philosophical Society, but Adams refused to do so until he had checked further, and revealed them to Challis, the then Director of the Cambridge Observatory. Adams was always renowned for modesty, so he did not hand on his calculations to Challis until September 1845, as he was too diffident to publish on his own, and too correct to do so without consulting his superiors. He was also too meticulous to publish before further checks and counter checks had been made. Challis did not show much animation in looking over the findings of a comparatively young graduate of twenty-six years of age. Also Adams was not a good correspondent which led to Airy's delays at Greenwich. Instead of writing to Airy, the Astronomer Royal at Greenwich, Adams had decided to hand over his findings to him in person, when Adams returned to Cambridge after a vacation in Cornwall in October 1845. He, however, made no appointment with Airy, who happened to be in France when he called. Adams then decided to call back a few days later, and on that occasion left his papers at the door with one of the servants, as the Airy's were at dinner. The Airy's dined at 3 p.m. – earlier than was customery. The message was never fully explained to Airy, and the papers were seemingly pigeon-holed at Greenwich till the following year, when Le Verrier's findings were announced. This lack of communication between Airy and Adams, largely arising from Adam's modesty and unwillingness to correspond even in answer to a query from Airy, led to all the controversy which was to follow, as a result of the delay in publishing Adams's discovery. Adams's accurate and correct calculations lay at Greenwich at least a month before Le Verrier *began* his calculations in November 1845.

By June 1846 Le Verrier had communicated his results to Galle in Berlin, and the planet was first sighted on the Berlin telescope. Challis had been making a perfunctory sweep of the sky on 4 August and 10 August 1846 with the Northumberland Telescope at Cambridge University Observatory, but clouds had intervened on a clear sky, while he had been drinking tea with a friend and Mrs. Challis at the Observatory at her suggestion for her husband's well-being on a cold summer night. In fact Challis had probably sighted the planet ahead of Galle, but failed to register what he had seen. It was not until Le Verrier made his announcement, and Berlin claimed the credit which Cambridge should have had, that Airy and Challis realized how they had bungled the findings of 'the young man called Adams'. Professor Adam Sedgwick of Trinity College, Cambridge, was heard to explode in the Trinity Combination Room in the autumn of 1846, 'Oh! curse their narcotic Souls', as he frequently lamented over the Cambridge delays, which led to the French claiming the victory. Le Verrier had announced his preliminary findings to the Academy of Sciences in France on 10 November 1845, and even then neither Airy nor Challis realized they had the clue too.

While Sedgwick was exploding in the Trinity Combination Room matters were equally confused in the Trinity Junior Combination Room, judging by a letter to his father dated 31 October 1846, written by F. J. A. Hort.*

In October 1846 Hort had just arrived at Trinity from Dublin for his first term as an undergraduate. He writes:

> Romilly asked me to wine on Thursday. Professor Sedgwick was there, besides 2 or 3 old pupils of Romilly's, who had come down for the day, and 3

*_Life and Letters of F. J. A. Hort_ by Sir A. F. Hort, Vol. I & II, 1896, Macmillian. F. J. A. Hort was eventually to become Hulsean Professor of Divinity in 1878 and to be editor with Westcott of a Greek New Testament.

> or 4 undergraduates, chiefly I think of other colleges. Romilly talked and laughed and joked incessantly for everyone else as well as himself. There was some interesting conversation about the new Planet, but I could not make it out, nor can I remember it clearly. Some observatory, I think here, thinks he has discovered a ring. It appears that Mr. Adams of St. John's had made his calculations in the spring and sent them to Greenwich to Airy, the Astronomer Royal; but he paid no attention to them, and to his neglect Sedgwick attributed the loss of the honour to England of the discovery. He mentioned that in the summer he and someone else had seen Mr. 'Nep' from the Observatory here, but did not recognise him as the planet that they were looking for.

Nearly two weeks later he writes again to his father on 12 November 1846:

> I had a treat on Monday night such as I am not likely often to have, and I am sure you would give something to have had; I heard from the lips of Professor Challis and Mr. Adams the account of their discovery of Neptune. _______ told me that that night was the first meeting for this term of the Cambridge Philosophical Society and asked me to go with him. Mr. Adams explained in some degree the difficulties and peculiarities of his calculations, but they were all but wholly unintelligible to me. One curious thing I fished out, that the well-known theory of a certain rule in the relative distances of the planets from the sun as compared with that of the earth is found false in Neptune's case. The rule was that, supposing the distance of one planet from the sun to be x times as great as that of the earth from the sun would be

> two $(x - 1)$ times that of the earth . . . There was then some discussion as to the respective honours of Adams and Le Verrier; Adams said that he gave Le Verrier the full credit of the discovery, but, as a matter of calculation, he claimed for himself the credit of prior independent conjecture. Challis said the same, and merely claimed credit for himself on the score of having laboured most, having taken between 3,000 and 4,000 observations between the end of July and September. He it seems actually saw the planet before its discovery at Berlin, and had suspicions of its being the planet, but did not examine it. On coming home I sat down to write an account of what I had heard, but when I had written a good deal, was obliged to go to bed by the hour; and unfortunately totally forgot till this afternoon; now on trying to complete it I find my recollections very imperfect.

So another 'Khubla Khan' is lost to the world owing to the intervention of a 'man from Porlock'. Both letters, however, give some idea of the impact of the Cambridge discovery on a young, and somewhat callow, undergraduate from Dublin, later to blossom out into one of the Theologians of his day, who eventually became a friend of Adams in their long time together in Cambridge. Hort eventually died a few days before Adams, in 1892.

The controversy over the discovery of the planet Neptune was still being mentioned in Adam's obituary notice in *The Standard* on 27 January 1892, where a further account is given of the whole complicated and confusing affair. The account gives a coherent scientific account of the discovery, and the respect in which Adams was held at his death in 1892, nearly fifty years later.

Again at the time of the Centenary Celebrations of the Discovery of Neptune in 1946, the controversy was once more revived. Letters passed between H. Spencer Jones, the Astronomer Royal, and W. M. Smart, of the University Observatory of Glasgow, in the magazine *Nature* for 7 December 1946, respectively defending and attacking Airy's part in the proceedings of 1846. The letter from Spencer Jones is as follows:

The account by Prof. W. M. Smart of the discovery of Neptune, of which a summary was published in *Nature* for November 9, depicts the part played by G. B. Airy, the Astronomer Royal, in a most unfavourable light. He describes the treatment of Adams by Airy as 'unbecoming to the leading astronomer of his generation'. Prof. Smart's verdict is not, in my opinion, justified, and I feel that, for the sake of historical accuracy, a reply is needed.

In judging Airy's actions, it is necessary to remember the tremendous load of work which he carried. Besides attending to all the details of the work of the Royal Observatory, he maintained an extensive correspondence with astronomers in all parts of the world and was consulted on a great variety of general scientific questions outside the range of his strict official duties. No man could have been more meticulous in replying promptly to all letters and inquiries. An examination of Airy's day-book shows that in the period covered by the investigations of Adams, Airy visited France for the purpose of examining and reporting upon the design and construction of the breakwater at Cherbourg; he went to York to see experiments on the running of engines; he visited Portsmouth to inquire into and report upon the defects of the engines of H. M. S. Janus; he was occupied with the Tidal Harbour Commission and he was frequently called to London for meetings of the Railway Gauge Commission, the draft report of which he prepared.

Airy first learnt that Adams was working on the theory of Uranus from Prof. Challis, who wrote to Airy in February 1844 asking for the errors of longitude of Uranus, as indicated by the Greenwich observations, for the years

1818–26. Airy by return of post sent the Greenwich data not merely for those years, but also for the whole period 1754–1830, data invaluable for the purpose of the investigation.

Adams twice called at Greenwich in the course of his investigations in the hope of seeing the Astronomer Royal and discussing the results he had obtained. It would have been a matter of ordinary courtesy for a young man like Adams, personally unknown to the Astronomer Royal, to have written and asked for an appointment, but Adams on each occasion called without any previous notice. On the first occasion, towards the end of September 1845, Adams called at Greenwich and left a letter of introduction from Challis; Airy was then in France on the Cherbourg breakwater investigation. Immediately on his return, he wrote to Challis and said: 'Would you mention to Mr. Adams that I am very much interested with the subject of his investigations, and that I shall be delighted to hear of them by letter from him.' This letter should surely have encouraged Adams to write. On the second occasion, on October 21, 1845, Airy was in London attending a meeting of the Railway Gauge Commission. Adams left his card and said that he would call later. The card was taken to Mrs. Airy, but the message was not given to her. When Adams made his second call, he was informed that the Astronomer Royal was at dinner; there was no message for him and he went away feeling mortified. This visit is not mentioned in Airy's day-book, and it is clear from Airy's private correspondence that he was not told either of Adams' intention to call again or of his second call. It may also be mentioned that this visit of Adams was made a few days before Mrs. Airy gave birth to a son, Osmund.

Adams left at the Observatory a paper with a summary of his results, and a comparison between the observed longitudes of Uranus and those computed from his theory. On November 5, Airy wrote to Adams putting his famous query about the errors of the radius vector of Uranus. Adams never replied to this letter. In a later letter to Airy of

November 18, 1846, he stated how deeply he regretted his neglect and mentioned that he had always experienced a strange difficulty in writing letters. But to a man so methodical and precise as Airy, it was a barrier to any further communication. As Airy afterwards wrote to Challis, 'It was clearly impossible for me to write to him again'. This is why Adams' statement remained, in Prof. Smart's words, 'in Airy's pocket for eight months'.

Prof. Smart seems to regard Airy's query as trivial. Airy was, of course, thinking of the possibility that perturbation by an unknown planet might not be the only possible cause of the irregularities in the motion of Uranus. His views were clearly expressed in a letter to Challis (December 21, 1846).

'There were two things to be explained, which might have existed each independently of the other, and of which one could be ascertained independently of the other: viz. error of longitude and error of radius vector. And there is no *a priori* reason for thinking that a hypothesis which will explain the error of longitude will also explain the error of radius vector. If, after Adams had satisfactorily explained the error of longitude he had with the numerical values of the formula for perturbation of radius vector into numbers, and if these numbers had been discordant with the observed numbers of discordances of radius vector, then the theory would have been false, not from any error of Adams' but from a failure in the law of gravitation. On this question therefore turned the continuance or fall of the law of gravitation.'

Prof. Smart mentions that even so late as 1844 Airy regarded as possible that gravitation might not be exactly according to the inverse square of the distance. It is perhaps well to recall that, fifty years later, the same suggestion was seriously examined by Simon Newcomb and other eminent astronomers in the endeavour to explain the anomaly in the motion of the perihelion of Mercury.

It is also stated that towards the end of June 1846 Le Verrier applied to Airy for assistance in the search for the planet, and that this request for practical aid passed unheeded. What were the facts? Airy had written to Le Verrier putting to him the query about the errors of radius vector which he had previously put to Adams, and had at once received a satisfactory reply. The assurance that the hypothesis of an unknown planet accounted for the errors of both longitude and radius vector of Uranus had convinced him of the reality of the planet's existence. He considered that the telescopes at Greenwich were probably of insufficient size to detect the planet and that the Northumberland telescope at the Cambridge Observatory was the most suitable for the purpose of the search. He therefore wrote to Challis on July 9, 1846, inquiring whether he could undertake the search and, if not, whether he would superintend the examination if Airy supplied him with an assistant from Greenwich for the purpose. He concluded by saying, 'The time for the said examination is approaching near'.

When Challis informed Airy that he would undertake the search, Airy drew up as a guidance for Challis his 'Suggestions for the examination of a portion of the Heavens in search of the external planet which is presumed to exist and to produce disturbances in the motion of Uranus' (dated July 12, 1846). In sending this paper to Challis he wrote, 'I only add at present that, in my opinion, the importance of this inquiry exceeds that of any current work, which is of such a nature as not to be totally lost by delay'. Airy could not have done more to further the search and to impress upon Challis its urgency. There is little doubt that if the search had been carried out by an assistant from Greenwich, the planet would have been found, for it was an essential part of Airy's system that reduction of observations proceeded *pari passu* with the observations themselves.

As regards the actual researches of Adams and Le Verrier, full abstracts of Le Verrier's investigations had been published in the *Comptes rendus*, but neither Airy nor Challis had received anything from Adams beyond the bare summary of his results; they knew nothing of the methods he had employed.

After the discovery of the planet by Galle at Berlin, Airy wrote to Le Verrier and informed him that collateral researches, which had led to the same result as his own, had been made in England, and that they had been known to him earlier than those of Le Verrier. His 'Account of some circumstances historically connected with the discovery of the planet exterior to Uranus' presented to the Royal Astronomical Society on November 13, 1846, left no doubt about the priority of the researches of Adams. In a letter of later date to Biot, Airy wrote, 'I believe I have done more than any other person to place Adams in his proper position'.

Prof. Smart agrees that the contemporary criticism of Airy, made in ignorance of many of the facts, was on some points unfair and unjustifiable. In my opinion, his verdict that Airy's treatment of Adams was unbecoming is equally unjustifiable.

H. Spencer Jones, Royal Observatory, Greenwich, London S.E.10 ('G. B. Airy and the Discovery of Neptune', Letters to the Editor, *Nature*, no. 4023, 7 December 1946.)

The letter from Professor W. M. Smart in *'Nature'* (December 1946) in reply to Spencer Jones reads as follows:

The Astronomer Royal does not see eye to eye with me in my judgement of Airy, in connexion with the Neptune controversy, as expressed in my article in *Nature* for November 9. This article, which was written in response to an editorial request, was a summary of the two addresses – dealing with different aspects of the discovery of Neptune – which I gave at the centenary commemoration on October 8; these addresses were themselves a summary of a fairly long 'essay' (if I may call it so) written at the invitation of the Council of the Royal Astronomical Society and accepted, as I understand, by the Council for eventual distribution to the fellows in one of the Society's publications. The 'essay' is a historical study of events of a century ago, and I was very conscious throughout its preparation that I must follow the methods of the historian as efficiently as I knew how. The job of the historian, as I see it, is to elicit facts, to present these in proper form, and to paint as accurate and complete a picture as possible. The 'essay' was accordingly built up on a very large amount of historical documents – I explain in the 'essay' how many of these became available, for the first time, for a study of the Neptune controversy, in which Sir Harold's great predecessor was in many ways the dominant figure.

All this, it seems to me, must be said before one turns to the criticism of the Astronomer Royal. Sir Harold's arguments, when documentary evidence is invoked, are based on Airy's letters alone. Most of his quotations will also be found in my 'essay', if – in one or two instances – not as direct quotations then as transcriptions of them. There is no suggestion in my article or 'essay' that Airy was to blame for Adams's failure to see the former on the occasion of his abortive visit to the Royal Observatory in October 1845 – it was far otherwise – and as to the famous query about the 'radius vector', Adams never failed to reproach himself for not replying to Airy, although he was convinced that the matter was 'trivial', an opinion shared at the time by Challis.

The main questions are: Why did Airy claim to know the whole history of the business? Why did he declare unambiguously that Le Verrier must be regarded as the real 'predicter' of the planet? Why did he affirm that there was noone (in England) in competition, as regards scientific insight, with Le Verrier, etc.?

It is to be remarked that Airy's correspondence with Le Verrier was understood by him to be 'private', and he was exceedingly indignant – and justly so – when his letters were published in the French press without his sanction being even asked. Later, Airy described Adams as his 'oracle' in all matters relating to lunar and planetary theory; but this has nothing to do with the Neptune controversy as a historical episode. Airy was unjustly criticized on many points, as the Sedgwick correspondence makes abundantly clear, and as I hope my article and 'essay' demonstrate.

Any judgement on Airy's actions must be based, not on his letters alone, but on the whole corpus of contemporary documents. I do not claim that my 'essay' is the last word on the subject, but I do claim that, whatever its faults may be, it was written as a purely historical study with all the implications that this description suggests.

W. M. Smart, University Observatory, Glasgow.

A contemporary account appears in the records of the Royal Astronomical Society (Vol. VII, 13 November 1846, No. 9). This is the meeting referred to (see p. 20) when John, Thomas and George Adams were present.

Captain W. H. Smyth, R. N., President, in the Chair.

John Riddle, Esq., Second Master of the Nautical School, Greenwich Hospital, was ballotted for and duly elected a Fellow of the Society.

The Astronomer Royal [G. B. Airy] read the following Memoir:-

1. Account of some circumstances historically connected with the discovery of the Planet exterior to *Uranus*.

It has not been usual to admit into the *Memoirs* of this Society mere historical statements of circumstances which have occurred in our own times. I am not aware that this is a matter of positive regulation: it is, I believe, merely a rule of practice, of which the application in every particular instance has been determined by the discretion of those Officers of the Society with whom the arrangement of our *Memoirs* has principally rested. And there can be no doubt that the ordinary rule must be a rule for the exclusion of papers of this character; and that if a positive regulation is to be made, it must absolutely forbid the presentation of such histories. Yet it is conceivable that events may occur in which this rule ought to be relaxed; and such, I am persuaded, are the circumstances attending the discovery of the planet exterior to *Uranus*. In the whole history of astronomy, I had almost said in the whole history of science, there is nothing comparable to this. The history of the discoveries of new planets in the latter part of the last century, and in the present century, offers nothing analogous to it. *Uranus, Ceres* and *Pallas,* were discovered in the course of researches which did not contemplate the possible discovery of planets. *Juno* and *Vesta,* were discovered in following up a series of observations suggested by a theory which, fruitful as it has been, we may almost venture to call fanciful. *Astraea* was found in the course of a well-conducted re-examination of the heavens, apparently contemplating the discovery of a new planet as only one of many possible results. But the motions of *Uranus*, examined by philosophers who were fully impressed with the universality of the law of gravitation, have long exhibited the effects of some disturbing body: mathematicians have at length ventured on the task of ascertaining where such a body could be; they have pointed out that the supposition of a disturbing body moving in a certain orbit, precisely indicated by them, would entirely explain the observed disturbances of *Uranus*: they have expressed their conviction, with a firmness which I must characterise as wonderful, that the disturbing planet would be found exactly in a certain spot, and presenting exactly a certain appearance; and in that spot, and with that appearance, the planet has been found. Nothing in the whole history of astronomy can be compared with this.

The principal steps in the theoretical investigations have been made by one individual, and the published discovery of the planet was necessarily made by one individual. To these persons the public attention has been principally directed; and well do they deserve the honours which they have received, and which they will continue to receive. Yet we should do wrong if we considered that these two persons alone are to be regarded as the authors of the discovery of this planet. I am confident that it will be found that the discovery is a consequence of what may properly be called a movement of the age; that it has been urged by the feeling of the scientific world in general, and has been nearly perfected by the collateral, but independent labours, of various persons possessing the talents of powers best suited to the different parts of the researches.

With this conviction, it has appeared to me very desirable that the authentic history of this discovery should be published as soon as possible; not only because it will prove a valuable contribution to the history of science, but also because it may tend to do justice to some persons who otherwise would not receive in future times the credit which they deserve. And as a portion of the history, I venture to offer to this Society a statement of the circumstances which have come to my own knowledge. I have thought that I could with propriety do this: not because I can pretend to know all the history of the discovery, but because I know a considerable part of it; and because I can lay claim to the character of impartiality to this extent, that, though partaking of the general movement of the age, I have not directly contributed either to the theoretical or to the observing parts of the discovery. In a matter of this delicacy I have thought it best to act on my own judgement, without consulting any other person; I have, however, solicited the permission of my English correspondents for the publication of letters.

Without pretending to fix upon a time when the conviction of the irreconcilability of the motions of *Uranus* with the law of gravitation first fixed itself in the minds of some individuals, we may without hesitation date the general belief in this irreconcilability from the publication of M. Alexis Bouvard's *Tables of Uranus* in 1821. It was fully shewn in the introduction to the tables that, when every correction for perturbation indicated by the best existing theories was applied, it was still impossible to reconcile the observations of Flamsteed, Lemonnier, Bradley, and Mayer with the orbit required by the observations made after 1781: and the elements of the orbit were adopted from the latter observations, leaving the discordances with the former (amounting sometimes to three minutes of arc) for future explanation.

The orbit thus adopted represented pretty well the observations made in the years immediately following the publication of the tables. But in five or six years the discordance again growing up became so great, that it could not escape notice. A small error was shewn by the Kremsmunster Observations of 1825 and 1826: but, perhaps, I am not in error in stating that the discordance was first prominently exhibited in the Cambridge Observations, the publication of which from 1828 was conducted under my superintendance.

While still residing at Cambridge, I received from the Rev. T. J. Hussey (Now Dr. Hussey) a letter, of which the following is an extract. It will be considered, I think, as honourable to that gentleman's acuteness and zeal. I must premise that the writer had lately passed through Paris.

No. 1. The Rev. T. J. Hussey to G. B. Airy.

[Extract.]

Hayes, Kent, 17 November, 1834.

With Mr. Alexis Bouvard I had some conversation upon a subject I had often mediated, which will probably interest you, and your opinion may determine mine. Having taken great pains last year with some observations of *Uranus*, I was led to examine closely Bouvard's tables of that planet. The apparently inexplicable discrepancies between the ancient and modern observations suggested to me the possibility of some disturbing body beyond *Uranus*, not taken into account because unknown. My first idea was to ascertain some approximate place of this supposed body empirically, and then with my large reflector set to work to examine all the minute stars thereabouts: but I found myself totally inadequate to the former part of the task. If I could have done it formerly, it was beyond me now, even supposing I had the time, which was not the case. I therefore relinquished the matter altogether; but subsequently, in conversation with Bouvard, I inquired if the above might not be the case: his answer was, that, as might have been expected, it had occurred to him, and some correspondence had taken place between Hansen and himself respecting it. Hansen's opinion was, that one disturbing body would not satisfy the phenomena; but that he conjectured there were two planets beyond *Uranus*. Upon my speaking of obtaining the places empirically, and then sweeping closely for the bodies, he fully acquiesced in the propriety of it, intimating that the previous calculations would be more laborious than difficult; that if he had leisure he would undertake them and transmit the results to me, as the basis of a very close and accurate sweep. I have not heard from him since on the subject, and have been too ill to write. What is your opinion on the subject: If you consider the idea as possible, can you give me the limits, roughly, between which this body or those bodies may probably be found during the ensuing winter? As we might expect an excentricity [inclination?] approaching rather to that of the old planets than of the new, the breadth of the Zone to be examined will be comparatively inconsiderable. I may be wrong, but I am disposed to think that, such is the perfection of my equatoreal's object-glass, I could distinguish, almost at once, the difference of light of a small planet and a star. My plan of proceeding, however, would be very different: I should accurately map the whole space within the required limits, down to the minutest star I could discern; the interval of a single week would then enable me to ascertain any change. If the whole of this matter do not appear to you a chimaera, which, until my conversation with Bouvard, I was afraid, it might, I shall be very glad of any sort of hint respecting it.'

My answer was in the following terms:-

No. 2. G. B. Airy to the Rev. T. J. Hussey.

[Extract.]

'Observatory, Cambridge, 1834, Nov. 23.

I have often thought of the irregularity of *Uranus*, and since the receipt of your letter have looked more carefully to it. It is a puzzling subject, but I give it as my opinion, without hesitation, that it is not yet in such a state as to give the smallest hope of making out the nature of any external action on the planet. Flamsteed's observations I reject (for the present) without ceremony: but the two observations by Bradley and Mayer cannot be rejected. Thus the state of things is this, – the mean motion and other elements derived from the observations between 1781 and 1825 give considerable errors in 1750, and give *nearly the same errors* in 1834, *when the planet is at nearly the same part of its orbit*. If the mean motion had been determined by 1750 and 1834, this would have indicated nothing; but the fact is, that the mean motions were determined (as I have said) independently. This does not look like irregular perturbation. The observations would be well reconciled if we could from theory bring in two terms; one a small error in Bouvard's excentricity and perihelion, and the other a term depending on twice the longitude. The former, of course, we could do; of the latter there are two, viz. a term in the equation of the centre, and a term in the perturbations by *Saturn*. The first I have verified completely (formula and numbers); the second I have verified generally, but not completely; I shall, when I have an opportunity, look at it thoroughly. So much for my doubts as to the certainty of any extraneous action. But if it were certain that there were any extraneous action, I doubt much the possibility of determining the place of a planet which produced it. I am sure it could not be done till the nature of the irregularity was well determined from several successive revolutions.'

It will readily be understood that I do not quote this letter as a testimony to my own sagacity; but I think it deserving of production, as shewing the struggle which was made twelve years ago to explain the motions of *Uranus*, and the difficulty which seemed to envelope the subject. With regard to my last sentence, I think it likely that the same difficulty would still have been felt, if the theorists who entered seriously upon the explanation of the perturbations had not trusted more confidently to Bode's law of distances than I did myself.

In the year 1836, having quitted the Observatory of Cambridge, I completed the reduction of the planetary observations made there during the years 1833, 1834, 1835, in such a form as to exhibit the heliocentric errors of the tabular places of *Uranus*, together with the effect of errors of the tabular radius vector. The memoir containing these reductions was subsequently printed in the *Memoirs* of this Society. The progress of the errors of the tables of *Uranus* was here clearly marked.

In 1837, I received from M. Eugene Bouvard a letter, from which I trust I may be permitted to make an extract. It will, I am certain, be received as creditable to the intelligence and industry of the astronomers of the Observatory of Paris.

No. 3. M. Eugène Bouvard to G. B. Airy

[Extract.]

'Paris, ce 6 Octobre, 1837.

Dans le peu de moments de loisir que me laissent mes fonctions, je m'occupe d'un travail que je crois n'être pas sans importance. Mon oncle [M. Alexis Bouvard] travaille à réfaire ses tables de *Jupiter* et de *Saturne*, en se servant des corrections apportées recemment aux élémens astronomiques. Il m'a cédé les tables *d'Uranus* a réconstruire. En consultant les comparaisons que vous avez fait des observations de cette planète avec les calculs des tables, on voit que les différences en latitude sont très grandes et qu'elles vont toujours en augmentant. Cela tient-il à une perturbation inconnue apportée dans les mouvements de cet astre par un corps situé au-delà? Je ne sais, mais c'est du moins l'idée de mon oncle. Je regarde la solution de cette question comme fort importante. Mais, pour réussir, j'ai besoin de réduire les observations avec la plus grande précision, et souvent les moyens me manquent.'

The remainder of this letter relates principally to the reduction of observations.

The following are extracts from my answer:–

No. 4. G. B. Airy to M. Eugène Bouvard.

[Extract.]

Royal Observatory, Greenwich, 1837, Oct. 12.

'I think that, probably, you would gain much in the accuracy of the reduced observations by waiting a short time before you proceed with that part of your labour. Some time ago, I presented to the Astronomical Society of London a very complete reduction of the observations of all the planets made at Cambridge in the years 1833, 1834, 1835. This paper will, as I expect, very shortly be printed. I have reduced the observations made at Greenwich in 1836 in the same manner: the volume containing these reductions will very soon be published. *** You may also know that I am engaged upon a general reduction of the observations of planets made at Greenwich, from the commencement of Bradley's observations to the present time. It may, perhaps, be a year before I can furnish you with the places deduced from these observations. ***** With respect to the errors of the tables of *Uranus*, I think you will find that it is the *longitude* which is most defective, and that the errors in *latitude* are not at present increasing. To shew this, I set down a few of my results. ***** You will see by this statement that the errors of longitude are increasing with fearful rapidity, while those of latitude are nearly stationary. **** I cannot conjecture what is the cause of these errors, but I am inclined, in the first instance, to ascribe them to some error in the perturbations. There is no error in the pure elliptic theory (as I found by examination some time ago). If it be the effect of any unseen body, it will be nearly impossible ever to find out its place.'

On the 24th of February, 1838, I addressed a letter to M. Schumacher, which is printed in the *Astronomische Nachrichten*, No. 349. In this letter it is shewn, by treatment of the results of the reduced observations of 1833, 1834, 1835, 1836 (to which allusion was made in my letter to M. Eugène Bouvard), that the tabular radius vector of *Uranus* was considerably too small. This deduction (which has been confirmed by the observations of all the subsequent years) has always appeared to me to be very important. It is, perhaps, worth while here to point out that the detection of this error arose, in the first place, from the circumstance that my observations of *Uranus* had not been confined to the mere opposition (as had too often been done), but had been extended, as far as possible, to quadratures; and, in the next place, from my having so reduced the observations as to exhibit the effect of error of the radius vector.

On the 14th of May, 1838, I transmitted to M. Eugène Bouvard the reduced observations of 1833, 1834, 1835, 1836; and referred him to the paper in the *Astronomische Nachrichten* which I have cited.

The following letter from M. Eugène Bouvard will shew how vigorously the attention of the astronomers of Paris was still directed to *Uranus*:

No. 5. M. Eugène Bouvard to G. B. Airy.

[Extract.]

'Paris, ce 21 Mai, 1844.

*** Je viens aujourd'hui vous prier de me communiquer, si c'est possible, les ascensions droites et les déclinaisons *d'Uranus* depuis 1781 jusqu'en 1800. *** J'ai réduit moi-même toutes ces observations en m'en tenant aux élémens imprimés, mais je crains qu'il n'y ait quelques erreurs. Il y a surtout une telle incertitude sur les erreurs de collimation du quart de cerecle depuis 1785 jusqu'en 1800, qu'il est presque impossible d'avoir une grande confiance dans les observations. *** Mon travail est fort avancé. Je suis arrivé à des resultats fort bons déjà, puisque je satisfais aux observations actuelles et aux premières de 1781, 1782, &c., à 15" de dégré près en longitude: tandisque d'après les tables de mon oncle les erreurs sont de près de 2′ de dégré actuellement. Si je mettais de côté les observations de Maskelyne faites depuis 1785 jusqu'à 1796, mes tables pourraient satisfaire aux observations à 7" ou 8" près. Mais je crains que cette période ne m'empêche d'y parvenir; et malheureusement c'est dans cette intervalle que les observations sont le plus défectueuses. **** D'après mes calculs, il faut changer considérablement les élémens elliptiques d'Herschel, surtout le moyen mouvement et le périhélie. J'ai determiné aussi la masse de *Saturne*, et je la trouve très différente de celle que l'on admet; il faut l'augmenter beaucoup. Mais j'attendrai une nouvelle approximation pour être tout à fait sûr de ma détermination.'

After some further correspondence, I transmitted to M. Eugène Bouvard, on June 27, 1844, the proof-sheets of the *Planetary Reductions*, containing the Right Ascensions and North Polar distances of *Uranus*; and M. Bouvard, in acknowledging the receipt of them, on July 1, 1844, pointed out an error in the refraction for June 15, 1819. I mention this to shew the extreme care with which M. E. Bouvard's collateral calculations had been conducted.

Although no allusion is made in the last letter to the possible disturbing planet, it would be wrong to suppose that there was no thought of it. In fact, during the whole of these efforts for reforming the tables of *Uranus*, the dominant thought was, 'Is it possible to explain the motions of *Uranus*, without admitting either a departure from the received law of attraction, or the existence of a disturbing planet?' I know not how far the extensive and accurate calculations of M. Eugène Bouvard may have been used in the subsequent French calculations, but I have no doubt whatever that the knowledge of the efforts of M. Bouvard, the confidence in the accuracy of his calculations, and the perception of his failure to reconcile in a satisfactory way the theory and the observations, have tended greatly to impress upon astronomers, both French and English, the absolute necessity of seeking some external cause of disturbance.

I have departed from a strictly chronological order for the sake of keeping in connexion the papers which relate to the same trains of investigation. Several months before the date of the last letter quoted, I had received the first intimation of those calculations which have led to a distinct indication of the place where the disturbing planet ought to be sought. The date of the following letter is Feb. 13, 1844:-

No. 6. Professor Challis to G. B. Airy.

[Extract.]

'Cambridge Observatory, Feb. 13, 1844.

A young friend of mine, Mr. Adams, of St. John's College, is working at the theory of *Uranus*, and is desirous of obtaining errors of the tabular geocentric longitudes of this planet, when near opposition, in the years 1818–1826, with the factors for reducing them to errors of heliocentric longitude. Are your reductions of the planetary observations so far advanced that you could furnish these data? And is the request one which you have any objection to comply with? If Mr. Adams may be favoured in this respect, he is further desirous of knowing, whether in the calculation of the tabular errors any alterations have been made in Bouvard's *Tables of Uranus* besides that of *Jupiter's* mass.'

My answer was as follows:-

No. 7. G. B. Airy to Professor Challis.

[Extract.]

'Royal Observatory, Greenwich, 1844, Feb. 15.

I send all the results of the observations of *Uranus* made

with both instruments [that is, the heliocentric errors of *Uranus* in longitude and latitude from 1754 to 1830, for all those days on which there were observations, both of right ascension and of polar distance]. No alteration is made in Bouvard's *Tables of Uranus,* except increasing the two equations which depend on *Jupiter* by 1/50 part. As constants have been added (in the printed tables) to make the equations positive, and as 1/50 part of the numbers in the tables has been added, 1/50 part of the constants has been subtracted from the final results.'

Professor Challis, in acknowledging the receipt of these, used the following expressions:-

No. 8. Professor Challis to G. B. Airy.

[Extract.]

'Cambridge Observatory, Feb. 16, 1844.
I am exceedingly obliged by your sending so complete a series of tabular errors of *Uranus.* **** The list you have sent will give Mr. Adams the means of carrying on in the most effective manner the inquiry in which he is engaged.'

The next letter shews that Mr. Adams had derived results from these errors.

No. 9. Professor Challis to G. B. Airy.

'Cambridge Observatory, Sept. 22, 1845.
My friend Mr. Adams (who will probably deliver this note to you) has completed his calculations respecting the perturbation of the orbit of *Uranus* by a supposed ulterior planet, and has arrived at results which he would be glad to communicate to you personally, if you could spare him a few moments of your valuable time. His calculations are founded on the observations you were so good as to furnish him with some time ago; and from his character as a mathematician, and his practice in calculation, I should

consider the deductions from his premises to be made in a trustworthy manner. If he should not have the good fortune to see you at Greenwich, he hopes to be allowed to write to you on this subject.'

On the day on which this letter was dated, I was present at a meeting of the French Institute. I acknowledged it by the following letter:-

No. 10. G. B. Airy to Professor Challis.

'Royal Observatory, Greenwich, 1845, Sept. 29.

I was, I suppose, on my way from France, when Mr. Adams called here: at all events, I had not reached home, and therefore, to my regret, I have not seen him. Would you mention to Mr. Adams that I am very much interested with the subject of his investigations, and that I should be delighted to hear of them by letter from him?'

On one of the last days of October, 1845, Mr. Adams called at the Royal Observatory, Greenwich, in my absence, and left the following important paper:-

No. 11. J. C. Adams, Esq. to G. B. Airy.

'According to my calculations, the observed irregularities in the motion of *Uranus* may be accounted for by supposing the existence of an exterior planet, the mass and orbit of which are as follows:-

Mean Distance (assumed nearly in accordance with Bode's law)	38.4
Mean Sidereal Motion in 365.25 days	1° 30′.9
Mean Longitude, 1st October, 1845	323 34
Longitude of Perihelion	315 55
Excentricity	0.1610.
Mass (that of the Sun being unity)	0.0001656

For the modern observations I have used the method of normal places, taking the mean of the tabular errors, as given by observations near three consecutive oppositions, to correspond with the mean of the times; and the Greenwich observations have been used down to 1830: since which, the Cambridge and Greenwich observations, and those given in the *Astronomische Nachrichten*, have been made use of. The following are the remaining errors of mean longitude:-

Observation–Theory

1780	+0.″27	1801	−0.″04	1822	+0.″30
1783	−0.23	1804	+1.76	1825	+1.92
1786	−0.96	1807	−0.21	1828	+2.25
1789	+1.82	1810	+0.56	1831	−1.06
1792	−0.91	1813	−0.94	1834	−1.44
1795	+0.09	1816	−0.31	1837	−1.62
1798	−0.99	1819	−2.00	1840	+1.73

The error for 1780 is concluded from that for 1781 given by observation, compared with those of four or five following years, and also with Lemonnier's observations in 1769 and 1771.

For the ancient observations, the following are the remaining errors:-

Observation–Theory

1690	+44.″4	1750	−1.″6	1763	−5.″1
1712	+6.7	1753	+5.7	1769	+0.6
1715	−6.8	1756	−4.0	1771	+11.8

The errors are small, except for Flamsteed's observation of 1690. This being an isolated observation, very distant from the rest, I thought it best not to use it in forming the equations of condition. It is not improbable, however, that this error might be destroyed by a small change in the assumed mean motion of the planet.'

I acknowledged the receipt of this paper in the following terms:-

No. 12. G. B. Airy to J. C. Adams, Esq.

'Royal Observatory, Greenwich, 1845. Nov. 5.

I am very much obliged by the paper of results which you left here a few days since, shewing the perturbations on the place of *Uranus* produced by a planet with certain assumed elements. The latter numbers are all extremely satisfactory: I am not enough acquainted with Flamsteed's observations about 1690 to say whether they bear such an error, but I think it extremely probable.

But I should be very glad to know whether this assumed perturbation will explain the error of the radius vector of *Uranus*. This error is now very considerable, as you will be able to ascertain by comparing the normal equations, given in the Greenwich observations for each year, for the times *before* opposition with the times *after* opposition.'

I have before stated, that I considered the establishment of this error of the radius vector of *Uranus* to be a very important determination. I therefore considered that the trial, whether the error of radius vector would be explained by the same theory which explained the error of longitude, would be truly an *experimentum crucis*. And I waited with much anxiety for Mr. Adams's answer to my query. Had it been in the affirmative, I should at once have exerted all the influence which I might possess, either directly or indirectly through my friend Professor Challis, to procure the publication of Mr. Adams's theory.*

From some cause with which I am unacquainted, probably an accidental one, I received no immediate answer to this inquiry. I regret this deeply, for many reasons.

While I was expecting more complete information on

* Here the Astronomer Royal explained to the meeting, by means of a diagram, the nature of the errors of the tabular radius vector.

Mr. Adams's theory, the results of a new and most important investigation reached me from another quarter. In the *Compte Rendu* of the French Academy for the 10th of November, 1845, which arrived in this country in December, there is a paper by M. Le Verrier on the perturbations of *Uranus* produced by *Jupiter* and *Saturn*, and on the errors in the elliptic elements of *Uranus*, consequent on the use of erroneous perturbations in the treatment of the observations. It is impossible for me here to enter into details as to the conclusions of this valuable memoir: I shall only say that, while the correctness of the former theories, as far as they went, was generally established, many small terms were added; that the accuracy of the calculations was established by duplicate investigations, following different courses, and executed with extraordinary labour; that the corrections to the elements, produced by treating the former observations with these corrected perturbations, were obtained; and that the correction to the ephemeris for the present time, produced by the introduction of the new perturbations and the new elements, was investigated, and found to be incapable of explaining the observed irregularity of *Uranus*. Perhaps it may be truly said that the theory of *Uranus* was now, for the first time, placed on a satisfactory foundation. This important labour, as M. Le Verrier states, was undertaken at the urgent request of M. Arago.

In the *Compte Rendu* for June 1, 1846, M. Le Verrier gave his second memoir on the theory of *Uranus*. The first part contains the results of a new reduction of nearly all the existing observations of *Uranus*, and their treatment with reference to the theory of perturbations, as amended in the former memoir. After concluding from this reduction that the observations are absolutely irreconcilable with the theory, M. Le Verrier considers in the second part all the possible explanations of the discordance, and concludes that none is admissible, except that of a disturbing planet exterior to *Uranus*. He then proceeds to investigate the elements of the orbit of such a planet, assuming that its mean distance is double that of *Uranus*, and that its orbit is in the plane of the ecliptic. The value of the mean distance, it is to be remarked, is not fixed entirely by Bode's law, although suggested by it; several considerations are stated which compel us, to take a mean distance, not *very* greatly differing from that suggested by the law, but which nevertheless, without the suggestion of that law, would leave the mean distance in a most troublesome uncertainty. The peculiarity of the form which the investigation takes is then explained. Finally, M. Le Verrier gives as the most probable result of his investigations, that the true longitude of the disturbing planet for the beginning of 1847 must be about 325°, and that an error of 10° is this place is not probable. No elements of the orbit or mass of the planet are given.

This memoir reached me about the 23rd or 24th of June. I cannot sufficiently express the feeling of delight and satisfaction which I received from it. The place which it assigned to the disturbing planet was the same, to one degree, as that given by Mr. Adams's calculations, which I had persued seven months earlier. To this time I had considered that there was still room for doubt of the accuracy of Mr. Adams's investigations; for I think that the results of algebraic and numerical computations, so long and so complicated as those of an inverse problem of perturbations, are liable to many risks of error in the details of the process: I know that there are important numerical errors in the *Mécanique Céleste* of Laplace; in the *Théorie de la Lune* of Plana; above all, in Bouvard's first tables of *Jupiter* and *Saturn*; and to express it in a word, I have always considered the correctness of a distant mathematical result to be a subject rather of moral than of mathematical evidence. But now I felt no doubt of the accuracy of both calculations, as applied to the perturbation in longitude. I was, however, still desirous, as before, of learning whether the perturbation in radius vector was fully explained. I therefore addressed to M. Le Verrier the following letter:-

No. 13. G. B. Airy to M. Le Verrier.

'Royal Observatory, Greenwich, 1846, June 26.

I have read, with very great interest, the account of your investigations on the probable place of a planet disturbing the motions of *Uranus*, which is contained in the *Compte Rendu de l'Académie* of June 1; and I now beg leave to trouble you with the following question. It appears, from all the later observations of *Uranus* made at Greenwich (which are most completely reduced in the *Greenwich Observations* of each year, so as to exhibit the effect of an error either in the tabular heliocentric longitude, or the tabular radius vector), that the tabular radius vector is considerably too small. And I wish to inquire of you whether this would be a consequence of the disturbance produced by an exterior planet, now in the position which you have indicated?

I imagine that it would not be so, because the principal term of the inequality would probably be analogous to the Moon's variation, or would depend on sin 2 (v–v'); and in that case the perturbation in radius vector would have the sign – for the present relative position of the planet and *Uranus*. But this analogy is worth little, until it is supported by proper symbolical computations.

By the earliest opportunity I shall have the honour of transmitting to you a copy of the *Planetary Reductions*, in which you will find all the observations made at Greenwich to 1830 carefully reduced and compared with the tables.'

Before I could receive M. Le Varrier's answer, a transaction occurred which had some influence on the conduct of English astronomers.

On the 29th of June, a meeting of the Board of Visitors of the Royal Observatory of Greenwich was held, for the consideration of special business. At this meeting, Sir J. Herschel and Professor Challis (among other members of the Board) were present; I was also present, by invitation of the Board. The discussion led, incidentally, to the general question of the advantage of distributing subjects of observation among different observatories. I spoke strongly in favour of such distribution; and I produced, as an instance, the extreme probability of now discovering a new planet in a very short time, provided the powers of one observatory could be directed to the search for it. I gave, as the reason upon which this probability was based, the very close coincidence between the results of Mr. Adams's and M. Le Verrier's investigations of the place of the supposed planet disturbing *Uranus*. I am authorised by Sir J. Herschel's printed statement in the *Athenaeum* of October 3, to ascribe to the strong expressions which I then used the remarkable sentence in Sir. J. Herschel's address, on September 10, to the British Association assembled at Southampton. 'We see it [the probable new planet] as Columbus saw America from the shores of Spain. Its movements have been felt, trembling along the far-reaching line of our analysis, with a certainty hardly inferior to that of ocular demonstration.* And I am authorised by Professor Challis, in oral conversation, to state that the same expressions of mine induced him to contemplate the search for the suspected planet.

M. Le Verrier's answer reached me, I believe, on the 1st of July. The following are extracts from it:

No. 14. M. Le Verrier to G. B. Airy,

[Extract.]

'Paris, 28 Juin, 1846.

**** Il a toujours été dans mon désir de vous en écrire, aussi qu'à votre savante Société. Mais j'attendais, pour cela, que mes recherches fussent complètes, et ainsi moins indignes de vous être offertes. Je compte avoir terminé la

* This sentence is copied from the written draft of the speech. Sir. J. Herschel appeared to suppose that the sentence had not been reported in the public journals as spoken. I did, however, see it so reported in an English newspaper, to which I had access on the Continent.

rectification des éléments de la planète troublante avant l'opposition qui va arriver; et parvenir à connaître ainsi les positions du nouvel astre avec une grande précision. Si je pouvais espérer que vous aurez assez de confiance dans mon travail pour chercher cette planète dans le ciel, je m'empresserais, Monsieur, de vous envoyer sa position exacte, dès que je l'aurai obtenue.

La comparaison des positions d'*Uranus*, observées dans ces dernières années, dans les oppositions et dans les quadratures, montre que le rayon de la planète, calculé par les tables en usage, est effectivement très-inexact. Cela n'a pas lieu dans mon orbite, telle que je l'ai déterminée; il n'y a pas plus d'erreur dans les quadratures que dans les oppositions.

Le rayon est donc bien calculé dans mon orbite; et, si je ne me trompe, M. Airy désirerait savoir quelle est la nature de la correction que j'ai fait subir à cet égard aux tables en usage?

Vous avez raison, Monsieur, de penser que cette correction n'est pas due à la perturbation du rayon vecteur produite *actuellement* par la planète troublante. Pour s'en rendre un compte exact, il faut remarquer que l'orbite d'*Uranus* a été calculée par M. Bouvard sur des positions de la planète qui n'etaient pas *les positions elliptiques*, puisqu'on n'avait pas pu avoir égard aux perturbations produites par la planète inconnue. Cette circonstance a nécessairement rendu les éléments de l'ellipse faux, et c'est à l'erreur de l'excentricité et à l'erreur de la longitude du périhélie qu'il faut attribuer l'erreur actuelle de rayon vecteur d'*Uranus*.

Il résulte de ma théorie que l'excentricité donneé par M. Bouvard doit être augmentée, et qu'il en est de même de la longitude du périhélie; deux causes qui contribuent, à cause de la position actuelle de la planète dans son orbite, à augmenter le rayon vecteur. Je ne transcris pas ici les valeurs de ces accroissements, parce que je ne les ai pas encore avec toute la rigueur précise, mais je les aurai rectifié avant un mois, et je me ferai un devoir, Monsieur, de vous les transmettre aussitôt, si cela vous est agréable.

Je me bornerai à ajouter que la position en quadrature, déduite en 1844 des deux oppositions qui la comprennent, au moyen de mes formules, ne diffère de la position observée que de 0''.6; ce qui prouve que l'erreur de rayon vecteur est entièrement disparue.

C'est même une des considérations qui devront donner plus de probabilité à la vérité de mes résultats, qu'ils rendent un compte scrupuleux de toutes les circonstances du problème. Ainsi, bien que je n'aye fait usage dans mes premières recherches que des oppositions, les quadratures n'ont pas laissé de se trouver calculées avec toute l'exactitude possible. Le rayon vecteur s'est trouvé rectifié de lui-même, sans que l'on l'eut pris en considération d'une manière directe. Excusez-moi, Monsieur, d'insister sur ce point. C'est une suite du désir que j'ai d'obtenir votre suffrage.

Je recevrai avec bien du plaisir les observations que vous voulez bien m'announcer. Malheureusement le temps presse; l'opposition approche; il faut de toute necessité que j'aye fini pour cette époque. Je ne pourrai donc pas comprendre ces observations dans mon travail. Mais elles me seront très-utiles pour me servir de vérifications; et c'est ce à quoi je les employerai certainement.'

It is impossible, I think, to read this letter without being struck with its clearness of explanation, with the writer's extraordinary command, not only of the physical theories of perturbation but also of the geometrical theories of the deduction of orbits from observation, and with his perception that his theory ought to explain all the phenomena, and his firm belief that it had done so. I had now no longer any doubt upon the reality and general exactness of the prediction of the planet's place. My approaching departure for the Continent made it useless for me to trouble M. Le Verrier with a request for the more accurate numbers to which he alludes; but the following correspondence will shew how deeply his remarks had penetrated my mind.

About a week after the receipt of M. Le Verrier's letter,

while on a visit to my friend the Dean of Ely, I wrote to Professor Challis as follows:

No. 15. G. B. Airy to Professor Challis.

'The Deanery, Ely, 1846, July 9.

You know that I attach importance to the examination of that part of the heavens in which there is ***** reason for suspecting the existence of a planet exterior to *Uranus*. I have thought about the way of making such examinations, but I am convinced that (for various reasons, of declination, latitude of place, feebleness of light, and regularity of superintendence) there is no prospect whatever of its being made with any chance of success, except with the Northumberland Telescope.

Now I should be glad to ask you, in the first place, whether you could make such an examination?

Presuming that your answer would be in the negative, I would ask, secondly, whether, supposing that an assistant were supplied to you for this purpose, you would superintend the examination?

You will readily perceive that all this is in a most unformed state at present, and that I am asking these questions almost at a venture, in the hope of rescuing the matter from a state which is, without the assistance that you and your instruments can give, almost desperate. Therefore I should be glad to have your answer, not only responding simply to my questions, but also entering into any other considerations which you think likely to bear on the matter.

The time for the said examination is approaching near.

In explanation of this letter, it may be necessary to state that, in common, I believe, with other astronomers at that time, I thought it likely that the planet would be visible only in large telescopes. I knew that the Observatory of Cambridge was at this time oppressed with work, and I thought that the undertaking – a survey of such an extent as this seemed likely to prove – would be entirely beyond the powers of its personal establishment. Had Professor Challis assented to my proposal of assistance, I was prepared immediately to place at his disposal the services of an efficient assistant; and for approval of such a step, and for liquidation of the expense which must thus be thrown on the Royal Observatory, I should have referred to a Government which I have never known to be illiberal when demands for the benefit of science were made by persons whose character and position offered a guarantee, that the assistance was fairly asked for science, and that the money would be managed with fair frugality. In the very improbable event of the Government refusing such indemnity, I was prepared to take all consequences on myself.

On the 13th of July, I transmitted to Professor Challis 'Suggestions for the Examination of a Portion of the Heavens in search of the external Planet with is presumed to exist and to produce disturbance in the motion of *Uranus*,' and I accompanied them with the following letter:

No. 16. G. B. Airy to Professor Challis.

'Royal Observatory, Greenwich, 1846, July 13.

I have drawn up the enclosed paper, in order to give you a notion of the extent of work incidental to a sweep for the possible planet.

'I only add at present that, in my opinion, the importance of this inquiry exceeds that of any current work, which is of such a nature as not to be totally lost by delay.'

My 'Suggestions' contemplated the examination of a part of the heavens 30° long, in the direction of the ecliptic, and 10° broad. They entered into considerable details as to the method which I proposed; details which were necessary, in order to form an estimate of the number of hours' work likely to be employed in the sweep.

I received, in a few days, the following answer:

No. 17. Professor Challis to G. B. Airy.

'Cambridge Observatory, July 18th, 1846.
'I have only just returned from my excursion. ***** I have determined on sweeping for this hypothetical planet. ***** With respect to your proposal of supplying an assistant I need not say any thing, as I understand it to be made on the supposition that I decline undertaking the search myself. **** I purpose to carry the sweep to the extent you recommend.'

The remainder of the letter was principally occupied with the details of a plan of observing different from mine, and of which the advantage was fully proved in the practical observation.

On August 7, Professor Challis, writing to my confidential assistant (Mr. Main) in my supposed absence, said,–.

No. 18. Professor Challis to the Rev. R. Main.

[Extract.]

'Cambridge Observatory, August 7, 1846.
'I have undertaken to search for the supposed new planet more distant than *Uranus*. Already I have made trial of two different methods of observing. In one method, recommended by Mr. Airy ****** I met with a difficulty which I had anticipated. **** I adopted a second method.'

From a subsequent letter (to be cited hereafter), it appears that Professor Challis had commenced the search on July 29, and had actually observed the planet on August 4, 1846.

Mr. Main's answer to the other parts of this letter, written by my direction, is dated August 8.

At Wiesbaden (which place I left on September 7), I received the following letter from Professor Challis:-

No. 19. Professor Challis to G. B. Airy.

[Extract.]

'Cambridge Observatory, Sept. 2, 1846.

'I have lost no opportunity of searching for the planet; and, the nights having been generally pretty good, I have taken a considerable number of observations; but I get over the ground very slowly, thinking it right to include all stars to 10–11 magnitude; and I find, that to scrutinise, thoroughly, in this way the proposed portion of the heavens, will require many more observations than I can take this year.'

On the same day on which Professor Challis wrote this letter, Mr. Adams, who was not aware of my absence from England, addressed the following very important letter to Greenwich:-

No. 20. J. C. Adams, Esq. to G. B. Airy.

'St. John's College, Cambridge, Sept. 2, 1846.

In the investigation, the results of which I communicated to you last October, the mean distance of the supposed disturbing planet is assumed to be twice that of *Uranus*. Some assumption is necessary in the first instance, and Bode's law renders it probable that the above distance is not very remote from the truth: but the investigation could scarcely be considered satisfactory which based on any thing arbitrary; and I therefore determined to repeat the calculation, making a different hypothesis as to the mean distance. The eccentricity also resulting from my former calculations was far too large to be probable; and I found that, although the agreement between theory and observation continued very satisfactory down to 1840, the difference in subsequent years was becoming very sensible, and I hoped that these errors, as well as the eccentricity, might be diminished by taking a different mean distance. Not to make too violent a change, I assumed this distance to be less than the former value by about 1/30th part of the whole. The result is very satisfactory, and appears to shew that, by still further diminishing the distance, the agreement between the theory and the later observations may be rendered complete, and the eccentricity reduced at the same time to a very small quantity. The mass and the elements of the orbit of the supposed planet, which result from the two hypotheses, are as follows:-

	Hypothesis I.	Hypothesis II.
	$\frac{a}{a'} = 0.5$	$\frac{a}{a'} = 0.515$
Mean Longitude of Planet, 1st. Oct. 1846	325° 8′	323° 2′
Longitude of Perihelion	315 57	299 11
Eccentricity	0.16103	0.12062
Mass (that of Sun being 1)	0.00016563	0.00015003

The investigation has been conducted in the same manner in both cases, so that the differences between the two sets of elements may be considered as wholly due to the variation of the fundamental hypothesis. The following table exhibits the differences between the theory and the observations which were used as the basis of calculation. The quantities given are the errors of *mean* longitude, which I found it more convenient to employ in my investigations that those of the true longitude.
[For the rest of this letter and mathematical details, see the Appendix.]

The fierce nature of the contemporary conflict can be gleaned from Airy's reply to a critical letter he had received from Professor Sedgwick, of Trinity College, Cambridge. Airy replies to this letter from the 'Royal Observatory, Greenwich, on December 4, 1846.

Dear Sedgwick,

I will answer your letter as explicitly as I can in the short time I have to spare. You need not be afraid of using any freedom in your letters – nor need anybody else in the matter as regards the disturbance of my temper – for when I thought of writing my account I repeated to myself

> 'Those who in quarrels interpose
> Must often wipe a bloody nose'

and I made up my mind to wipe my nose accordingly.
Charge 1 'Of [one word that I cannot read] and apathy towards Adams, and of having snubbed him'

As touching 'apathy' look at my letter November 5, 1845 and see whether it looks like apathy. As touching 'snubbing', I never had any opportunity of doing this. My whole epistolary communication with Adams is printed in the 'Account'; and I never saw him but twice; – once, somewhere with Challis (I totally forget where) and once when Hansen and I came for half a day to Cambridge, and we were walking over St. John's bridge. The interview on each occasion might last 2 minutes. I have had no other opportunity of seeing him. I am sorry to have wasted so many words on this; it is purely ridiculous.
Charge 2 'That Adams called when I was at home, and that I refused to give him audience.' Untrue.

(Did it occur to your friend to inquire how my being at home on this supposed occasion was established?)
Charge 3 'Had the results communicated to Airy and Challis been sent to Berlin I am told they came so near the mark that to a certainty the new Planet would have been made out in a very few weeks, perhaps a very few days.'

What in the name of goodness has Berlin to do with this? The powers at Cambridge Observatory much exceed those of Berlin. And as it was the planet was found at Cambridge before it was found at Berlin. But in 1845 I did not even urge Challis to observe, because (in consequence of Adams not having answered my critical question) I regarded the whole matter as doubtful. The results of Adams' first calculations were quite near enough to enable anyone to find

the planet. The only thing needed was, sufficient grounds for trusting the results.
Charge 4 'Adams is a very young man – and he had no backer to urge him on, and says *"I did my best in sending my results to two natural observatories"* '.

I am quite certain that no person can read my letter of November 5th, 1845 without seeing that I took very great interest in what Adams was about, and that I entered so far into it as to ask for fuller and more critical information. Adams, by not answering my letter, not only left the matter in an unsatisfactory state, and thereby 'did not do his best in sending results', but also entirely stopped me from writing again.
Charge 5 'When about June last Le Verrier published *one* of the results Adams had attained before (September 1845), why in the name of wonder was not all Europe made to ring with the fact that a B.A. of Cambridge had done this 10 months previously?'

In the name of wonder what had *I* to do with this publication? No understood rule of Society would have justified me in doing so. The *first* person to publish was Adams. The *second* was Challis. The *third* was I. But there was a very serious difficulty in the way of *my* doing so, because Adams had declined to answer my letter. Moreover, in consequence of my question not having been resolved, I had not till I received Le Verrier's explanatory letter the security for the truth of the theory which I desired.

You insist much on Adams being only a B.A. etc., etc., which was probably known to you, and Challis, but was not known to me. (I supposed him to be an M.A. of some standing, and addressed him as Reverend.) But this has nothing to do with the matter. Now, my dear Sedgwick I do not write this *to be published*, but *to give you information* on which you may act; and I desire that you should, in conjunction with it, read my printed Account again, I shall wipe my bloody nose quietly at home. Yours most truly G. B. Airy.' (Letter at St. John's College, Cambridge, Box 12 of Adam's papers.)

In a letter previous to this one Airy had written to *Rev.* Mr. J. Adams on 14 October 1846 in a semi-apologetic manner as he had been in Germany but he offers to write to the R.A.S. on *Account* of what he knows of the English transactions

1) For the History of Science
2) To do justice to England
3) To do justice to individuals
4) He could do it as he had most of the history and yet had taken no part in theory on observation.

The letter continues 'it would be wrong for me to compromise anymore, and therefore I ask no advice about this. All I ask is – will you permit me to publish your correspondence with me on the subject in extracts taken from the correspondence taken at my discretion? Have the kindness to give me an answer *in a day or two.* I am, dear sir, faithfully yours G. B. Airy'.

A further note of 20 November 1846 from Airy to Adams shows that Adams had replied as Airy writes – 'I am greatly obliged, by your note of 18th. I should not in my account of the planet have made any mention of my waiting for your answer to my query, but that (as you will have seen by the French discussion) the similar inquiry addressed to M. Le Verrier had already been seized upon as proving that you had done nothing whatever, and any supposition of the whole seemed necessary for a general History.'

The correspondence continues on to 29 April 1847, addressed this time to J. C. Adams, from G. B. Airy when the question is discussed as to whether Lalande had certainly seen the planet, but thought it was a star, because of the difficulties involved in searching the sky. This letter has Le Verrier's backing for Lalande's mistake and concludes with Airy's sentence 'Let no one after this blame Challis.'

A letter from a niece of J. C. Adams, Mary Roseveare,

(a daughter of Mary Ann Adams, his youngest sister) written on 21 April 1947 to Prof. W. M. Smart, thanking him for his Essays in *Nature* on the Centenary Celebrations for Neptune, shows the family's attitude to the saga. She was at Newnham College, Cambridge 1891–95, and saw J. C. Adams when a frail old man, and knew the story of Neptune as family folklore. She writes

> It was a great grief to my Aunt that Sir Donald Macalister (busy man that he was) never succeeded in writing Uncle's life. You may guess that we are the more grateful for the accurate and sympathetic study you have written of the Neptune discovery. Uncle John's dislike of leaving his calculations to written letters was fully recognised by his family, and Sir Harold Spencer-Jones criticises him justly for not answering Airy's letter, but that surely does not absolve the Royal Astronomer of responsibility for his neglect of papers handed in by person on his return from his vacation in Cornwall. His want of sympathy, so patent by contrast with his attitude to Le Verrier, must have had a chilling and depressing influence on one so modest, and unable to push, as my uncle. For him it was scientific worth that mattered and not credit, and his refusal to accept the Knighthood offered him, and other high office, proves his devotion to his work, especially on the moon's mean motion, which meant more to him than the much talked of Neptune discovery.
>
> As children we put most blame in the end on Professor Challis, who should have accepted Airy's offer of an assistant from Greenwich, or have seen that observing was more thorough. The story of the cup of tea, published in a picture paper not long ago is regarded as true by the Misses Challis of Cambridge. One of my old col-

leagues knows them well and asked them if it was true or not.

The Knighthood was offered to Adams in 1847 by Queen Victoria. The reasons why he refused it are made clear in a letter he wrote to the Rev. Prof. Adam Sedgwick from St John's College on 15 June 1847. Adams was aged just twenty-eight years on 5 June 1847.

My Dear Sir,

I have been thinking seriously on the subject of which we were speaking the other day. There are certainly some strong reasons to induce me to accept the honour if it should be offered me.

To receive from the hand of the Sovereign such a mark of distinction, and one conferred on a similar occasion on Newton, could not fail to be very gratifying to my ambition. It would place me in a satisfactory position in the eyes of the world, as being a public recognition of my claims connected with the discovery of the new planet. It would also, no doubt, tend to promote the cultivation of science in England, by showing that the Government is disposed to sympathize with and to encourage those who devote themselves to such pursuits. But on the other hand there are two objections one of which I partially stated to you the other day, about which, there is no one whose opinion I value more, I wish to ask your advice. The first is, that it is doubtful whether I could *afford* to accept such an honour. I have no private fortune, and a title would prevent me having recourse to several means of obtaining a sufficient income, such as taking pupils, while it could hardly be expected that the Government would grant me sufficient pension to render such means unnecessary. I do not insist upon the obstacle to my taking orders, as I have not yet decided that I should do so, however this matter may turn out.

Again, if I were to wish to marry, my choice would be seriously restricted by the necessity there would be for keeping up appearances, in some degree corresponding to the title.

My next difficulty is that my connections occupy a comparatively humble position in life. My father is simply a farmer, and it might appear rather incongruous that his son should be Sir John.

You would much oblige me by giving your opinion whether there is sufficient weight in these objections, and also whether you think the Government would be disposed to do anything in the matter, if the title were not accepted.

I remain, my dear Sir,
Ever your obliged faithful servant
J. C. Adams.

There is no trace of Sedgwick's reply, but the title was refused, and it never was 'Sir John'. Had it come later in his career perhaps he might have thought differently, though this letter to Sedgwick shows the true reasoning nature of the man, looking on all angles before deciding, and eventually taking the most simple, and maybe the most honest and humble course.

The same modesty is shown when Adams graduated. A reference to this appears in *The Queen* 11 November 1893, eighteen months after Adams's death, when someone, signing himself as Peregrine, writes to the magazine under the title 'Adams's Year'.

I was an undergraduate of St. John's College, Cambridge, when the late Professor Adams was there as an undergraduate also. I well remember his appearance. He was rather a small man, who walked quickly, and wore a faded coat of dark green. As I had entered as a pensioner and he as a sizar, we did not sit at the same table in hall, or, indeed, dine at the same hour. In my time, the Fellows' hall and ours was at four o'clock, the sizars' (who had some dishes left from the Fellows' table) at five. Chapel was at six when every member of the College was due, and when some came. Fellow commoners and pensioners saw but little of the sizars as a rule, and I fear they were looked down upon on account of their poverty, except, indeed, those few who were certain to do great credit to the college. The fastest and the vainest man would have been civil to Adams, for he was known to be a pretty certain Senior Wrangler, besides, men bet on him and backed him as they would a racehorse. But he was so exceedingly good, so, unusually safe, so utterly and entirely the favourite, that odds were laid on him at three, or even four, to one. Men little thought, indeed, that, he would very shortly discover a comet [*sic*], and that science all through the world, would 'cap' him in concert with the undergraduates, to whom he soon became a mighty don, though, I believe, one of the most gentle and unassuming that ever lived.

A couple of days after Adams had come out Senior Wrangler, I knocked in late, and had a chat with Ballard, the porter, before going to my rooms. I said, 'Well, Ballard, we've got the Senior Wrangler, but that was of course'. Ballard looked glum. I could not understand it, for he was as proud of the college as any of its members. 'Ah, Sir,' he said, 'Mr. Adams did not behave well to me.' 'Not well to you! Why what on earth had he done?' 'I have lost £5 by him, Sir.' 'How?' 'Mr. Adams is not a gentleman as often knocks in late, but two nights before he went in to the Senate House, he did, and I made so bold as to say, "Mr. Adams, I hope no offense, Sir, but I suppose you are certain to be Senior Wrangler; because I have laid £10 on it already, and I have a chance of laying another £5." Now, you'd hardly believe it, Sir, but Mr. Adams told me there was no certainty about it, and that he might come out second or third, when all the while he must have known he was dead certain.' 'Well,' I said, 'I don't know what he knew, but all the University knew; but how did you lose your £5?' 'By not putting it on, Sir; which I should have done if he hadn't knocked in late. I kept £10 on, however, and won what came of that.' So really Mr. Ballard had not very much to complain of.

It was said among us that Adams never read more than six hours a day; and in a certain sense, that was perfectly true. In my time – and I should think now –, Freshmen, and men in their last term, had to 'keep' out of college; in other words, they lived in lodgings licensed by the authorities and their knockings-in were reported just as strictly as if they had been in college. Oddly enough, I had lodgings in my last term which Adams, somewhat my senior, had inhabited long before; I think in his last term but one. I naturally asked my landlady if she could tell me anything of the Senior Wrangler's habits. How long did he read? and so forth. She said that she sometimes found him lying on the sofa, with neither books nor papers near him; but not infrequently he was standing at a desk he had fixed against the wall, and that when she wanted to speak to him, the only way to attract his attention, was to go up to him and touch his shoulder; calling to him was of no use. I found out afterwards that the great man was in the habit, after he had accomplished a certain piece of work at the desk, of thinking the whole matter out on the sofa, and, it was there, probably, that his brain-work was at the greatest.

The above facts are within my experience, and mine only. His homely manner of living and dressing when he was an undergraduate I have already mentioned, as well as his modesty when he became the pride of his college and of his university. But these were known to all.

Peregrine.

By 1851 he was a Junior Proctor contending with perturbations in Senate House examinations, rather than in the heavens.

> We, the Proctors and Moderators for the current year, having had our attention called to the existence of certain dishonourable practices in the

Examinations for the Degree of B.A., and acting upon a recent decision of the Vice-Chancellor to the effect, that a Candidate who had taken a paper from his pocket and copied it in the Senate-House, brought himself, in spite of explanations, under 'very grave suspicion,' wish to make it known, that, in similar cases, we shall reject every Candidate who, by his own deed, renders his Examination equivocal. We feel assured that the great body of Undergraduates, in common with our selves, consider it essential to the honour of the University that its Public Examinations be above suspicion.

W. Nind, Senior Proctor
J. C. Adams, Junior Proctor
H. Goodwin, Senior Moderator
S. Parkinson, Junior Moderator.

Cambridge
Nov. 1851.

A letter addressed to Adams dated 30 December 1856 among the Adams's papers at St John's College Cambridge, proves that abuses continued. It gives a good picture of the cheating still going on, and concludes 'The remedy is with you and surely the man that discovers planets can find some practical way of conducting an examination fairly, and stop the low system of copying.' The correspondent states 'It seems that this year a notice against the system of copying at examinations has been issued and the reason for this is made to rest upon a single case. But why upon a single case? Do you not know that it is a *system*? If not, will you allow me to lay before you a statement of facts, that perhaps may open your eyes a little wider? Listen to a plain unvarnished tale. When last year I passed the Poll exam, all round me, on the right-hand and on the left, men copied freely. Some got assistance from their friends: some worried their neighbours into helping them; some boldly produced *books* from pockets artfully contrived in their gowns or in wonderfully constructed overcoats; *occupat extremum scabiis* was the order of the day. The most common method of all was to take in many of the most likely answers, especially propositions in mechanics, Hydrostatics in Euclid and the like, ready written out, and to produce them from the pocket – if they were in too crumpled a state to show up to re-write them then and there; if not too dog-eared,– to show them up just as they were. *And as the paper itself had been taken from the Senate House on the previous day* detection was not feared. I do not hesitate to say that half the men are copying. Some more, some less; some in one subject, some in *all*; it was a regular system; in so much that one man who sat in an *unlucky* place (i.e. close under the examiner's nose) cut the examination after the second day, saying it was no use going on, as no man could pull through who had such bad luck as to be placed as he was. He never dreamt of any man's getting a degree by any other means than copying. In May he succeeded, but as he modestly remarked, a man must be a fool not to be able to get through when there was only one examiner in the room, and he reading a book all the time! It appears that examiners are not sufficiently alive to the perverted ingenuity of those they examine. To sit in the Senate House looking over papers, reading novels, or otherwise amusing themselves as best they please, is not doing their duty. Twenty examiners, all parading the Senate House, and all looking sharp too, would not be too many to detect the numerous tricks imployed to hoodwink an examiner.' It was also pointed out that it was the Arithmetic paper which 'plucked most men' as it was difficult to take in ready made answers for this paper. So much for one aspect of Cambridge University life half way through the nineteenth century. Something must have been done about this situation, as the modern undergraduate probably finds the paths of dishonesty more fraught with difficulty – or does he? No evidence has come to light as to how far J. C. Adams remedied the situation.

A few pages from J. C. Adams's diary for May in Cambridge in 1854 show other angles on University life, which do not differ so much from May week, or its preceeding weeks, today. The entries show some of his wider interests, eight years after the discovery and controversy of Neptune.

1854: 3 May (Wed.): Went to Stephen's lecture on the power of the King, and the function of the *conseil d'etat* as derived from those of the old feudal court. After went to the Senate House. (Studies Syndicate)

4 May (Thurs.): Wrote to accept the Lord Mayor's invitation on the 18th. Finished reading 'Hyperion'. Motto an excellent one. Went to Stephen's lecture on the Constitution of the Army, Courts of Justice etc. After, walked to Trumpington alone, and came back with Cope. Then wrote to Airy on Hansen's note. Moon's secular equation. It has been a beautiful day.

5 May (Fri.): Began Longfellow's Kavanagh. Attended College meeting, which lasted a long time. Then to Sir J. Stephen's lecture on the state of the Gallican Church before the Revolution. Called at the Library, and then took a short walk with Bashforth.* A very heavy shower about 5. Afterwards it cleared and I walked to Lestourgeons to dinner. Met M/s Burbage, Dr. Fisher etc., and spent evening. Played at Vingt-un till late.

6 May (Sat.): Read more of Kavanagh. Then read the papers and took a walk with Bashforth on Observatory Road, and returned by Coton. Headlam was thrown from his horse but is going on well. Dined at St. John's on their great day. Sat by Overton. Very large party. Enjoyed myself

* Fellow of St John's, Second Wrangler when JCA was Senior? Took orders. Later Professor at Greenwich Military Academy. Expert in Ballistics, frequently consulted Adams.

very well. Authentic account of bombardment of Odessa this morning.*

7 May (Sun.): ['3rd Sunday after Easter' printed in J. C. A.'s Letts Diary] Rose late. Mr. Nevile on Conscience in his defence of Paley†. Elliot preached on the History of the Prophet sent from Judah to denounce Jereboam's idolatory, and the apparently severe manner in which he was punished for disobedience. Finished Nevile's defence of Paley, but am not satisfied by it.

8 May (Mon.): Wrote a letter home. Got a ticket for the Choral Festival of to-morrow. Borrowed Forbes on Glaciers of Norway etc. and Switzerland from Parkinson. Rain and hail. In evening Ferguson and I walked to Ditton to see a boat race. Lady Margaret bumped Trinity and got head of the river. Called at Phil. After read some Forbes. In afternoon looked over some investgs with Bessel in Sch. Alln.

9 May (Tues.): Rose late. Went with Ferguson to King's Chapel. Well pleased with the music, parts with Tarrant, Elvey, and the Hallelujah Chorus. Afterwards went to luncheon at Mr. Barrett's. Met Prof. and Mrs. Challis. Mrs. Fullerton. Went to a party at Godfray's. Had a little dancing; evening passed off pleasantly. The Hopkins there, and Miss Craig with Mrs. Fawcett. Finished Longfellow's Kavanagh.

10 May (Wed.): Made some further notes on Bessel's Comet paper. Sir J. Stephen lectured on Social life in France in middle of 18th C. Remains on Feudalis etc. Walked with Overton round Trumpington and Grantchester. We had a feast in hall, and a large party. I had no

* Crimean War – England embarked on war with Russia on March 27 1854 – Russia had attacked Turkey – war ended with Treaty of Paris March 1856.

† Paley, 1743–1805, Christ's College, Cambridge, 1763 Senior Wrangler, 1794 *A View of the Evidences of Christianity*.

guest. Afterwards Stokes* and I went to the Ray Society at Babington's.

11 May (Thurs.): Worked a little more at Bessel's paper. Sir J. Stephens on the Financial system of France during the 18th Century. Met with Nevile after the lecture. Then walked with Bainbridge and Parkinson. Read the papers and then dined at Dr. Clarke's. Met Henslow, Cumming,† Paget,‡ Fisher etc. Read a little of Forbes's Norway.

12 May (Fri.): Read some more of Forbes's Norway, and returned it to Park. Also returned Schemate to St. John's Library and Humboldt's§ Cosmos, which I had taken for Airy. Stephen lectured on the Financiers Administration of Law, National Bank, Mississipi Scheme etc. Afterwards walked to Trumpington. Met with Brown and friend. After Hall played at Bowls. Took tea at Godfray, and spent evening looking over Challis's paper on Lunar.

13 May (Sat.): (Old May Day) [printed in Letts' Diary] Looked at letter which Ferguson is about to send to the Times. Read the papers. Walked with Bashforth, and after with Parkinson and Overton. Just began my report on Challis's paper. In evening went to a large party at Hopkins. Gave some songs. Had some pleasant chat. I have been very idle to-day.

14 May (Sun.): (4th after Easter) Went to Chapel in morning. Then called at Philosy, and afterward walked in Jonsian grounds. Talked of synodic action and revision of Prayer Book. Then with Field, and discussed some points

* Prof. G. G. Stokes (1819–1903) Irish Mathematician. b. Skreen, Co. Sligo – Pembroke Coll. Camb. Lucasian Prof. of Maths 1849. Sec. (1854–85) and Pres. (1885–90) of Royal Society and Fellow (1841–57), Master (1902) of Pembroke. MP of Cambridge 1886 Married a daughter of Prof. Robinson of Armagh Observatory, Ministry of Mines for a time.

† Prof. of Chem (Paget attended his lectures 1852)

‡ 1852 Nominated for Master of Caius. Guest appointed.

§ Humboldt 1769–1859, Naturalist. *Cosmos* 1845–58. Series of lectures given in Berlin–one of the greatest scientific works ever published.

about the war. Elliot preached on our Lord's appearance to disciples going to Emmaus. Took a turn with Bashforth. After Chapel, took tea with him.

15 May (Mon.): Wrote some of my report on Challis's paper. A college meeting at 11, which lasted a long time. Challis gave an account of Galvanic Signals. He is much offended at the hesitation shown with regard to his paper.

16 May (Tues.): Finished writing out my Report for Challis's perusal; showed it to Godfray. Wrote a note to Challis to accompany my remarks. Went to Sir J. Stephens' lectures on religious controversy of France of 18th Century. Walked with Overton & Bert. On return found a note from Challis and took my papers to him at Phil. Had some bowling after Hall. In evening went to a party at Wm Martin's of Grantchester. Had some Scotch songs from Miss Craig and Miss Haycock, and some good music from Miss Reece. Walked home with Godfray.

17 May (Weds.): Rose late. Went to the Senate House. Challis gave me a note, and I had some talk with him afterwards – not of a very pleasant nature. He presses me to enter into a public controversy. In evening went to a large party at Phear's. Danced with M/s H, and had some talk with Mrs. Martin.

18 May (Thurs.): Went by express to London. Mr. and Mrs. Lestourgeon and Romilly* in the same carriage. Some pleasant conversation. Went to Exhibition of Academy. Spent some time over the pictures. Afterwards met with Mr. Sheepshanks.† Dined at the Mansion House. Sat next to Lagand. Had a good deal of talk on the Eastern Question and other topics of the day. After dinner had some 'idiotic conversation' with Urquhart. Some good singing after dinner. The Lord Mayor paid me some flattering compliments.

*Romily Registry

† Sheepshanks (Richard 1794–1855) Astronomer – operated a pendulum in Cornwall with Airy 1828. Determined longitude of Antwerp, Liverpool by chronometric observation. Helped to restore standard weights and measures, destroyed by fire in 1834.

19 May (Fri.): Rose rather late. Called on Sir J. Lubbock.* Came to Cambridge by 11½ train. Escorted M/S Dewey and had some agreeable conversation with her. Played some games at bowls. In the evening went to a large party at Mrs. Skinner's. Introduced to Miss Matthias. Dancing was kept up rather late. Had some conversation with Miss Croker, Miss Hawthorne etc.

20 May (Sat.): [sole entry] Read the 'Rape of the Lock'. Took tea with Bashforth.

21 May (Sun.): (Rogation) Elliot preached on the contribution for the poor saints of Jerusalem and a collection was made for the Sons of the Clergy.

22 May (Mon.): Dined at Prof. Stokes and met Mr. and Miss Phear. Longfellow's Hyperion etc. mentioned in conversation. After went to a large party at Mrs. Hopkins. Danced with Miss Hawthorne, Miss Hopkins, Miss Phear, and Miss Dewey.

23 May (Tues.): Went with Brown to the University Concert. Had a good deal of Italian singing from Gardiner, Coleridge. Sat next to Overton. Met with a Trinity man whose acquaintance I had made on the Col de Baline.

24 May (Weds.): Sir J. Stephen lectured on the character and writings of Voltaire.

3 June: [Printed in Lett's Diary Oxford term ends–Cam divided June 1] Went to London by express. In same carriage with Bateson.† Met with Mrs. Challis at station. She was very cold. Called on Sir J. Lubbock. Bought a hat etc. Went to Lord Ross's.

4 June (Whitsun Day): Left London by early train, but we were a long time on the way. In the same carriage with the Master of Trinity and Mrs. Saltin. Late breakfast. Skinner gave a somewhat flowery but dull sermon in afternoon. Walked in our garden after Chapel.

5 June (Whit Monday): My 35th Birthday. Went to a

* Founder of August Bank Holiday in Great Britain. MP for Maidstone 1870–1880 b 1834, Principal of London Working Man's college.
† Master of St John's College

meeting of examiners to settle the Lists. Then to college meeting which lasted till Hall time. Settled scholarships.

12 June (Mon): Wrote a note home this morning. Ordered a new pair of boots. Fined for breaking an inkstand. Played at Bowls pretty successfully. In evening wrote a letter to Challis containing some criticisms of his paper, showed it to Stokes* and remained late with him.

13 June (Tues.): Rose late. Rec'd catalogue of Arago's library and looked through it. Also a letter from Lubbock. Made a list of the periods of Lunar Inequ^{s}. whose coeff^{s}. are to be examined with the no. of corresponding Argts. in American Tables. Called on Bashforth with umbrella. Then went to Johnian bowling green with Park. Played till near Hall. Aft^{s}. on our own Green.

14 June (Wed.): Called on Bashforth, & aft^{s}. at the Phil. rooms and at the Library. In the evening played at bowls with some success. Went to tea at Bashforth's and then he divided for me several scales showing the no: of days cont^{d}. in mult^{s}. of halfperiods of Lunar unequalities whose coefficients require examination. Wilson of Belfast came in late.

15 June (Thurs.): Did a little more to my calcul^{ns}. of dates when Lunar Argt^{s}. vanish . . . Dined with Clark of Trinity to meet the College Examiner's Looked at some gd photographs of Jerusalem in Constantinople &c brought from the East by Luard.

16 June (Fri.): Rec'd a letter from Thomas. Called at the Library & looked through D'Alembert's Opescules, met with Stokes & Fischer.–Afts. Walked with them to botanic garden. Called at Bashforth's in evening & he divided some more Lunar scales. I wrote to Jeff's for Argo's books.

17 June (Sat.): My gyp having omitted to post my letter to Jeffs, I was fortunate to be able to send it by a friend of Wilson's, who is going to London. Thought about my answer to Challis. Walked with Rayner on Sheep's Green. Then with him to St. John's bowling green and played till

* G. G. Stokes, M.A., FRS (Pembroke College) Lucasian Prof. of Maths, Uni. of Cambridge. Prof. of Physics Gov't School of Mines.

Hall. Aft^{s}. on our own & after having given up once, resumed on Croker & Power coming. Went to Bashforth's & divided some more scales. After I had left he finished all that remained.

18 June (Sun.): Went to Chapel this morning. Bashforth & Watson called & walked with me round Trumpington & Grantchester. Then lunched with me. Aft^{s}. went to hear rather a dull Univ. sermon by Grant. Wilson, Fischer, & Power of Clare dined with us. Searle extemporised a pretty good dinner. After coffee we all walked for a long time in the garden. Then adjourned to Power's room, & had tea. Looked at maps.

19 June (Mon.): Rose early. Wrote to Mr. Francis. Wrote part of my answer to Challis. Power called & I *accepted* the Mathematical Lectureship.

So apart from difficulties over disagreements with Challis's scientific theories, and problems of university discipline, life was very pleasant and leisurely in 1854. By this time Adams had settled the problem of taking orders, had given up the St John's Fellowship and moved to Pembroke.

3

Cambridge: 1855–61
St Andrew's University 1857–59

While John Couch Adams was enjoying the usual variety of occupations of May Week in Cambridge, criticisms of the organization and curriculum of the University were rife, which suggested reforms were necessary. George Peacock, the Dean of Ely, and a former Lowndean Professor of Mathematics and Geometry, had published, in 1841, his 'Observations on the Statutes of the University'. Here he had stated that 'at least half the students in the University are designed for the Church, and no provision (the lectures of the Norrisian Professor alone excepted) is made for their professional education'. Attendance at all Professors' lectures had been waning since the end of the eighteenth century, and by 1842 the decline continued unabated. Some Professors never gave lectures, and some who did, did so to audiences of two or three. The tutorial system, however, maintained its strength in the University. There was a strong faction in the Universities of Oxford and Cambridge who wanted to preserve the status quo, which the Universities had enjoyed through the ages; this faction resented any outside criticism of curriculum or practices. However, Royal Commissions were being mooted in the early 1850s, and the preserves of the academic elite of Oxford and Cambridge were to be open for inspection, question, and criticism. Parliament, under Sir Robert Peel, was pressing for such Royal Commissions to inspect the inner structures of Oxford, Cambridge and Dublin. Prince Albert had been appointed in 1847 Chancellor of Cambridge University and was known to be a reformer. He had previously visited Cambridge with the Queen in 1843, when he had become a member of Trinity College, and a Doctor of Laws.

D. A. Winstanley in *Early Victorian Cambridge* (1940, Cambridge University Press, Ch. 11, p. 235, 'The Royal Commission'), gives a few vivid clues to the political, clerical, and University problems and tensions ahead for the Royal Commission. Personal rivalries, and dislike of Reforms, can be sensed in the following account.

> In November 1849 Professor Corrie, having been for many years a Fellow and Tutor of St. Catharine's was promoted by his friend and former colleague, Dr. Turton, Bishop of Ely, to the Mastership of Jesus, and twelve months later, in accordance with the established system of rotation, he succeeded Dr. Cartwell as Vice-Chancellor. It was unfortunate that he entered upon this office when the Royal Commissioners were beginning their labours, as he was an extreme Tory in academic and national politics and the last ditch was his spiritual home.

Adam Sedgwick, Vice-Master of Trinity, and later one of the Commissioners, when writing to Colonel Grey on 19 January 1851 (a letter now in the Royal Archives, Windsor) adds further information about Corrie.

> He is a thoroughly conscientious man and book-learned in his own way; and I am told that he is both respected and loved by the circle of his

> personal friends. But he is physically reserved, timid and shy, bearing this character in his person and manner. Over and above, he is on many points singularly narrow-minded, and on all points he is, I believe as obstinate as a mule; so that no power on earth would turn him when he thinks himself right, and like other honest men of narrow views, he perhaps never believes himself in the wrong.

This was the man Prince Albert, as Chancellor, had to work with. He was also evidently strongly prejudiced against the Chancellor, never sought his advice, rarely communicated with him, and in fact declined an invitation to dine with him, as he did not wish to be considered as an appendage of the Court.*

These comments help to show the climate of Cambridge University when Prince Albert became Chancellor. Even his election, in 1847, had divided the University.

The apparently calm waters of the Cam flowed on, in spite of personal vendetta and Government interference in University affairs. While Corrie remained as Vice-Chancellor, on 2 December 1850 he had informed Heads of Houses whom he had summoned to attend him, that he had decided not to answer two questionnaires about the finances and degree courses of the University, which the Commissioners had sent to him early in November 1850. He sends a note to the Commissioners, declaring war on them.

> After having ascertained from high legal authority, that the University Commission is without the form of law, and is, moreover, regarded as unconstitutional, and of a kind that was never issued except in the worst times, I feel obliged by a

* G. Corrie to Rev. Augustus Phipps, 5 Nov. 1850, Royal Archives, Windsor.

sense of public duty to decline answering any questions which I had the honour to receive from you a short time ago.*

He also refused, as Master of Jesus, to supply any information about his college. Dr Ainslie, Master of Pembroke, strongly disapproved of Corrie's attitude, eventually supplied the information about the degree courses, and Richard Okes, Provost of King's, on succeeding Corrie as Vice-Chancellor, answered the Commissioner's questions about the University Finances.† Progress was being made.

These glimpses into the affairs of Cambridge University in the mid-nineteenth century, reveal clashes of personalities and ideas, which have a way of recurring in institutions, whether ecclesiastical, academic or political.

A similar division of opinion had arisen in 1847, a year after the discovery of the planet Neptune, when Cambridge opinion was divided between the two rival candidates for the Chancellorship – either Prince Albert, or Lord Powis. It was felt that Prince Albert, in spite of his German education and lack of knowledge of English universities, might rid the office of party strife, and, with his close connection with the Crown might be able to wield more influence with the government than previous Chancellors, and in spite of his reforming zeal might fend off the looming possibilities of a Commission. Whewell, and Trinity, therefore made tentative suggestions as to the possibility of Prince Albert being willing to stand as Chancellor. Whewell heard, however, to his great disgust, that the Trinity proposition might be scuppered by a counterattack from the Master and Seniors of St John's, who immediately, on learning of the sudden death of the previous Chancellor, the Duke of Northumberland, at Alnwick on 12 February 1847, had invited Lord Powis, a former undergraduate of their College, to be a candidate.

* University Commission Report 1852.
† p. 235, Winstanley.

Powis, even when he heard of the Prince's nomination, refused to withdraw, and an election was held. Sir Robert Peel advised the Prince to compete in spite of a rival competitor.

Among the Whewell papers quoted by D. A. Winstanley in his *Early Victorian Cambridge,* is a letter from William Frederick Pollock, a distinguished Trinity man who was against the Prince's nomination. Writing to Whewell he states his reasons for writing:

> First to prevent the election of the Prince Consort, and so to maintain the true dignity and independence of the University, which would be sacrificed by committing its highest functions to the keeping of a personage, without any substantial existence of his own but wholly merged in the Crown; from his position inaccessible in the ordinary ways in which a Chancellor is addressed, and even disqualified from discharging the usual courtesies as well as the duties of office; Secondly, to protest against the proceeding of the resident members of the Senate. The Senate now consists of about 3,500 members of whom only some 300 are resident. Railway communications now brings us all much nearer to Cambridge, and the strongest feeling exists among the non-residents that no important step should be taken without, at least, some endeavour to ascertain their opinion, if that step is to be assumed to be the act, or to represent the wishes, of a majority of the body.

St John's had not taken non-resident opinion into account before inviting Lord Powis to stand; and many quite reasonable men were prejudiced against the Prince, suspecting he might wish to remodel Cambridge University on the lines of a German University and be reluctant to defend the University against the government. Religion also reared an ugly head in some arguments: 'Good Protestants were also called upon to save the University from Popery disguised as Tractarianism.' Trinity men were called upon to show their hatred to St John's by voting against the candidate of that college; and loyal subjects were called upon to vote for 'the noble-hearted husband of our noble-hearted Queen'.

D. A. Winstanley *Early Victorian Cambridge*, in a footnote on page 116, refers to a poem among the Whewell papers which describes the Tractarians voting for Lord Powis because they wished to restore the papal authority in England, and the Johnians as voting for him because 'the Dons of Trinity and King's oppose him'. Another poem in the same collection accused Lord Powis' supporters of 'wounding their Sovereign in her woman's heart'.

According to the *Autobiographic Recollections of George Pryme* (1870, p. 314) he had found it difficult to know where to cast his vote, though a Trinity man and a Whig, he voted eventually for Prince Albert. The election began on Thursday 25 February 1847 and lasted three days. Voting took place in the Senate House amid remarks from the undergraduates in the gallery. Lord Fitzwilliam, in scarlet gown, was greeted with 'here she is – the Lady of Babylon', as he cast his vote for Lord Powis. Voting took place from 10 a.m. to 5 p.m. and again from 8 p.m. to 9 p.m. in the evening on the first day. During the evening hour the undergraduates 'howled and hooted, and made themselves hateful', according to the Diary of J. Romilly, the Registrar. Of the 1219 votes recorded on the first day a 'prodigeous number' – 617 – were for the Prince and 602 were for Lord Powis. Old friends of opposite camps managed to dine together at 5.30 p.m. that day. It is reported that 240 Trinity graduates dined together in their college Hall. Adam Sedgwick, as Vice-Master, presided and proposed 'in a kind way for both sides' the toast of the non-resident voters, for which Lord Nelson, Chairman of Lord Powis's London Committee returned thanks and proposed Sedgwick's health, which was 'received with great applause'. On the second day of voting only 445 votes were recorded in the eight hours – 258 were for the Prince – which gave him a lead of 86 votes. The undergraduates grew more unruly, blowing horns, braying and pelting the voters with peas, shot, and halfpence. Polling ceased at noon on the third day, and Prince Albert was declared elected, having received 117 more votes than Lord Powis, out of the record 1791 votes cast. Church bells rang and flags flew, though there was some doubt whether Prince Albert would accept it on such a small margin. Eventually, after consulting Sir Robert Peel, Prince Albert was installed as Chancellor at Buckingham Palace on 25 March 1847 in the presence of a deputation from the University; some of the more distinguished of them were entertained to dinner by the Prince. The Public Orator (a supporter of Lord Powis – and therefore not over-effusive in his Latin address to Prince Albert) had been warned not to ask for beer, his favourite drink, at this dinner. He was disgusted to learn that Romilly had enquired of a servant in a humble way 'Is it possible to have a glass of beer?', and had immediately been brought some 'in a short glass with a handle (much like a teacup)'. The rest drank claret and sherry as the only drinks available, apart from the Master of Clare who was deaf and had asked for port. The Master of Clare, who had been out of sorts for some days was indiscreet enough to venture on a glass of punch after the turtle soup, which so disagreed with him that he had to be got out of the room. The after dinner sitting lasted only twenty minutes, 'the wine was handed round twice only'.

These are some of the insights into Cambridge University life in the mid-nineteenth century, just before John Couch Adams's Fellowship at St John's College was running out in 1852, and just after he had become famous with his discovery of the new planet in 1846. According to the details of the poll, Adams, with the majority of John's men, voted for the Earl of Powis – 318 of St John's College voted for the Earl of Powis and 53 for Prince Albert. The majority of Trinity men voted for Prince

Albert, including G. B. Airy, and Professors J. Challis, and Adam Sedgwick, and both the Romilly's, and both the Sheepshanks, and George Peacock; as well as Sir John Frederick Wm. Herschel Bart, and S. Earnshaw of St John's, who were two who broke away from the main trend of voting in St John's.

Meanwhile by 1854, decisions were being made in the University for the reform of its organization and curriculum; Professors' lectures were to be resumed; subjects in addition to Classics and Mathematics were to gain in status and be encouraged; Heads of Colleges were to be stripped of some of their absolute power, and there were even rumours that Dissenters might eventually be considered as entrants according to the 1854 University Reform Act. 1848 had been a year of revolution on the continent, and reform had been in the air as far back as 1832. However, the Eastern Question and the rivalry of Russia and Turkey were to dominate the early 1850s. The Crimean War of 1854–56 became of more paramount interest to governments and citizens than university reforms. This war kept John Couch Adams awake at night, as did most national crises. There was a fear of Russian advances and victories against Turkey, and their allies the English, Austrian, and French troops. The Fall of Sebastapol in September 1855, when the Russians eventually silently evacuated the town after a lengthy siege, brought the war to an end.

It was not only of interest to those in England; but it was also a topic of concern in Australia, where the war news was followed as anxiously by Thomas Adams, as by his brothers in England. On 28 August 1854 Thomas Adams writes to his parents in Cornwall, from Sydney, Australia, where he had returned from Tonga for a few years because of ill-health

> The great subject, which excites attention is the European War, and the newspapers are eagerly sought after when an English Mail arrives. We

> have English news up to the 10th July received in Sydney on 9th inst. To us the war seems a very perplexing subject, a complicated affair, and it is difficult to say where it will end and what may be its probable results. Will it tend to open Mohamedan Turkey to the preaching of the Gospel?

This was written just after his brother John Couch had been enjoying May Week in Cambridge in 1854, and just after Thomas and his wife Maria had returned to Australia with four children, aged seven years, five years, three years and eighteen months, after burying a three months-old son, christened John Couch, at Vavau, Tonga on 13 January 1854. They left Tonga for Australia via New Zealand on 7 February 1854 and arrived in Sydney June 1854.

The following year on 5 March 1855 Thomas and his family have just heard in Australia of the Battle of Inkerman (5 November 1854). In another letter to his parents, Thomas mentions further concern about the Crimean War:

> and of the awful strain in the Black Sea with the loss of shipping, stores, etc., with so many precious lives, and we hope large re-inforcements have been promptly sent to relieve our valient troops in the Crimea. I rejoice at the Exhibition of such a patriotic feeling in the Colonists. We are just now engaged in a subscription for the widows and orphans of those who have shed their blood in their country's cause. I am on the Committee for Parramatta and have been collecting for the object. Many handsome donations have been presented. One gentleman in Sydney has presented a donation of £1,000 and promised £500 a year to it, while war continues. We pray that the Lord may speedily scatter those who delight in war.

In England Cobden and Bright of the Manchester School of Economics, had led a Peace Movement denouncing the war, but a certain bellicose patriotism prevailed among the majority of their fellow citizens.

News travelled slowly to Australia in the mid 1850s but by 25 January 1856, Australia had heard about Sebastopol, which had fallen in September 1855.

> We were pleased to hear that the south side of Sebastopol had fallen into the hands of the Allies – and we are now looking out for what followed. Truly we hear of wars and rumours of wars, O that the time may speedily come when men shall learn war no more! The last Mail informed us of some misunderstanding between England and the United States of America. We sincerely hope there may be no disruption in that quarter or we might expect an unwelcome visit from Bro. Jonathan in this part of the world.

This difference did not develop into war, though the Indian Mutiny of 1856 to 1858 was still to come to disrupt the Victorian peace still further, and to show that all was not sweetness and light in the Empire over which the sun never set. The Victorians were never, however, to involve themselves in world wars, such as were to face the twentieth century.

There had been Potato Famines in Ireland 1845–47, leading to distress, when John Couch Adams was turning to planets. While many peaceful occupations were being pursued in university circles governments came and went in the United Kingdom. The Conservatives, under Peel, were not really united, as Disraeli and Bentinck, sometimes known as the Protectionists, were going their separate ways. The Whigs, beginning to be called Liberals (a name borrowed from Continental politics, as the Social Democrats of the 1980s) were not fully united, as Russell and Palmerston were pulling them in different directions

– Irish and radical members were also loosely attached to them. The Manchester Radicals, under Bright and Cobden, also formed a Liberal school of their own, mainly based on Free Trade, and a desire for peace abroad. No government stayed in power for long from 1841–65. Peel managed to stay in office from 1841 to 1846, in spite of Irish troubles, and anti-Corn Law agitators, and reforms in Income Tax, and the birth of the Young England Movement under Disraeli. Peel's government had repealed the Corn Laws in 1846, and had been a moderate reforming middle-class Conservative government. Then came the Liberals, under Lord John Russell of 1846–52, with Palmerston as Foreign Secretary. 1848 developed into the Year of Revolutions on the continent, and saw the rise of Chartism in England. In 1851 the Great Exhibition in Hyde Park, largely brought about by the efforts of Prince Albert, had appeared to herald an age of peace and commerce, though unfortunately, and ironically, a long series of wars was to follow. 1850–51 saw fears of Papal power asserting itself once more in England, when the Pope appointed bishops with titles from English towns. A Derby–Disraeli Government followed in 1852 from February to December, when it fell. Whigs and Peelites had joined to defeat Disraeli's budget (Peel had died in 1850 from a fall from a horse). 'I am attacked by a Coalition', cried Disraeli; 'but England does not love Coalitions, and your triumph will be short.' 1852 saw the death of Wellington. A coalition government of Whigs and Peelites followed the December fall of Disraeli's Government. 'This is the realisation of the country's and our own most ardent wishes', wrote Prince Albert, 'and it deserves success'. Gladstone was Chancellor of the Exchequer, Lord Aberdeen became first Lord of the Treasury. However, the mismanagement of the Crimean War led to the fall of this government in 1855, and Palmerston then formed a Liberal government from 1855–58. His government fell in February 1858 when trying to please the French with his Conspiracy to

Murder Bill after Orsini had tried to murder Napoleon III with explosive bombs, made in England, thrown into his carriage. A large majority of English feeling rose in revolt that France should dictate to England to abandon her right of asylum and alter her laws. There was a brief Derby–Disraeli government once more (1858–59) but this fell over Disraeli's 'fancy franchises', which sought to give votes to people of property and education, even if they were not householders. Palmerston's second Ministry was then formed, which survived from 1859 to 1865, during which time the American Civil War was raging (1861–65) and the sudden death of Prince Albert, in 1861, shook the nation. Palmerston, himself, died in 1865, eighty-one years old. These events heralded the end of a chapter in English history (1832–65) during which time a generation came and went. Some of the nineteenth century events mentioned have a familiar ring to occupants of the twentieth century.

Against these events the Universities of Oxford and Cambridge fought their own battles of reform and scholarship and forged ahead with scientific progress and discoveries. National and personal decisions were proceeding against national and international events. John Couch Adams's Fellowship at St John's College expired in 1852; his Pembroke Fellowship followed in 1853, a Fellowship that did not require him to take Holy Orders. It was while Adams was at Pembroke that he received a letter from Sir David Brewster, Principal of St Andrews, dated 22 April 1855 and written in answer to a letter he had received from Adams about the Newton papers he was working on. Brewster adds

> I hope you will excuse one for asking a question of some importance. Would you accept the Mathematical Chair in our University? It is worth £500 a year at present, and we have reason to expect a considerable addition to the income of the Professor from the Crown. We have only one session

of six months and a vacation of six months. The vacancy is expected ere long. I am, my dear Mr. Adams ever most truly yours, D. Brewster.

A further letter from Brewster is dated 6 May 1855 from St Leonard's College, St Andrew's referring to Sir Isaac Newton's papers and giving further information about the Mathematical Chair about to become vacant.

On the day on which I wrote you I had an interview with Sir George Gray on the subject of our Mathematical Chair, and I mentioned to him that I thought it probable you might accept it. The answer was that when a vacancy took place it would be given to the most distinguished candidate.

The fees amount to about £200 and the salary to about £300. I am sure you would like a Residence here. In the University we have at present two Professors from Cambridge and three from Oxford. The Society is very agreeable, and the climate in winter and summer exceedingly salubrious. Like every place on the East Coast of the Island, we have bad east winds in Spring but not more than you have in Cambridge.

If the Chair had been in the gift of the College we would, of course, have made you an offer of it; but being in the gift of the Crown it is necessary to apply for it, I presume. How this will be done you will be the best judge. Whatever you think I can do in the matter I will readily undertake.

The present Professor is about seventy years of age and is in very bad health. No time should be lost in making the application. I am my dear Mr. Adams ever most truly yours D. Brewster.

P.S. To your list of Addendum as in the 3rd. Edition of the Principia, I am adding a considerable number from Pemberton's letters.

And finally, a further letter from Brewster, dated 9 May 1855 adds

> I think it might be mentioned to you that I have just written to Prof. Sedgwick, as your friend, proposing to him to get an application made to Sir George Gray on your behalf for the Mathematical Chair in the same manner as was recently done for Sir Roderick Marchison, I hope you will approve of this step which will render any movement on your part unnecessary.

This shows some of the workings of University appointments, but judging by a letter from Dr L. Fischer of 22 December 1856 from St Andrew's to Adams at Pembroke College – but forwarded to Laneast, Launceston (arriving 26 December) from Cambridge (24 December 1856), the matter of the St Andrew's Chair was not yet settled, as the present incumbent must have lived longer than was expected. However, by 1856

> our Mathematical Professor is very ill, and being above eighty years old, not very likely to recover, I have been urged by friends to write to you, but have been restrained by friends partly from delicacy towards the poor living sick man, partly and mainly from the wish of not again disturbing you with thoughts about the Chair, now likely to become vacant. But I hear now for certain, that his medical man does not think he will live another fortnight, and that a party is already very busy in making interest for Dr. Lees who you may recollect was appointed Assistant to the Professor, rather more than two years ago; an appointment against which a majority of Senators raised a lawsuit, which is still pending. Under these circumstances further delicacy would become weakness and longer delay a blunder. It would be

of great importance to the University if men like you and Stokes were to become candidates. Surely even the present Lord Advocate, in whose hands the Crown appointment virtually is, and who sent us his protége, Dr. Lees, who taught Euclid to his predecessor, would not venture to pass such men over in favour of Dr. Lees. Public opinion, one would hope, would be too strong for such an act to be perpetrated. The Income of the Chair is rather more than £470 a year (on an average); the Professor has thirteen hours teaching a week during a session of 5 months (from the first Thursday in November to the last Thursday in April, with a fortnight's vacation at Xmas); all the rest of the year he has entirely to himself. Also the classes are so elementary that the teaching would require little or no preparation in a good Cambridge man. Our University Library is capital; our Society very good, considering how small the town is. I write by the same post to Stokes, begging him to let you know at once what decision he has come to as regards himself. Of course, you would be amicable rivals, and not wish to stand in one another's way. If neither of you would become candidates can you recommend anyone of note who would, I mean of note, not only at Cambridge but in the scientific world at large? Should I, in that case become a candidate myself, as the Professorship is worth nearly half as much again as mine? Applications would have to be sent to the Home Secretary, who I believe has promised Sir D. Brewster that there shall be an open competition when the vacancy occurs. If that is the case, I have no fear of the results; it will make Lees impossible.

Let me hear from you as soon as possible. I shall write, if anything occurs. Can you send me Stokes's exact address? I wrote to him in duplicate, one note addressed to the Atheneum, the other to the care of Dr. Robinson, Armagh. Won't you follow his example soon? [In 1857, Stokes married a daughter of Dr. Robinson, of Armagh.]

A Merry Xmas to you, and all my friends near you, Yours sincerely L. Fischer

P.S. I doubt though, whether I have not destroyed any chance I might have had by having taken part against the Crown in Dr. Lees case. Will you write to Stokes too?

After all this cloak-and-dagger diplomacy in action behind university appointments John Couch Adams was eventually appointed to the Chair of Mathematics in St Andrew's University in 1857. He was only to hold it for a year as the Lowndean Professorship of Astronomy and Geometry at Cambridge University became vacant in 1858 with the death of the Dean of Ely, Dr George Peacock. It must have been another disappointment to St. Andrew's when Adams returned to Cambridge so soon after his arrival in Scotland in 1857. The letter from Sir Spencer Walpole, dated 17 November 1858 to the Vice-Chancellor of Cambridge University announces the appointment of the new Lowndean Professor.

My dear Vice-Chancellor,

I am now in a position to inform you that those in whom the choice of the Lowndean Professor is vested have selected Professor Adams of St. Andrew's University, so that he will come back, as you all of you wish, to his own Alma Mater. I wish you joy of this result most heartily.

The lamented death of the Dean of Ely, has occasioned two vacancies in which the Crown is concerned, viz. The Deanery, and the Cambridge Commission.

In the first of these I have sent the following names to Lord Derby, viz. The Master of St.

Catharine's, Professors Terence, Selwyn and Brown, and Mr. Harvey Goodwin. I mention this as the choice may have an effect on University matters. The Master of St. Catharine's has had the Deanery offered to him.

With regard to the Commission, I have endeavoured to look for a man with moderate views, clear judgement, academical distinction, and unpronounced and unbiased opinions. I have recommended W. H. Waddington.

His mind is the fairest and most judicial I ever had dealings with. I hope the appointment will give satisfaction. Excuse me for troubling you with this long letter. In your position I thought it my duty. Yours ever very faithfully. S. H. Walpole.'

John Couch Adams had evidently applied for the Lowndean Professorship on 10 November 1858, supported by the Master and resident fellows of Pembroke College. 'It would be superfluous for us to testify to his scientific acquirements', they stated. He was appointed on 11 March 1859, and the signing and sealing was dated 18 March 1859, from 10 Downing Street. The appointment was in the hands of the Lord High Chancellor since a certain Thomas Lowndean, late of Overton, in the County of Chester in a will of 6 May 1748, bequeathed his property to the University of Cambridge for such a Professorship. Adams's appointment was signed by such as the Marquis of Exeter, witnessed by M. Cecil, while the Earl of Hardwicke was witnessed by none other than William Grylls Adams, St John's College, Cambridge. This document can still be seen among some miscellaneous papers at St John's College, Cambridge.

The above-mentioned William Grylls Adams, eventually graduated in 1859, when aged twenty-three. Though not as brilliant as his elder brother John Couch (who was three months short of forty years years old in

1859, when appointed Lowndean Professor), William was eventually to become Professor of Natural Philosophy at King's College, London, and also to add ScD. and F.R.S. to his name. He also edited some of his brother's papers and wrote many lively letters to his brothers and sisters. He was evidently, a better correspondent than his elder brother, and had wide ranging interests as a Member of the Alpine Club, together with rowing, cricket, walking– the latter a very popular activity in Victorian England.

Two letters from the Cambridge brothers, written from Cambridge in 1857 to their youngest sister, Mary Ann, still in Cornwall and just eighteen years old, show their different styles and occupations and give a glimpse of the Adams family life. William writes on 26 April 1857:

> I see by the date that the day [28 April] on which you will be 18 years of age is very near at hand, and wish you many happy returns of that day. How fast our time slips away, I sometimes for a short space think of times gone by when we used to have joyful frolics, and how we used thoroughly to enjoy our little day, hopping and skipping about, with sometimes little accidents, never amounting to knocking teeth down the throat, although I once had one knocked out of my head. I recall old scenes with pleasure and after think with respect to the time between this and that, that I might have paid a little more attention to general reading, particularly when I had the advantage of so many books at home and at Birkenhead, however, youth must be youth. . . . I shall be glad to hear that you read some of Longfellow's poems and of Wordsworth when you have time.

John Couch's letter to his young sister is dated 9 December 1857, written from Pembroke College, and takes on a more sober tone – but then he was twenty years older than Mary Ann and William was only three years older than her. John Couch writes:

> I was very glad to get your note, though it reminded me of my neglecting to write to you as I had fully intended to do long ago. I have been very busy all this term, but very little has happened which it would at all interest you to hear about. I met with Mr. West one day who was a missionary with Thomas in the Friendly Islands, and we had a good deal to talk about the place etc. Last Friday I heard a very interesting lecture from Dr. Livingstone, the great African discoverer, which was delivered to an immense audience of University men in our Senate House. I sent home a paper containing a pretty good report of the lecture which you will see. I had heard him give a somewhat similar lecture in Dublin, and was very glad to hear him again. I met him at a friend's house the same evening. He is a most remarkable man and is soon going out again on his mission to open the interior of Africa to christianity and civilization. You have indeed had a very long time of it away from home [at Trevolland School, Saltash, run by Mrs. Nepean]. I am glad that you have been able to be useful to Mrs. Nepean. William goes into his College examination to-morrow. I hope he will do well. He seems well, and in good spirits. He will leave Cambridge I suppose on 16th, and will probably bring home little Thomas with him. [The eldest son, aged ten, of Thomas Adams, the missionary brother in the Friendly Islands. The ten-year-old had just arrived in England from Australia, for school at Taunton.] I have not quite made up my mind whether I shall come home or not this Christmas. If I do, it cannot be till a few days after William's coming. Did you hear anything about Uncle and Aunt Smith when you

> were at Saltash? [Aunt Smith (née Grylls) was Tabitha Adams's sister – John Couch Adams had lodged with them when at school at Devonport.] I have a letter from the Clergyman of that place saying that both of them were ill, and in very straightened circumstances and asking me to send them some relief. I have sent them a small sum, but I wish George [the third brother, who remained on the farm in Cornwall] would make some enquiries about them. Give my kindest love to all at home and believe me your affectionate brother John.

In April 1858, just before John went to St Andrew's to be inducted to the Professorship, which he took up in November 1858, the two Cambridge sons had been entertaining their mother, Tabitha, then aged sixty-two, in Cambridge and London. This gives yet another insight into the close-knit family.

William in his letter to Mary Ann on her nineteenth birthday, dated 17 April 1858, writes enthusiastically: 'Mother has been quite delighted with her trip. I think she has seen very nearly everything in Cambridge, and a great deal in London that is worth seeing. John and I were busy going about as long as we could stay in London, and she has seen some things since.' As a postscript he adds 'I should like for you to come to Cambridge next, perhaps when I take my degree'. He had previously mentioned that he intended to go to Birkenhead for his summer vacation,

> among my own friends there and recalling old associations connected with every little nook and turn of the Park and the country round and I also hope to have a little cricketing again while I stay there; I have begun to pull in the boats again this term, and during this hot weather I think it is very much better than walking, because we have not so

> much clothes on, and we must have a good amount of exercise, because it is absolutely necessary to preserve health; for this reason and also because I am strong enough for it, I am going to pull in the races which begin on May 10th.

He also wishes her 'Many happy returns' of her birthday, and adds, 'May each one be happier than the previous one and may the day soon come when Thomas will again be at home to spend his and your birthday together.' He concludes with 'Kind love to Father, George and Grace,' who were the only members still at Lidcott Farm, Laneast, in company with Mary Ann. The other sister, Elizabeth had died in 1848 at the age of sixteen.

Meanwhile Thomas, the son who had travelled furthest from home, and the only married member of the family in 1856, was also making decisions for himself and his family. He had been invalided out of Tonga in 1855, but was asked to return in 1856 for a final term of service before returning to England. This return to Tonga necessitated sending his son Thomas to England for the sake of his education, as he 'will be too old to take back to the Islands and education here [Australia] is too expensive.' He and his wife, and four young daughters, all born in the Friendly Islands, aged eight years, six years, four years and a few months returned to Tonga, when the Friendly Islands had just been

> visited by a fearful hurricane. The crops of the Islanders have been destroyed. The cocoa huts blown down. Nearly half the chapels on the station of Vavau destroyed. Brother Amos's house blown to pieces, so that our prospect is not very delightful. But I hope the appointment is from God and we wish to go where he appoints. Our little girls are all well. Of course, all future movements are uncertain.

Movements in Cambridge were more certain than those of the families of Wesleyan Missionaries in the 1850s. John Couch was listening to Dr Livingstone, and University sermons, and voting for Chancellors of the University; William was 'pulling in the boats', and taking exams, while the rest of the Adams family worked on the land in Cornwall. Governments came, and went; wars started and ceased; and railways spread all over the British Isles, and John Couch Adams became Professor Adams twice over. The first time he acquired this honour of Professorship is recorded in William's birthday letter to Mary Ann dated 27 April 1858. Its phrasing is typical of a younger brother, still an undergraduate at St John's College, writing about his more illustrious elder brother: 'John has been to St. Andrew's and has been inducted into the Professorship in due form, and is going there to reside in November; he has taken lodgings. He returned to Cambridge on Saturday; so now your brother is Professor J. C. Adams, M. A., F.R.S., . . . as long as your arm.' By 17 November 1858, John had been selected as the Lowndean Professor of Astronomy and Geometry at Cambridge on the death of the former Lowndean Professor Peacock. So John's return to Cambridge was assured, and by 1861 he was to succeed Challis at the Observatory of Cambridge University.

4

The Observatory, The University of Cambridge: 1861–72

Two major aspects of the character of John Couch Adams emerge from his letters and diaries, stored at St John's College, Cambridge, as well as from his contribution to scientific research and discoveries: one was of a shy, retiring, humble and modest solitary genius; the other was of a man who made friends easily, and kept them, who enjoyed music and dancing, and Cambridge parties, which he seemed to attend frequently as part of the social order of the day in mid-Victorian England. Though not as interested in rowing (apart from watching May Races), cricket and mountaineering as his younger brother William, nevertheless, he gave time to croquet ('vigorous' at times, when later he played with his teenage nieces, the daughters of his brother Thomas) and to bowls on College lawns, and whist in College rooms, though apparently he never excelled at the latter, judging by his winnings. Vingt-et-un may have suited him better. He enjoyed good conversation, was a voracious reader, and in course of time built up a large library of books, 960 of which were bequeathed to the Cambridge University Library at his death. A catalogue of these books shows the breadth and depth, and catholic tastes of his reading. Novels were always his standby in times of national crises, when sleep was elusive.

The shy and modest genius was more of a 'loner', especially where mathematics was concerned; his private calculations transported him to other worlds, where he made himself entirely at home, and where he tended to outsoar his fellow human beings. Some of his academic Cambridge contemporaries recognized a similar mind in John Couch Adams as had been sighted in Newton previously. In fact it was John Couch Adams who was called on to edit Newton's papers when they were bequeathed to Cambridge University by Lord Portsmouth in 1872. Adams had always been Newtonian in his allegiance and in his thinking when exploring the Universe mathematically. Adams enjoyed wrestling with apparently insoluble problems, and never abandoned them until a solution was achieved. Yet this transcendence never excluded him from his fellow men; he was always willing to help them with their problems, great or small. There are still many letters among the Adams' papers at St John's College, Cambridge, from correspondents, known and unknown, asking him for advice on scientific problems, especially concerning lunar problems, tides, ballistic missiles and projectiles (the latter were fields where his Cambridge friends Bashforth and Professor Stokes were at work at the War office and the Ministry of Mines). In spite of his having 'always experienced a strange difficulty' in the writing of letters, according to his own confession to Airy, he must have answered many of his correspondents, judging by their replies of thanks. In spite of some procrastination over correspondence, he could also forget to attend University business meetings – greater matters no doubt having intervened.

He enjoyed walking several miles daily, sometimes alone, or with one or two companions. In his undergraduate days he walked from Cambridge to London with his friends Drew, and Campbell. The popular Cambridge walk was to Trumpington and Grantchester, and sometimes Madingley and Coton, in all weathers. He mentions floods on the road to Trumpington near the Mill, and sometimes snow and ice making the roads slippery. He watched skating at the back of Scrope Terrace. He visited London by train, once or twice a term, usually meeting some Cambridge academic in the same carriage. When in London he was usually visiting the Royal Society, or Royal Astronomical Society meetings. On one occasion in 1847 he was the guest at the Lord Mayor's Banquet, and was flattered by the Lord Mayor. On other occasions he watched Royal Processions among great crowds in London streets, or in a good seat in St Paul's Cathedral. On one occasion he returned by Mail train to Cambridge in the company of Miller and Browne, when the latter gave him a lift from the station in his pony and carriage. When in London he dined at Simpson's, stayed at the Craven, visited Miss Adams in Albion Road, Hammersmith, who gave him a chop for breakfast, after an hour's visit with her on the previous day to Kensington Museum. Chops and tea were frequently enjoyed by him when visiting hotels. All this was happening in 1861, just before he accepted the Directorship of the Cambridge Observatory.

The first suggestion that he is being considered as a successor to Challis is recorded as an entry in Adams' diary of 1861:

4 January (Fri.): Rose late. Challis called and tried to persuade me to think of the Observatory after his own retirement. Went on with Froude. [Froude's *History of England* was just being published from 1856 onwards to 1870.] *From the Fall of Wolsey to the Defeat of the Spanish Armada*, [Adams had begun Volume VI on 3 January.]

The next entry referring to the Observatory reads 1861:

12 February (Shrove Tuesday): Stokes called and we walked round Grantchester and Trumpington talking over Observatory business. Resumed my work and then took a walk with Power [Master of Pembroke]. A good dinner in Hall though we were only three. Did some more work and about 9¾ went to a party at Trinity Lodge to meet the Prince (Later Edward VII). Much music. Rather too much etiquette. Read 'The Cosmos'.

13 February (Ash Wednesday): Stokes called and we talked of Lord Derby's letter to me.

14 February: Forster's Account of 5 members. Wrote to Drew. Walked to Observatory and talked with Challis about the work etc. Stayed to dinner and spent the evening there. Found great difficulty in knowing what to think about it. Had some Christy Minstrels. A wet evening.

15 February: Wrote a letter to the Vice-Chancellor with a conditional acceptance. [Then he adds that he went to Kingsley's lecture on 'The State of England' after almost making his final decision.]

16 February: Wrote to the Vice-Chancellor accepting the terms proposed by the Syndicate for the Superintendance of the Observatory. Walked round Trumpington and Grantchester. Wrote to George.

So by mid-February 1861 the Lowndean Professor of Mathematics was to become the Director of the Cambridge Observatory from October 1861.

Some entries from his diary of January and February 1861 show his occupations and varied reading. In January he is reading Dundonald's Autobiography, Rawlinson's Bampton Lectures, Layard's *Nineveh and Babylon*, various articles in *The Quarterley* on 'The Cape and the Kaffirs', and 'Stonehenge', Tulloch's account of Latimer, Macaulay, Motley's *Struggle with Spain*, Delaunay's first volume just published with 'a present from the author', inscribed together with Rowland Williams's *Essay on Bunsen's Biblical Prayer Book*. He regularly listened to sermons at Great St Mary's, where in January 1861 Kennedy was preaching on the Epiphany, on 'No man has seen God at any time', and on the differences in Ancient and Modern

Palestine. In January he received two letters from his young nephew Thomas, then aged fourteen, at School in Taunton since his return from the Friendly Islands, and enclosing his school report; and John Couch himself on 23 January was in London again 'at a Pantomime "Lady-bird" at the Haymarket'.

He moved into the Observatory some time in the summer of 1861, as a bachelor. He had no wife in mind at that time, though in a letter to his brother Thomas, written in 1846 congratulating him on his marriage, he had hinted that he never intended to remain a bachelor all his life, although unmarried Fellows were the only ones allowed to remain in College. His family seemed to have expressed concern about him living alone at the Observatory. A letter from his younger brother, William, dated 6 October 1861, written from The College Marlborough where he was then teaching, written to his youngest sister, Mary Ann, in Cornwall, shows his concern:

> I suppose John will be going to the Observatory now in a few days. I expect he will feel rather lonely in such a large building all by himself. He will very much wish for your company. It will be very different to being in College and with you he would be quite comfortable and go on pretty much as he does when at home, except that he will not go out so much, except perhaps to dine at college or some college meeting, or something of that sort. I must say I don't see much objection to your taking care of him as I seemed to do, when I was at home. The society at Cambridge is by no means high and there are some nice people there. Clever men, I find, are oftener found in the middle classes than among those in a higher station in life, and most of them who, remain, and in fact most of John's associates are clever men. Professor Babington, who was here examining in Botany last half, told me that John ought to get one of my

> sisters to keep house for him. With kind love to Mother, and George, and yourself and kind regard to all friends. Your affectionate brother W. G. Adams.

So 'class' was becoming an issue for William, who was also an adept at giving advice to his family, as many of his letters show.

The period 1859–61 had also seen changes in the rest of the Adams family. Thomas Adams Senior had died on 28 March 1859, which meant that his wife, Tabitha, as well as George, Grace and Mary Ann had had to move from Lidcott Farm on Lady Day 1860 to Badharlick, near Egloskerry – a good old stone farmhouse, given to Tabitha by Aunt Couch at her death, and renovated by John Couch Adams. Thomas, the second son, had returned from Tonga in May 1861, on the death of his wife in the Friendly Islands, and Grace went in September 1861 to live with Thomas to look after his household of six young children. In August/September 1861 John moved to the Observatory, and in 1862 George to a farm called Trewen, at St Tudy, near Wadebridge. Mary Ann had evidently been in Cambridge in the summer of 1861 to help John Couch with furnishing for the Observatory. A letter from John Couch dated 10 September 1861 refers to the help she gave:

> I have made great progress in my furnishings since you were here. I wish you were here now to see what has been done. The curtains are up in the drawing room, and the carpet, which we both liked so well, laid down and I assure you the effect is very good indeed. I have also got a sofa, two easy chairs and half a dozen other chairs covered with damask, uniform with the curtains and having loose chintz covers over all. I have still to get a drawing room table and some light chairs but I have already ordered about them. The car-

> pets are all down in the bedroom and look very well, particularly the Brussels one in the best room. The wardrobe is up in this room and sets it off capitally, and I have also had chintz curtains put up to match the bed furniture. The plate about which you were rather nervous has come all right. My new dressing tables arrived while Grace and Thomas were here. So you see that I have been making progress since you left. With kindest love to all, I remain your affectionate brother J. C. Adams.

In the same letter he refers to George's new farm Trewen, at St. Tudy, near Wadebridge: 'I am uncommonly glad that George has got into some business at last, and I hope he will do very well in it.' After the death of his father it was necessary for George to continue farming, but on another farm, as they no longer rented Lidcott.

What was worrying Tabitha in 1861 was the fact that she had three bachelor sons – John, George and William – all in separate establishments, and Thomas was already a widower with six children, ranging in age from three to fourteen years. She writes to Grace in 1861 from Badharlick to Newark, where Grace was keeping house for Thomas and his young family – it gives us a glimpse of the mother of John Couch Adams, with her concern for all her children, her somewhat erratic spelling, her lack of punctuation, and the sound of the Cornish lilt in her speech and sentence formations:

> My dear Grace, I hope this will find you all in good health. I be just as usuall I have had a very bad cold but thank the Lord I feel better now I hope twill pass off now the weather is fine now, my cough is easear than it was, we have been rather in a bustle latly George has been away about the estate that he has taken people say that

it is a very good place good grownd and full of grass mostly for sheep tis a great undertaking he ought to have a wife to help him I hope he will git a good one I tell him to make it a matter of Prayer. I trust he will be directed all right I wish he may be so lucky as his brother Thomas was to git such a good wife as she was it has been quite sudden his taking this place the sale is to-morrow for all the cattle etc George went off his morning they be valuing all the stock and cattle and household goods Mrs. Major says he may take whatever he likes of the household goods he likes in the valuation she dont wish to be particular in nothing. George says she appears to be a nice lady she tells others she likes the appearance of George very much indeed. So I hope that he will git on but she says that he must git a wife she has given him some ducks and fowls to begin with. I think Mary Ann will go down next week we are ordering things for him she was to Market last week got some things we are ordering two beds for him he thinks he shall have some of theirs Tammy is covering his quilt she is going to cover another next week we be rather busy now I should be glad if it was all settled I suppose the same housekeeper will stay on for some time and the servant maid they have kept too menkind in house perhaps they may stay I don't know yet he wishes us to give up and go with him but we can't think of that we must try to git some of them married soon their be three of them ought to have wives. Mr. Roseveare was here again last week came here with George from Northill Farm he seems to be determin'd he appeared rather freer not so reserved as he used to be [his object of attention was Mary Ann].

Judging by another letter from William to Mary Ann,

written from Cambridge, marriage was still not in John's sights. He writes on 31 January 1862:

> You will perhaps be surprised to hear that you have been enquired for here. Mrs. & Miss Challis enquired of me when you and mother were coming and so did Mrs. Miller who is a very nice person. I don't think John thinks anything about getting married and they think it would be very comfortable for him, if you were here. I don't think he will dine very much at the Observatory if he is alone but will often be coming in here [St John's College]. It would be a good thing if he had company to keep him there, otherwise I fear he will not be so much at the Observatory as he ought now that he has taken it, of course he should attend to it properly.'

William once more is willing to give advice to his family. He concludes this letter to his sister, aged twenty-three (he himself is twenty-six), with his opinions of her suitor, Henry Roseveare:

> Before I left home I wanted to have some talk with you about Henry Roseveare, but opportunity did not occur. I must speak plainly, and I hope you will consider my advice. When he was at our house, I must say that I was not favourably impressed by him; he has very little to say: when I was out for a walk with him I tried to talk with him about the railway and various ordinary things, but his ideas seemed to be contained within a small compass. I like Mr. Roseveare pretty well, he is a spirited man, but Henry has not a bit of his father's spirit. I was not favourably impressed either by Mrs. Roseveare, when I saw her. Henry seems to be urged on strongly by the people about Trevollard and I was astonished and

> grieved to hear that Trevollard people (Miss Welch etc), were driving it (Miss W on the ground that old Mr. R was such a nice man). Of course the Vospers are in favour of it as they are related, but I hope you will never be drawn into it that way.

In spite of all this brotherly advice, Mary Ann eventually married Henry Roseveare, but not until after her mother died in 1866. It would be interesting to know what Henry made of William, and his conversation on 'the railway and various ordinary things', when farming and Mary Ann must have been a more burning concern with him at that time.

John, in the meantime, was getting on quietly in Cambridge with his marital affairs without William's advice, and without consulting his family at all. The first time his future wife's name appears in John's Diary was on Sunday 19 October 1862: 'Rose rather late. A cold morning. At St. Mary's Howson gave us a capital sermon on the conscientiousness and integrity of St. Paul. Afterwards spoke to Miss Bruce.'

On the day before, Saturday October 18 1862, there is an interesting entry in the diary. In fact, the *only* entries in the 1862 diary are 18 October to 26 October – a memorable week! 18 October reads:

> Called at Stokes and Stayed to lunch. Saw the Robinson's leave. Very kind and cordial. Mrs. Stokes told me of something Mrs. Goodwin had been telling to my disadvantage. Called at Miller's. Then called at Pares to talk about the dispute with Hobson about the boiler. Dined there, and after going to Chapel returned to tea. Hobson has written rather a strong letter to P.

Two significant names appear in this Saturday entry – Stokes and Robinson. Both families have Irish links, and possibly Miss Bruce of Dublin was sighted at the Stokes's that Saturday, before the Sunday when 'Spoke to Miss Bruce' became a reality, more lasting than talk of boilers, or the sly comments of Mrs. Goodwin.

Developments that week become significant. After visiting booksellers to inquire about some stolen books, by Wednesday 22 October matters are advancing: 'Called at Porter's to get "Rossetti's early Italian Poets". In evening went to Ray at Miller's. Took Rossetti to Miss Bruce. Sedgwick at Ray. Talked about Kew and Greenwich Magnetic Observatory. Challis after observing late stayed the night here.' So the die was cast: 'Took Rosetti to Miss Bruce'.

Little is known of Elizabeth Bruce of Dublin before John Couch Adams met her in Cambridge in 1862. He had moved into the Observatory in September 1861 as a bachelor. For some time Professor Adam Sedgwick, Professor of Geology at Trinity College, Cambridge had advised marriage for John Couch Adams but no one had emerged as a prospective wife, though many feminine names had flitted in and out of the pages of the diary. John Couch Adams had visited Ireland on various occasions, both to Dublin to Professor Humphrey Lloyd, Provost of Trinity College, Dublin, and also to the Observatory at Armagh where Dr Thomas Romney Robinson was in charge. Dr Robinson, the son of a painter, a pupil of Romney, was born in Ireland where his father had emigrated; Thomas Romney Robinson was a precocious child and was sent in 1801 to Dr. Bruce's Academy for 200 boys in Belfast, later to be the Royal Academical Institution. However, it is not until a letter to Professor Sedgwick dated 30 December 1862, written from the Observatory, Armagh that all is revealed:

> My dear Professor Sedgwick,
>
> After the lecture which you gave me at our last Philosophical dinner I felt it a duty as well as a pleasure to tell you that I have followed your advice, have boldly put the important question,

and have been rewarded with a favourable reply. The lady who has taken pity on my lone condition is Miss Bruce, an Irish lady, who was lately staying with the Stokes, and who dined with you on one occasion, though you unaccountably forgot to invite me to meet her. I feel certain that I have found the one solution of a problem, which I had well nigh come to look upon as insoluble.

Miss Bruce is thoroughly good, generous and true, with a cultivated mind and a loving heart, and I am sure it will be my fault if she does not make me very happy. Already I feel as if in a new world, and look back with pity on my former state as on a glacial period, removed from the present by long geologic ages. Soon I hope to bring my new assistant to the Observatory, though the lawyers threaten to cause some delay, but not I trust, a long one. I write from Dr. Robinson's of Armagh, where you may imagine that I am spending my vacation very happily, as someone else is staying here too.

Believe me Dear Professor Sedgwick, Yours most sincerely, J. C. Adams.

Elizabeth Bruce was the daughter of Mr Holiday Bruce of Dublin. She was born in Ireland, though the family of Bruce may have emigrated from Scotland in past centuries. Rumour had it that there might have been a tenuous connection with Robert The Bruce. Some of her closest friends throughout life were the sisters of Professor Humphrey Lloyd, at one time Provost of Trinity College, Dublin. Professor G. G. Stokes, with whom she stayed in Cambridge, was of Irish extraction, born in Skreen, Co. Sligo, and educated at Pembroke College, Cambridge, where he was appointed Lucasian Professor of Mathematics in 1849. He was born in 1819, and was therefore the same age as John Couch Adams. Professor G. G. Stokes was Secretary of the Royal Society (1854–85) and President (1885–90). He was Fellow of Pembroke (1841–57), and eventually Master in 1902, ten years after the death of John Couch (1892). He represented Cambridge University in Parliament from 1886 and died in 1903. Sir George Gabriel Stokes had been a friend of Adams since their undergraduate days, and when Stokes was at the Ministry of Mines Adams had helped him with ballistic problems. How Elizabeth Bruce came to be staying with the Stokes is not known, but it may have been due to the Irish connection, and her friendship with Lady Stokes, stemming from the Academic life of Dublin, where Miss Bruce was evidently at home. In 1857 Professor G. G. Stokes had married Mary Susanna Robinson, daughter of Dr. T. R. Robinson of Armagh, by his first wife, Eliza Isabelle Rambaut of Huguenot stock.

It was not to be a long engagement. They were married at Bray, Co. Wicklow on May 2nd 1863 by Dr Humphrey Lloyd, Provost of Trinity College, Dublin. The immediate Cornish family seems to have been rather critical of John's lack of communication on these matters; and he is slightly 'huffy' that his family have not congratulated him on his engagement, and later marriage. It was a very happy partnership, and the Cambridge life at the Observatory increasingly absorbed them both as time went on. Visits to Cornwall grew less after the death of his mother in 1866 though no rifts developed in the close-knit family–only circumstances dictated different paths and Elizabeth Adams (née Bruce), always took a great interest in the Adams family in all its ramifications.

One reason why the Cornish Adamses did not congratulate John on his engagement as rapidly as he expected was the fact that they were entertaining Thomas's young family for Christmas 1862, and were by 2 February 1863 preoccupied with the death of the youngest of the four girls, Alice Ellen aged eight, caused by scarlet fever contracted when she returned to school at Trevolland, Saltash after Christmas. She was a lively little girl, born in the Friendly Islands, who had suffered with chilblains in the two English winters she had known. All the family, bar John Couch in Cambridge, were heavily involved in this. William writes to Grace saying he has also written to John from Callington 'to ask him to go down to Newark to see you, if he could. I know that he is busy with Smith's Prize Examn, which is over on Friday, and his lectures begin next week; but perhaps he may be able to run down on Saturday to see you in your loneliness.' Grace was keeping house at Newark for her widowed brother Thomas, the father of 'little Ally', and had stayed in Newark with the youngest of the six children, Freddie, when Thomas went to the funeral in Cornwall. There is no indication that John went to Newark, but he writes to his sister Grace from the Observatory on 4 February.

> My dear Grace, I got the sad intelligence yesterday afternoon by letter from Mary Ann. I cannot tell you how much it grieved me. I wrote last night to Thomas, but got too late for post, so that this will probably reach you at the same time. You can open the letter and if you like forward it to Thomas when you write to him. It will be a sad shock to poor Mother, weak as she is, and occuring so soon after the children have been home with her for the holidays. Believe me, my dear Grace Your affectionate brother, J. C. Adams.

J. C. Adams was obviously not so heavily embroiled in Cornish family affairs as the rest of his family. His Cambridge days were occupied with other matters, during the time between his engagement in December 1862 and marriage in May 1863. Elizabeth Adams was not involved in this family crisis, though she writes very sympathetically a few years later when Thomas's eldest daughter, Maria, when nearly fifteen years old, becomes seriously ill in February 1864 at Newark, just before they moved to Wigan in September 1864. Elizabeth Adams writes from

The Observatory, Cambridge (on headed notepaper with lilac-coloured Gothic script). The letter is dated Monday night, and the envelope shows it was posted in Cambridge on 1 March 1864 and received in Newark on 2 March 1864.

My dear Polly [who was once more rallying round the family; she was the one who had been most heavily involved with the death of Alice], I was truly glad to receive your letter this morning and to learn that the accounts of Maria are more favourable. I cannot express how I feel this sore trial for her and for all of you who witness her suffering. I can hardly fancy a greater trial in its way for a young girl just on the threshold of life, than to be confined to bed in one position with the prospect of being so for a long time, – and the dreadful anxiety hanging over her of what the result may be – still we must hope that as so little time was lost, her limb may recover its strength and her restoration to health may be complete.

I am sorry your dear Mother has had any anxiety about John – I would have written sooner except that he so often spoke of writing to his brother. He is quite well. We are going up to London on Thursday to return on Saturday.

You would not know this place the walks are finished, gravelled and rolled. The flower beds cut out and a number of shrubs planted. The back avenue is completely shut out from view by shrubs and it really looks very pretty.

Alas! there is no hope of Pierce getting his dismissal – he sticks on like a bur – doing nothing overt enough for his gentle master to be roused into the necessary state of righteous indignation – so I live in the hope of something turning up. The hens have laid four eggs since you left, in other words, we have had four eggs of their laying! –

and they eat such a quantity. I have not yet gotten a servant in Mary Anne's place.

John unites with me in very kind love to all your circle and begs me to say how truly he rejoices in your better account of his dear niece. Believe me to remain dear Polly your affectionate sister Eliza Adams.

The Mary Anne mentioned in this letter was at the Observatory in March 1862 when John gave her and the Cook £1 each for dresses 'for his wedding', and dismissed them with a month's notice. Eliza must have re-employed them, when she arrived as the Mistress of the Observatory.

Though we have no details of Eliza Adams's wedding, she herself furnishes details of the wedding of her niece, Maria Adams; having fully recovered from her illness of March 1864, she was wed in August 1871. Maria's family had moved to Cambridge in 1869 when her father, Thomas, was appointed Wesleyan Minister at Hobson Street Chapel. Maria's wedding to John Smith Simon, of Welsh and Scottish parentage, took place at Hobson Street Wesleyan Chapel, with the wedding reception at the Observatory. Eliza writes an amusing and scathing letter to her sister-in-law, Grace Adams, who had not been present at the wedding. It shows Eliza well enmeshed in the Adams (and Simon) family by 1871. She writes it from Crewe Station as she travels to Scotland after the wedding reception:

Crewe Station 12 o'c at night. – Here I am stuck till nearly 2 o'c and I am afraid to drop asleep so I shall write my promised letter to you by the very dim light I have got. The wedding went off very well – Maria was very brave and did not break down – and they said Mr. Simon's responses might be heard in the next street! She looked very pretty indeed – and so did the others. The bridesmaid's dresses were not of the expensive material I call grenadine, they were more like Tarlatan muslin – but I find more than one was shocked at so much style as 5 carriages and pairs, coachmen with favors and white gloves, and such gay dressing on the daughters of a minister! Mr. Graham looked very grave over it and I hear it was remarked on. When they got to the Observatory the whole party was *photographed* near the fernery – Mr. Simon having ordered a photographer to be up there to do it!! – I am *sure* all this extravagance and attempts at style, is Miss Simon's doing. I do not like her at all – and she ordered everybody about and went on as if the Observatory were *her* place and *she* the hostess – but I don't let a word of this go beyond Polly [Mary Ann] – I think she quite rules her brother – and is a regular Commander-in-Chief and fond of display.

I never saw in my life a girl of fourteen flirt like Gracie. She is really dreadful – asking a Mr. Wilton to walk with her round the grounds, allowing him to keep whispering in her ear – sitting on the grass beside him and gazing into his face. She perfectly amazed me – at her age, to be so forward! This too is only for you and Polly. Thomas was a good deal put out at the style and probable expense. He told us he had never asked any questions not knowing anything about the matter – and he had no idea Mr. S. would have gone in for such a fussy wedding – for he would have told him he disapproved of it. He says his character as a Minister will be compromised by it. I wonder if you will agree with *my* idea of Mr. S. which I told you? He is better than his sisters! Carry Sibley is a very nice contrast to them – very quiet in her manner, and with a look of character – and she had a *decided* and ladylike way of checking Tom when he was paying more attention to *her* than was good manners at a party. I was glad to see this – it showed nice and proper womanly feeling on her part. She looks very delicate.

There were 18 at the breakfast–
Our two selves
6 from Thomas' house [Thomas, Maria (the bride), and her sisters and brothers Emily, Gracie, Tom, Fred]

4 Simons [John (the Bridegroom), his mother and his sisters Maie, and Sara, who ran a school in Southport, Wintersdorf]
1 Miss Moulton [sister of first Headmaster of Leys School, friend of Maria Adams]
1 Mr. Lee [Rev'd – Chief Groomsman]
1 Mr. Rushbrooke
1 Mr. Wilton
1 Miss Sibley
1 Mr. Williams [Rev'd]

I am afraid it was not stylish enough to please Miss Simon but there was plenty and everything nice I thought.

Four quarter of lamb before John, piece of spiced beef before me. three fowl – a ham – a raised pie, a pigeon pie – a mayonnaise of salmon, and lobster done into a mould with meat jelly – two creams – two jellies and two fruit tarts and a head and foot dish of some sort of cake and cream made by the French cook. Champagne, claret and sherry and ale for any who liked it. Mr. Simon is a Tea Totaller! In the afternoon I had tea and coffee handed about as the party took to croquet after Maria left. She and Mr. Simon went to London by the 5 train. John went away at 6 o'c and the party remained on till 8 o'c very nearly.

I had magnificent roses and hollyhocks for the rooms so the flowers were very pretty. John met the gentm. who had examined Fred lately and he told John he had done very well indeed–and he could hardly believe he was so young [thirteen years]. I can hardly see to write but I hope you can read it.–Did your dress come safely? If not I will write at once as it was sent off the very day my letter ordering it reached Dublin. Yesterday and to-day were glorious for the harvest. I told Thomas I hoped when his next daughter marries he will take more control over the arrangements. I must stop. With much love to all ever your affectionate sister, E. Adams.

The Mr Graham mentioned in this letter as looking

'very grave' was an Assistant at the Observatory, with Methodist connections. Mr Wilton was eventually engaged to Emily Adams, not Gracie, and was later a Master at the City of London School for Boys, until he died on Snowdon in August 1874 keeping an appointment with Rushbrooke, which Rushbrooke never kept owing to bad weather. John Simon and Thomas Adams were eventually involved in the search for Wilton, who was 'found by a party of guides with me on Monday, August 24th 1874', according to a letter from J. Rushbrooke, written on 26 July 1935 from Melrose (34 The Mall Southgate) to my mother, G. E. Harrison, the daughter of Maria Simon and niece of Emily Adams. Emily eventually married George Yeld, a master at St Peter's School, York, and Gracie married the Rev. Hyatt Warner – an Anglican cleric. The letter from J. Rushbrooke continues:

> The inquest was held the same evening following. We laid him to rest in the little churchyard at Llanberis where it is said the very spot where his body was found is visible to one with good sight. I can remember the funeral quite well. We sang round the grave led by the Rector 4 verses of Son of my Soul. I think on the gravestone is an inscription drawn up by my brother. It is supposed that he took a little water course known as the Miner's Path as a real path and hence the fatal accident. It comes back so vividly to me.

A contemporary letter dated 24 August 1874 from Castle Hotel, Llanberis, North Wales, from Thomas Adams, the brother of J. C. Adams, and the father of Emily, engaged to Wilton, written to Henry Roseveare, his brother-in-law, states:

> My dear Henry, On reaching Torquay we heard that Mr. Wilton to whom Emily was engaged had been lost on visiting Snowdon. I came on to

Welshpool and this place. And to-day we found the body. Mr. W. had evidently missed the path in coming down from the mountain and had fallen over an awful precipice. It will be a fortnight tomorrow since he was missed. Poor Emily is in a sorrowful condition. I left Jane [his second wife] at Taunton [home of his first wife]. The inquest has been held to-night. Excuse haste. I am your affectionate brother, Thomas Adams.

The inscription on the tomb reads,

> To the memory of Frederick Roberts Wilton B.A.
> Assistant Master at the City of London School
> whose brief life cut short suddenly in his 26th year
> by a fall on Snowdon on August 11th 1874 was yet
> long enough to endear him to Friends, Colleagues
> and Pupils to whom he has bequeathed the
> example of his unselfish work a legacy for ever.

The Wilton legend became a part of the family saga, handed on to succeeding generations as an example of the morality of always keeping appointments, and sticking to promises made though in this case the promise kept also led to disaster; but *had* Rushbrooke only *kept* his appointment what might have been the upshot?

Through the ages the tapestry of human life is interwoven with names and events in family sagas. Once more John Couch remained in academic calm, in spite of turbulances of family weddings and eventual family disasters stemming therefrom.

5

The Observatory, The University of Cambridge: 1872–80

The academic calm of Cambridge in which John Couch Adams found himself, from 1839–92, was rippled, at times, by a few pebbles, thrown into that 'Ocean of Truth' which permanently flowed around those who dwelt on the banks of the Cam. Throughout the ages universities, and the colleges, which constitute universities, have attracted men of mental calibre and imagination, who have stimulated their contemporaries to explore new realms of thought, and to adventure into deeper realms of the human spirit. The University of Cambridge has been no exception. Medieval scholars had trekked from Oxford in the twelfth century to pioneer houses of learning at Cambridge, which expanded the work that the monastic settlements had already begun there. As far back as 1112 an Augustinian Priory of Barnwell was established, from which sprang the Hostel of St John in 1135, especially for the benefit of students. Peterhouse, the earliest College, was founded in 1284. A number of students before the end of the thirteenth century were migrating from Paris to Oxford and Cambridge. In 1209 a number of students migrated from Oxford to Cambridge because of town-and-gown disputes, only to find eventually that even more ferocious and frequent rows were developing between town-and-gown in the parishes of St Bene't and St Edward in Cambridge, than those that had been experienced originally in Paris. Other monastic houses had developed prior to the growth of the University at Cambridge. These were the Nunnery of St Rhadegund, about 1133, which eventually developed into Jesus College; the Carmelite White Friars at Newnham about 1250; the Friars of the Penitence of Jesus in the parish of St Peter-the-less on the site of Peterhouse; and the Friars of Bethlehem in Trumpington Street. Later came the Dominican Black Friars on the site of Emmanuel, the Franciscan Grey Friars on the site of Sidney Sussex, as recorded in John Steegman's *Cambridge*, published by Batsford in 1940.

Something of this monastic and scholarly atmosphere still lingered on in Cambridge through the centuries. John Couch Adams and his Victorian contemporaries were to inherit it. Those able to loiter in Cambridge for most of a lifetime are indeed privileged persons. The life of some other members of his family, who had stayed on Cornish soil as farmers or housewives, were having life of a different order, while brother Thomas, who had ventured to the southern hemisphere, in Australia and among the native culture of Tonga and Vavau in the Friendly Islands, was experiencing life of an entirely different order from that into which he had been born at Lidcott Farm on Laneast Down in Georgian England.

The Ivory Tower existence in Cambridge is reflected in Karl Capek's *Letters from England* (1925). He writes as 'a foreigner in Cambridge':

> At first you have the impression of a provincial town; but suddenly you wonder whose this old castle can be. It is a students' college, with three courtyards, a chapel of its own, a royal hall where students eat, a park, and I know not what else.

> And here is a second one, bigger still, with four courtyards, a park beyond the river, a cathedral of its own, a still bigger Gothic dining-hall, rafters five hundred years old, a gallery of old portraits, still older traditions and still more famous names. Then there is a third one, which is the oldest, a fourth one distinguished for scholarship, a fifth for athletic records, a sixth because it has the finest chapel, a seventh for I know not what, and as there are at least fifteen of them, I have mixed them all up; I see only the castellated places in perpendicular style, the huge quandrangles, where the pupils move about in black gowns and square tasselled caps, each of whom has his two or three rooms in the wings of these castles; I see the Gothic chapels disembowelled by Protestantism, the banquet halls with a dais for the 'masters' and 'fellows', the venerable smoked portraits of earls, statesmen and poets, who went forth from there; I see the renowned 'backs', i.e. the rear of the colleges above the river Cam, over which there are bridges leading to the ancient college parks; I float on the gentle river between the 'backs' and the parks. I bow down to you, O Cambridge. . . .

Some of this adulation may be difficult for modern Cambridge undergraduates to grasp, who very infrequently now go gowned and in 'square tasselled caps', and who may find themselves in scantier accommodation. Yet much of this view of the lavishness of the architecture in an attractive setting is still very true today. John Couch Adams would recognize much of Cambridge if he returned to it today, over a hundred years after he left it. The trams have gone; the bicycle and cars have appeared, though the bicycle was not unknown to him. Some modern buildings have arrived on the Backs, and in the centre of the city, in King Street and Petty Cury in particular. Many old shops have disappeared gradually.

Grays, the bookbinders were still in Green Street in 1982, but not in 1983. Here he used to take his books to be rebound, or renovated. James Neal, the tailor, on the corner of Silver Street, has only recently become Ede and Ravenscroft's. James Neal used to visit the Observatory to measure for suits and overcoats, and return the finished article within a few days. The inhabitants of the Observatory in the nineteenth century would miss the sight of hansom cabs, of flies, which they used to hire from time to time from Cambridge to the Observatory, or at times the astronomer shared one with Mr De'ath, who frequently called and often provided an afternoon drive. Both John Couch, and his wife Eliza, however, would frequently walk into Cambridge from the Observatory, and also 'take a turn' almost daily up the turnpike road to the Madingley or Comberton turn, about two miles, or to the windmill on Madingley Hill. Sometimes it would be a walk over the fields to Girton, when the college was being built in the 1870s, or across the Coton fields to Newnham. Grange Road was on St John's land, but only being developed in Adam's day, and of course neither Cranmer, Herschel, nor Adams had bequeathed their names to the later roads to be made off Grange Road. It was no doubt a more peaceful place in many ways, but a man had to be reported to the police for creating a nuisance at the Observatory Gates, and one unfortunate postman dropped dead on the same drive after delivering letters to the Observatory.

William Everett, writing in 1866 in *On the Cam* describes the peace and beauty of Cambridge in glowing terms.

> There is nothing of the kind lovelier in England. The velvet turn – the ancestral elms and hoary lindens – the long vistas of the ancient avenues – the quiet river – its shelving banks filled with loiterers, its waters studded with a scene of gay boats, and crossed by light graceful stone bridges;

the old halls of grey or red or yellow rising here and there – the windows peeping out from among the trees, and the openings into the old courtyard with their presage of monastic ease and learning – the lofty pinnacles of King's Chapel o'er topping all; – there is no such scene of repose and of beauty in Oxford or any other place of learning . . . I do not believe a single student ever paced under these ancient trees without some word of praise bursting from his lips for the beauty and glory of dear old Cambridge.

And one more aspect of Cambridge life is praised in 1765 by Samuel Parr (1747–1825), the pedagogue and pamphleteer, in his works in 1765 when he writes:

The unreserved conversation of scholars, the disinterested offers of friendship, the use of valuable books, and the example of good men, are endearments by which Cambridge will keep a strong hold on my esteem, my respect, and my gratitude, to the latest moment of my life. Never shall I have the presumption to disclaim her as a mother, and never may she have just occasion to renounce me as a son.

It was to this human aspect of Cambridge that John Couch Adams made his contribution during the time he lived in Cambridge. Some interesting people and ideas were afoot in Victorian Cambridge, and John Couch Adams made his own quiet, yet remarkable, contribution. In 1850 in Leigh Hunt's autobiography he states:

Oxford, I found, had greatly the advantage of Cambridge in point of country . . . the town, however, made amends; and Cambridge has the advantage of Oxford in a remarkable degree, as far as regards eminent names. England's two great

> philosophers, Bacon and Newton, and (according to Tyrwhilt) three out of its four great poets, were bred there, besides double the number of minor celebrities. Yet they are divine places, both; full of grace, and beauty, and scholarship; of reverend antiquity, and ever-young nature and hope.

Finally, Charles Tennyson writing in 1913 on *Cambridge from Within*, may give a clue as to why John Couch Adams felt so entirely at home in Cambridge:

> Though Cambridge studies less philosophy than Oxford, though she stands not cramped in a steaming valley but in a wide place swept and purged by every wind of heaven, yet she breeds more philosophy and a more passive spirit in her children. Her ancient houses dominate less nobly the streets of the surrounding city, about which they lie scattered behind discreet walls and modest gardens. The hand of restoration has been heavier upon her, the calls of science in all its branches have met with a readier response at her hands, as many a bleak laboratory and lecture-room bear witness. . . .
>
> Yet in spite of all this, Cambridge is less of the world than Oxford and more definitely of the past. Something is perhaps due to the vast spaces of the plain on the face of which our forefathers planted her. On that expanse where every molehill commands blue distances and pigmy man walks every hour beneath the complete vault of heaven, witness of the whole compass of its interminable splendour, the mind's eye insensibly turns upward. In a land arched by the whole circuit of days naked splendours, ringed by all the legionary fires of night, shadowed by the full concourse of flying tempests, lit from rim to rim with the flush of dawn and evening, her generations have

> grown to a certain breadth, a certain austerity of temper foreign to her more worldly rival, a temper with more reserve, with a power of enthusiasm keener if less sustained; less human perhaps and less responsive to the calls of practical life, but nearer in kinship to the winds and stars.

This last sentence could sum up some of the character of Adams. He would forget to turn up at committees, lose his luggage when travelling across England, drop his gloves, and mislay his umbrella on many occasions; practical life was of less consequence to him than his 'kinship to the winds and stars'. It dated back to his youth on Laneast Downs, when he took an interminable time in rounding up the cows on his father's farm; his mind was on his calculations in the heavens. Losses of personal property, and mislaying things, worried him, as did national crises, which kept him awake at night, but he was always abreast of his times, and always willing to discuss politics, and world affairs; his vision, however, was more frequently on the world of mathematics, and solving lunar theories, and the mysteries of winds and tides and the moon's motions, as well as the practical science of ballistics.

During his early days at the Observatory in the 1860s he was busy with many calculations. Lunar theory on the moon's motions occupied some of his time. In 1853 there was a Memoir to the Royal Society on the secular acceleration of the moon's mean motion. Halley had first detected it. Newton had agreed, but controversy followed in which Adams joined in his century. Adams queried Laplace's findings. In 1864 Delaunay gave a clear account of the controversy. Lubbock and Caley agreed with Adams. The controversy developed into an extraordinary episode in the history of physical astronomy. By 1866 the Gold Medal of the Royal Astronomical Society was awarded to Adams for his contribution to Lunar Theory.

Adams' scientific papers can be seen at St John's

College and were edited by his brother, Professor W. Grylls Adams. Professor R. A. Sampson, Fellow of St John's College, has studied Adams's manuscripts and believes the investigations he has left on the Lunar Theory will form a treatise on the subject. Adams's disinclination to prepare his work for publication was always one of his drawbacks. It was usually due to a desire to obtain a still higher degree of simplification or perfection. When researching on Jupiter satellites in great detail he was asked for a paper on them: 'I have still some finishing touches to put to it.' He rarely put pen to paper until he had carefully thought out the subject, and when he proceeded to write out the investigation he developed it rapidly, without interruption: 'His accuracy and power of mind enabled him to map out the course of the work beforehand in his head, and his mathematical instinct, combined with perfect familiarity with astronomical ideas and methods, guided him with perfect safety through the intricacies and dangers of the analytical treatment.' So Dr J. W. L. Glaisher explains the methods in his Biographical Notice in Volume I of the *Collected Scientific Papers of John Couch Adams*, published in 1896 by Cambridge University Press. Glaisher goes on to comment on Adams's methods:

> He hardly destroyed anything he wrote, or performed rough calculations. His manuscripts are written carefully and clearly, so that it is difficult to believe they are not copied out carefully. The sheets are dated, and his diary shows his progress in calculations, form and substance are equally vital to him. This had been a characteristic with him always. In his Tripos papers it was noticed that in the problem papers when everyone was writing hard, Adams spent the first hour looking over the questions, scarcely putting pen to paper the while. After that he wrote out rapidly the problems he had already solved in his head.

This proved his mental powers, for he was not a rapid writer, and as was proved in the case of the discovery of Neptune not an eager correspondent.

In 1872 Lord Portsmouth presented a large mass of Newton's scientific papers to the University of Cambridge. Adams catalogued them willingly, in spite of the difficult and laborious task of Newton's notes on lunar theory. Glaisher states: 'His mind bore naturally a great resemblance to Newton's in many marked respects, and he was so penetrated with Newton's style and thought that he was peculiarly fitted to be his interpreter . . . Only a few intimate friends were aware of the immense amount of time he devoted to these manuscripts or the pleasure he derived from them.'

In 1887, the bicentenary of the publication of Newton's *Principia* was celebrated. Adams was asked by Trinity College to deliver the commemorative address, but he was too ill at that time to accept, so handed on his information to Glaisher, who delivered it.

While at the Observatory Adams was constantly asked to undertake calculations regarding eclipses, phenomena, etc., and never hesitated to lay aside his own work in order to comply. 'His readiness to help, and his magnificent ability to help, will always be remembered at the Nautical Almanac Office', according to Mr Downing.

From 1874–76 Adams was President for the second time of the Royal Astronomical Society (R.A.S.). In 1870 he had been Vice-President and delivered an address on presenting a medal to Delaunay, whose general treatment of Lunar Theory he had admired.

In 1881 he was offered the position of Astronomer Royal, on the retirement of Airy, but declined.

In 1884 he was one of four British delegates to the International Prime Meridian Conference at Washington. In the course of the years he had gained Hon. Degree D.C.L. (Oxford), LLD (Dublin and Edinburgh), D.Sc. (Bologna and Cambridge), was Correspondent of the French Academy, and the Academy of Science at St

Petersburg. He had travelled far by virtue of his calculations from the time of his preliminary excursions in mathematics on the barn door at Lidcott Farm.

Some of his scientific papers published between 1844 and 1890 give an idea of the exact work on which he was involved on a variety of subjects. About fifty Astronomical papers appeared in the Memoirs or Monthly Notices of the Royal Astronomical Society; there are eleven papers on pure mathematics. There is unpublished work on Legendre's and Laplace's co-efficients, and terrestrial magnetism. More exact expressions of the co-efficients for Jupiter Satellites II, III and IV were found among unpublished papers at his death. In March 1867 a paper 'sur les etoiles filantes de Novembre' was published in Paris. A paper on lunar inequalities due to ellipticity of the earth was also published after his death. Earlier, in 1852, he gave the R.A.S. new tables of the moon's parallox, to be substituted for those of Burckhardt. Methodically he had given the table of corrections to be applied to values in the Nautical Almanac for every day of the year from 1840 to 1855 inclusive. As Glaisher comments:

> This contribution to Astronomy is very characteristic of the Author. It contains the results of a great amount of intricate and elaborate mathematical investigations carried out with great skill and accuracy in all its details, both analytical and numerical, but no part of the work itself is given. The method of procedure is briefly sketched, and the final conclusions are stated in the fewest words and simplest manner possible. No one unacquainted with the subject would imagine how much careful research was represented by these few pages of results.

He can, however, describe in simple language and at length a total eclipse of the sun he saw when thirty-two years old on 28 July 1851 at Frederiksvaern, five years after the discovery of Neptune. He sends an account of this eclipse to R.A.S. (See Memoirs of R.A.S., Vol. XXI (1852)). He and Mr Liveing, also of St John's College, 'left Hull, by steamer, on the evening of Saturday, July 19, together with a large party of Astronomers bound on the same errand with myself.' He shows his modesty, and scientific approach to the subject at the beginning of the article:

> The approach of the total eclipse of July 28 1851 produced in me a strong desire to witness so rare and striking a phenomenon. Not that I had much hope of being able to add anything of scientific importance to the accounts of the many experienced astronomers, who were preparing to observe it; for I was not unaware of the difficulty which one not accustomed to astronomical observation would have in preserving the requisite coolness and command of the attention amid circumstances so novel, where the points of interest are so numerous, and the time allowed for observation is so short. Certainly my experience has shown that I did not exaggerate these difficulties; but I have at least the satisfaction of having formed a far more vivid idea of the phenomenon than I could have obtained from any description, and I think that if I should ever have another opportunity of observing a total eclipse, I should be prepared to give a much better account of it than I can at present.

He used a telescope of Dolland's 'kindly lent me by the Master and Fellows of St John's College.' In a postscript he adds further thanks: 'I cannot close this account without expressing my sense of the kind hospitality which I met with during a subsequent tour of six weeks in Norway. To Mr. Crowe, Her Majesty's Consul-General at Christiana, whose kindness is so well-known to all

English travellers in that country, I feel particularly bound to return my warmest thanks.'

This is yet another glimpse of the younger astronomer. He continued to be interested in phenomena, and during his time at the Observatory (1861–92) met many interesting people, and contended with many scientific problems in a gracious manner.

In 1872, 29 July, he visited Lord Portsmouth's estate in connection with his work on the Newton papers. The diary records:

29 July (Mon.) 1872: One hour late at St. Pancras. Great bustle at Waterloo Station. Met with Stokes. Lord P's omnibus met us at Whitchurch Station. Lady P. received us very kindly and pleasantly. Lord P. returned from London. Good deal of talk with Lord Portsmouth before going to bed. Wrote to E.

30 July (Tues.): After breakfast began to look over the Newton papers with Stokes. Found some papers containing interesting and important calculations by Newton respecting atmosphere refractions. Also a few bearing on the motion of the Moon's apogee. In the afternoon Lord Portsmouth took us out for a drive. No party at dinner. Lady P. retired early, and we had a good deal of talk with Lord P. Before going to bed read a good deal of 'Goodbye Sweetheart.'

Another visit to Lord Portsmouth is recorded on:

12 May 1877 (Sat.): E to Brighton (+ heavy cold). Lunched at the Atheneum. Then back to Waterloo. Met with Oscar Browning and left for Whitchurch. Took a fly to Hurstbourne, and were rather late for dinner. We had some dancing in the evening. To bed late.

13 May (Sun.): Heavy rain last night. Brought up diary before going to bed. We breakfasted at half past nine. Day very dull at first but soon improved. After service in the private chapel took Colonel and Mrs. Lloyd Lindsay a long walk in the Park to the Terrace Walk and back by the old Yew trees and the cottage. Met with Lord Portsmouth and some others of the party as we returned. Lord Carnarvon arrived just as we returned to the house. After luncheon walked with Lord Carew, Mr. Browning and Mr. Lowther through the village, and looked at fine old Yew in Churchyard. Had afternoon tea and looked at Spectator. Took Lady Camilla into dinner. After talked with Lord Carnarvon about burials bill. Evening Service in Private Chapel. In afternoon heard Teddy play on violin, and tuned it for him.

14 May (Mon.): Mr. Matthew Arnold left this morning before breakfast. Wrote in diary. Left with Mr. Oscar Browning and most of party by 11.27 train. Lady P. was to leave immediately afterwards to see the little daughter of her maid who is very ill at Romsey. Drove with Mr. Browning to the Atheneum and had lunch. Then took a Hansom, called at Astronomical Society, and drove to Liverpool Street, where I met with E. Bought a ready-made overcoat. Both felt the air colder at Cambridge.

These parties at Lord and Lady Portsmouth's were evidently features of the time. In G. S. Haight's *George Eliot– a Biography* (Cambridge University Press, 1968), he records a note from George Eliot's diary. '18 April 1876 Lyceum (Lewes's 59th Birthday) – saw Henry Irving and Kate Bateman in Tennyson's *Queen Mary*. "All the interest and excitement of a FIRST NIGHT" – Lewes noted – "Play horribly acted, throughout – not one of them able to speak." ' Then on 18 May she [G. Eliot] dined at Lady Portsmouth's 'with a distinguished company including Lord Carnarvon (who took her down); Lord and Lady Abercromby; Lord Ramsay; Lord O'Hagan, the Lord Chancellor of Ireland; Mountstuart Grant-Duff; J. C. ADAMS, the discoverer of Neptune; Meredith Townsend, the proprietor of the "Spectator"; and two of the Earl of Portsmouth's daughters. One of them exclaimed to Lewes what a delight it was to see Polly's "saintly face again".'

[i.e. *Mary Ann* Evans]. In 1877 George Eliot and Mr. Lewes evidently were in Cambridge for May week as there is an entry in Eliza Adams' Diary for 2 June 1877 (Saturday) 'Grey and windy. Hans [J. C. A.] went to Greenwich. Revd. Thomas [J. C. A.'s brother] left us. I lunched at Mrs. Sidgwick's to meet G. Eliot and Lewes.' According to the diary 'Rev Thomas Adams came' on Sunday 28 May, and 30 May 'Thomas spent afternoon in Cambridge.' Whit Monday that year was 21 May, when Eliza Adams held a 'Dinner Party for sixteen at the Observatory.' On 4 June William and Mary Adams came down for the one day [from London] – took them to Newnham Hall, and Girton. Miss Clough and Madlle. Rasche to tea – sheet lightening all evening. On 5 June I took Mary to Mr. Jebb's lecture then to King's Chapel. Had lunch in Pembroke, Carrie joined us. Fitzwilliam Museum and Dante Reading.' It was certainly 'all go', day by day, for Eliza Adams. Previous to May Week activities on March 8th 1877 Eliza enters in her diary 'Hans to Joachim [Famous Violinist.] to get him Hon. Degree. Met Robert Browning and Mr. Grove. Hans and I had tea at Professor Colvin's and met Robert Browning. *March 9th 1877* We all lunched at Burns. Met Joachim and Prof. Macfarren and on 24th March 'Lunched at Pembroke, lionized Trinity to Miss Fishbourne and Miss Allen, 'Lionize' was the order of the day' for the wife of Professor J. C. Adams in 1877.

J. C. Adams himself continued with visits to Lord Porchester, and further study on the Newton papers. On 27 March 1883 he visited Lord Porchester at Eggesford, Chulmleigh, Devon, in connection with the Newton papers and his diary records:

> Had a middling night. Breakfasted and started just after eight. Drove by Leicester Square to Waterloo. Had a lovely day for my journey, and went to Eggesford without changing. Telegraphed to E. from the station. Kindly received by Lady P.

Found telegram from Cambridge and answered it. Took Lady Winifred Herbert into dinner. Had games and dance in evening. Afterwards copied some of Newton's Ms. at back of Pemberton's letter.

28 March (Wed.): Started a little before 11 in the waggonette with ladies to go to meet of Staghunt. Drove along road and through fields getting beautiful view. Then Mr. Harrison and I left the carriage and had a splendid walk to watch the hunt. Returned to lunch about 3. Afterwards copied some ms. Had pleasant evening. Sat by Lady P. at dinner. Curious case of dreams. I told her of Professor Stuart's Case. [Prof. J. C. A. and Mrs. Adams were part of the group that met with the Sidgwicks to discuss and practise Mesmerism, and explore the Occult. The Cambridge Club for Psychical Research, started in Cambridge in 1882, has now celebrated its centenary. In 1887, J. C. A. declined the office of President. Eliza Adams was more involved and interested. Her diary records on 25 February (Sunday): 'The Caleys called. Miss Bernard and Miss Harrison came up. Hans and I not to bed till 3 a.m. because of occultation.' This event, however is not mentioned in his Diary for the same day.] March 28th at Eggesford concludes they had a rather wild dance.

29 March (Thurs.): Walk in grounds and a long talk with Lady Dora. Wrote to E. and George before lunch. Afterwards went to the kennel to see hounds fed. At dinner sat by Lady P. and Lady Maud Cecil. Afterwards some of us were decked in crinolines and masks, and there was a wild dance, which way kept us till late.

Apart from scientific work, and social occasions, and the occult, J. C. Adams was also concerned with higher education for women, which was becoming an issue in the country. Bedford College for Women had been founded in 1849 in London, in connection with the University of London, to provide a liberal education for women. The first students were allowed to sit in at University lectures, always carefully chaperoned. A start was made in London therefore, towards higher education for women, twenty years earlier than in Cambridge. One of the early students at Bedford College was Nellie Adams, who eventually married a nephew of John Couch Adams, Fred Adams, the youngest son of Thomas who was born 1858 in the Friendly Islands. (In 1895 she writes a lively account of unveiling the medallion at Westminster p. 251). In 1878 London University admitted women to degrees. Progress was therefore afoot in London University once more before Cambridge University followed tentatively later. John Couch Adams was President of the Cambridge Association for the Higher Education for Women in 1877 – for on 27 December 1877 it was recorded that in his absence at one meeting of the Association, Mr H. Sidgwick took the chair. Present at that meeting were Mrs Bateson, Miss Clough, the Misses Kennedy, Rev. Prof. Mayor, Mr and Mrs Peile, Madame Rusche, Mr and Mrs Sidgwick, Mr Temperley, Rev. A. T. Torry, and Rev. Prof. Westcott. In 1879 J. C. Adams was made a member of Girton College, which had moved from Hitchin to Girton in 1869. It was in 1864 that a Government Committee had been set up to look into middle-class women's education. Miss Davies, Miss Beale and Miss Buss had given evidence, and various petitions were to be presented from the many reputable Girls' Schools already well-established in the country. On 3 June 1880 the Syndicate, which was

to consider 4 memorials relating to the encouragement to be given to the Higher Education for Women, and to report to the Senate before the end of the Lent Term 1881, beg leave to report to the Senate as follows:-

(a) A Memorial signed by 8500 persons forwarded by Mr. W. S. Aldis of Newcastle [see *C. U. Reporter*, 11 May 1880, p. 522].
(b) A Memorial from the Executive Committee of Girton College [See *C. U. Reporter*, 11 May 1880, p. 525].
(c) A Memorial from the Committee of the Association for Promoting the Higher Education of Women in Cambridge. [*C. U. Reporter*, 11 May 1880, p. 527].
(d) Memorial from 123 resident members of the Senate. [*C. U. Reporter*, 18 May 1880, p. 542].
(e) The Managers of University College, Nottingham.
(f) The London Association of Schoolmistresses.
(g) The Governors of Bradford Girls' Grammar School.
(h) The National Union for improving the Education of Women of all classes.
(i) The Council of St. Andrews' School for Girls.
(k) The Association of Head Mistresses of Endowed and Proprietary Schools, signed by 40 Head Mistresses.
(l) The Council of the Teachers' Training and Registration Society.
(m) The Governors of the Salt Schools, Shipley.
(n) The Trustees of Manchester High School for Girls Ltd.
(o) The Council of the Edgbaston High School for Girls Ltd.
(p) A Memorial, with 567 signatures, from non-resident Members of the Senate. [These Memorials will be found in an Appendix to this Report (Appendix II) *C. U. Reporter*, 357, p. 199.].

(c) and (d) ask the University formally to sanction the admission of women to Examinations which are open to Members of the University.
(a) (h) (k) ask that women may be admitted to the Examinations of the University and to degrees conferred according to results of examination; the remainder ask that women may be admitted to the B.A. degree. [Syndicate agrees with Honours degrees; more dubious of Ordinary degrees. Must have passed Previous (p. 334)].

The Signatures of Cambridge University approving of these Memorials were:-

S. G. Phear (Deputy VC)

W. H. Bateson	J. C. Adams	R. M. Burn
N. M. Ferrers	C. D. Liveing	Henry Sidgwick
B. F. Westcott	James Stuart	John Peile
E. G. Clark	G. F. Browne	G. W. Prothero
A. Cayley	E. W. Blore	

More than 8500 signatures were collected in favour of these memorials; among them the Countess of Portsmouth, the Rev. E. A. Abbott, D.D. (Doctor of Divinity) Head of City of London School for Boys, Rev. Montague J. S. Hawtrey, Rev. James Martineau, Principal of Manchester New College, and about 200 Non-conformist Ministers, E. Garrett Anderson MD, S. Jex-Blake M. D. Edinburgh, Miss Buss HM of North London Collegiate School, and twenty-eight HMs of Girls' Schools and more than 1000 other teachers, Professor Huxley, Asmund Airy, Philip Burne-Jones, G. A. Spottiswoode, Isabella M. S. Tod.

Eliza Bruce had also been involved with Committees at Newnham Hall, and on Monday 8 December 1879 she had attended 'a meeting at Mrs. E. C. Clark's about a High School for Girls', according to J. C. Adams' diary. This was eventually to become the Perse School for Girls, Cambridge, opened on 17 January 1881. The Rev. Thomas Adams had been very busy in the 1870s collecting money to start the Leys School in Cambridge. The end of the nineteenth century was an era for promoting more educational opportunities, and the Adams family took its part in this progressive movement. William Grylls Adams came down to vote on the women's issue in the Senate and also Fred Adams, his nephew, the son of Thomas.

Much new thought was abroad in Cambridge among scientists and theologians during the last few decades of the century. James Clerk Maxwell had been appointed the first Professor of Experimental Physics in Cambridge, moving from King's College, London to be succeeded by William Grylls Adams as Professor of Natural Philosophy at King's College, London. Clerk Maxwell made his name for his important researches in electricity and magnetism in 1864–66 and later in his investigations into the molecular constitution of matter. In one of his Cambridge lectures he alleged it was not Creation that was the Miracle, but what it was created from was even more marvellous when molecules were examined. Unfortunately he died at the early age of forty-eight in 1879. John Couch Adams refers to Maxwell's illness on 2 November (Sunday) 1879 when he saw Dr Paget at Great St Mary's: 'He says poor Maxwell cannot last long. He is perfectly calm.' On 5 November (Wednesday) 'Dr. Paget told us of Maxwell's death about 11–12 a.m.' when he met Paget at a meeting of the Royal Society. And on 10 November (Monday) 'Went to funeral service in Trinity Chapel for Professor Maxwell. Got there early. Large gathering. Solemn service. Walked a little way with Professor Cowell afterwards, who told me of Mrs. Maxwell.'

Various names of interest flash through the Diary during the weeks of Maxwell's illness in 1879. As well as minor personal matters and affairs in Cambridge.

10 October (Fri.): Called to inquire for Professor Maxwell who is dangerously ill as I heard yesterday.

12 October (Sun.): Both to St. Edward's and heard a heavy sermon from Dr. Lumby. Lunch at Prof. Stokes. Good sermon but too long at St. Mary's.

13 October (Mon.): Excellent news from Cabal in Standard. Electric clock brought back by Theodore Calliphrim. I asked him into lunch with us – only cold beef and stewed rice. 'Phineas Finn' – V. Good.

16 October (Thurs.): Failed to get in my teeth, which I have left off using for some considerable time.

17 October (Fri.): Again failed with my teeth. Called at Beale's about new stove in our bedroom, the tiles being of wrong colour. E. Busy classifying her shells. 'Phineas Finn'.

19 October (Sun.): Walked to Trinity Church, which is now opened after the alterations. It is immensely improved. Mr. Barton preached a good sermon. Very plain spoken. St. Mary's Dr. Barry preached a rather ponderous sermon 'Forgetting those things that are behind'. The Master [of Pembroke – Power] asked about my leather vests.

20 October (Mon.): Walked in with E and lunched at the Cookery School. Dined alone as E is going to Kennedy's. Drove in with her and went to Club Book Sale at Campion's. Hamblyn Smith was auctioneer and we had a good sale. After we talked a little about opening of Ridley College.

21 October (Tues.): Left note for Miss Jebb at Gonville Nurseries.

22 October (Wed.): Bought horse and cart for Tommy [Roseveare]. Dined at Hort's.

24 October (Fri.): Our new young servant, Annie, made her appearance this morning, having arrived last evening.

25 October (Sat.): Pottered and showed the Miss Days some of my Bibles. Won 5s at whist. Girton for tea. Walked home across the fields. Then E and I went to dine at St. John's Lodge. Some lively talk at dinner. Talked afterwards with Sedley Taylor.

26 October (Sun.): Elsie Day, and sister Emma, came over to us to sleep last night, having been the night before over at Mr. Graham's [Assistant at Observatory]. Mr. Barton's good sermon but I felt sleepy in parts of it. Then to Bishop of Carlisle at St. Mary's to Freshmen 'Come now and let us reason together'.

27 October (Mon.): Showed Miss Days Trinity Library & Hall. Elsie and sister Emma then went to lunch at Newnham Hall. [Elsie Day was Headmistress of Grey Coat Hospital, Girls' School in Westminster – where he called later when in Westminster. The first Headmistress of the Perse Girls', Miss Street, was on the staff of the Grey Coat Hospital before being appointed to the Perse Girls' School. Elsie Day and John Couch Adams may have been the link in this appointment.] In evening read the paper and looked over Missal with Miss Day.

28 October (Tues.): The Miss Days and E left by 10 o'clock train. After College meeting Searle walked out with me and I went part of the way back with him talking chiefly of ritualistic follies in the Church.

30 October (Thurs.): Mrs. Sidgwick called with articles of agreement respecting Newnham College.

31 October (Fri.): E had looked at Bazaar at Trinity Church. E and I to Prof. Calvin's. Introductory lecture on Raphael.

2 November (Sun.): E to Presbyterian Service in Town Hall.

3 November (Mon.): Again began to wear my chamois leather vest.

4 November (Tues.): Chamber Concert in Town Hall.

5 November (Wed.): Maxwell's death. Called at Glaisher's. Spoke of Lord Rayleigh.

9 November (Sun.): Cold nearly gone. William went in at 10 to hear Dr. Abbott preach at St. John's Chapel. B and E to Mr. Macleod at Town Hall, alluded feelingly to Maxwell's death. E and B [Lloyd] lunched in my room. To St. Mary's. Hussey preaching on Esau 'the Prodigal Son of the O. T.' – More favourable view of E's later care than usually taken – found B still in my room and waited for E. Then all walked out by Wallis Farm. Met with Wm and Miss Dingle.

10 November (Mon.): William got satisfactory letter about Clifton and Jack [his son]. Maxwell's funeral service.

11 November (Tues.): Wm left by 10 o'clock train. Niven called with requisition to ask Lord Rayleigh to stand for Professorship which I signed.

12 November (Wed.): Miss Clough told us of sudden death of Miss Jebb's maid. After lunch at Cayley's called at Newnham Hall and went with Miss Clough and Miss Jebb to the inquest and heard Mr. Carver give his evidence of natural causes.

15 November (Sat.): Found all well at Wm's [London]. Willy [William's small son] calls me 'a bird of passage'.

17 November (Sat.): Dinner at Fawcett's. Some skirmishing about Memorial to Rayleigh.

16 November (Sun.): Dr. Macleod preached at Guildhall – a capital sermon on 'Be careful for nothing' Translate your cares into prayers. Niven on Laplace's co-efficient. St. Mary's Montague Butler on 'Your Citizenship is in heaven'. Spoke beautifully of Professor Maxwell.

17 November (Mon.): Finished 'Travels with A Donkey'.

18 November (Tues.): Pottered with my calculations but made little progress. We were invaded by hunters and the hounds killed a fox in Mr. Graham's garden. Perkins of Downing prominent among them and introduced me to the Master of Hounds. He promised to have the brush mounted for me.

20 November (Thurs.): Did a little to my calculations about Jupiter's satellites.

23 November (Sun.): Dr. Stevenson of Dublin at the Guildhall 'Jesus of Nazareth passeth by' Luke 18^{37}. He was more eloquent but I did not like the sermon so well as Dr. Macleod's.

24 November (Mon.): To Mrs Power [wife of Master of Pembroke] and left Rabbit skin chest protector with her. E. made it. [For Master of Pembroke]

25 November (Tues.): To Colvin's lecture on Architecture.

26 November (Wed.): Snowing most of the day.

29 November (Sat.): Phil.Soc.dinner at Pembroke Hall. Large party and many visitors. Speeches rather heavy except Huxley's. I had to propose 'The Visitors' and floundered somewhat. Forgot to make any point of the November Meteors. Sat next Mr. Marten at dinner and had some pleasant talk. We kept the fly waiting a long time, and then home. I wore my Ulster and found it very comfortable.

30 November (Sun.): Professor Chalmers at Guildhall on Syro-Phoenician women. He was at times eloquent but I did not care much about the Sermon. Staunton 1st Hulsean lecture at St. Mary's on significance of our Lord's claim to be Messiah.

3 December (Wed.): Heard that Lord Rayleigh had sent round a circular consenting to become a candidate for Professorship. Read Mrs. Tait's life – affecting account of death of her five daughters.

4 December (Thurs.): In the afternoon went to a meeting in Peterhouse Combination Room to protest against the Commissioner's scheme. Fawcett brought a paper well drawn up of nine objections to the scheme. The meeting then considered and accepted the resolutions brought forward by Cobb. Adjourned after a good deal of talk. Sir H. Mains thought the Commissioners had gone beyond their legal power.

5 December (Fri.): Pleasant party at Dr. Paget's.* Beresford Hope was of the party.†

6 December (Sat.): Agreed to a College [Pembroke] order accepting Mr. Scott's plans for the new building. Walked in and out – brought up diary then in afternoon to adjourned meeting at Peterhouse. After a long speech from Campion and some discussion I moved a resolution about attachment of Profs. to Colleges which was carried unanimously. Sat by Fawcett. We appointed a Sub-Committee to draw up Memorial.

7 December (Sun.): Began reading 'The American' by Hy James. V. cold night. Them. 0.5 below zero.

10 December (Wed.): Took some books to Gray's for repair and then went to meeting in Trinity Combination Room to consider Maxwell Memorial. I was put on Committee to settle form of Memorial and agreed on picture or bust or both. Also enquiry to be made about publishing M.S.S.

* Sir George Edward Paget (1809–92) Fellow of Caius College, Cambridge (1821) MD (1838), FRS (1855), Physician to Addenbrooke's Hospital (1839–84), Professor of Physic, Cambridge University (1872), gave stimulus to education of medical practitioners.

† English politician (Conservative) and writer 1820–87; MP 1841–87; 1855 founded *Saturday Review*; Wrote *Worship in Church of England, English Cathedral's in the Nineteenth Century* and *Popular View of American Civil War*.]

works. After called at Union. Walked out – Not a pleasant evening for walk. Fred [Thomas's son] arrived rather late from Oxford and v. cold.

11 December (Thurs.): Took my cold bath and felt better for it. Fred went off soon after breakfast skating down the river. Miss Bernard leaves for Rome to-morrow. Fred returned to dinner and helped us in reading 'The American'.

12 December (Fri.): R.A.S. London. Got a majority for Huggins for the Medal. Hind elected President unanimously and Lindsay for Secy. Dined at Atheneum with Stokes. Streets dirty so drove to station early for 7.45 train. Wm. met me and drove home. Had difficulty in making them hear. Felt v. well and lively.

13 December (Sat.): Had syndicate meeting at 2½. The VC did not appear and Challis took his place. Audited Sheepshanks' Account, and agreed to recommend £100 augmentation for Mr. Graham. Challis, Darwin, and Niven came in afterwards for tea. Rather late in afternoon E and I walked with Fred. He went to dine with the Read's, and afterwards to dine at Caius. In evening we went on with 'The American'. Fred returned from his dinner rather late. I brought back some brown paper from Matthews for packing parcels.

14 December (Sun.): Dr. Oswald Dykes at Guildhall on the Trinity. I liked the sermon much. It was on the practical view of the doctrine. Then to lunch with Master of Pembroke and were rather a large party – Mrs. Power, Mr. and Miss Fowler, Searle and ourselves. Searle and I to St. Mary's to 3rd Hulsean lecture. I was rather sleepy. In evening Fred had a long talk with his aunt telling her of his engagement to E. W. [later Nellie Adams]. I read Laland's article on Russian Gypsies in 'Macmillan'. [This E. W. was at Bedford College for Women, London, the college which had been opened in 1849.]

15 December (Mon.): E and I and Fred shopping in Cambridge and University Library, but failed to get Bertrand's 'Integral'. Found Fred at Union and we went to call at Jesus Lodge. The Master was lively telling ancedotes about Woodham.

16 December (Tues.): In evening we finished 'The American' – the later part of which seems to us very poor.

17 December (Wed.): Fred left early in a great hurry for him, having to go out to breakfast and start by 9.45 train for Bedford. In evening began to read 'Phyllis', which we found very clever and amusing.

18 December (Thurs.): Mr. Hort called out in the morning to see B. [Lloyd]. [Hort was a native of Dublin, before coming to Cambridge Univeristy in 1846.]

20 December (Sat.): Mrs. Hort and Frank came out this a.m. to see B. E to children's party at Mrs. Hort's. In evening 'Phyllis', and E was busy making up rabbit skin vest for Miss Lloyd.

22 December (Tues.): Called at Library to see that I had no books out. Left the Protest signed at Peterhouse Lodge.

23 December (Tues.): Packed up hurriedly this morning for 11.32 train, which however was very late both in starting and arriving. At Liverpool Street we got lunch comfortably. On getting to New Cross found our train had left and we were sent back to London Bridge, and then by four o'clock train to Horsham and thence to Brighton. An old lady and her daughter in train, very civil to us. Kept warm and comfortable. Nearly past 7 when we got to Montpelier Crescent. [Home of the Misses Lloyd – sisters of Professor Lloyd, Provost of Trinity College, Dublin.] Found all well waiting dinner. Being rather tired we went to bed in pretty good time.

24 December (Wed.): In aft. went out with E and B and bought some Xmas cards. Then left them and took a walk along the sea and back by Montpelier Road. It had got foggy. In aft. read some of 3rd Vol of 'Phyllis' to E and B before dinner time. In course of evening glanced through the remainder of it alone.

25 December (Thurs.): Foggy cold day. To Railway Station and to town to get 'Standard'. Walked along by sea and got to St. John's Church as they were coming out. Lunch rather late. In evening to General Post with twenty-two letters or cards – thinking of Lunar theory.

26 December (Fri.): Dreaming a good deal. E much better.

27 December (Sat.): Niven's papers arrived from Graham – looked over it.

28 December (Sun.): Read Dublin Express and Life of Wm. Pennefather. Chats with Miss Lloyd (in bed). Takes aconite for himself and reads Trollope's 'Cousin Henry'.

31 December (Wed.): Read Standard and Times pretty fully.

1880 1 January (Thurs.). Went to bed last night just at twelve o'clock and then had my milk. Had a pretty good night but dreamt a good deal. Woke rather early. Had my bath. Ordered a new pair of trousers at Shelley's [Brighton – delivered on Saturday night, 3 January].

So began a new year for the Professor, now in his sixty-first year.

The Presbyterians used the Guildhall for services before their present Church in Downing Street was built in 1890. (See p. 150) Hence, the frequent visits to Guildhall and many sermons mentioned during this period of Adams' life. There is a Memorial plaque to J. C. Adams on the present Organ in Downing Street.

6

Cambridge 1880–84: The Contemporary Scene and Life at the University of Cambridge Observatory

The year 1880 for Professor and Mrs Adams began in Brighton, at the home of the sisters of Professor Humphrey Lloyd, Provost of Trinity College, Dublin. They had been lifelong friends of Elizabeth (née Bruce), the wife of John Couch Adams, and the Adams were frequent visitors to their home in Brighton. Miss B. Lloyd was also almost a permanent guest, at times, at the Observatory in Cambridge. Their brother, Professor Humphrey Lloyd, was the eldest son of the Rev. Bartholomew Lloyd of Trinity College, Dublin, who had established the Magnetic Observatory at Dublin, with observation stations in Great Britain and India. His son Humphrey, was President of the Irish Academy (1846–51) and Provost from 1867 until his death in Dublin on 17 January 1881. His sister, one of the three Misses Lloyd of Brighton, had died four days earlier on 13 January 1881.

January 1881, therefore, had a more gloomy start than 1880 in Brighton. It is mentioned in J. C. Adams's diary for 13 January 1881: 'Miss Lloyd died at 8 this evening without suffering.' The next entry followed immediately for 16 January (Sunday): 'Telegram from Dublin saying that no hope remained of life of Dr. Lloyd,' and then on 17 January (Monday):

'Arthur Lloyd arrived and we went to Miss Lloyd's funeral. Maria [Lloyd] stayed at home by our persuasion. In aft. about 2 came news telling of Dr. Lloyd's death. Afterwards Arthur and I took a walk, and afts. he went out with E.

18 January (Tues.): A great snowstorm and no one could go out.

19 January (Wed.): Arthur left.

20 January (Thurs.): Frost intense but calm and sunny. I went out to Hove Bank to cash a cheque for B. [Lloyd].

23 January (Sun.): Bishop of Bloemfontein gave a v. poor sermon on behalf of his work in the Orange Free State.

After funerals and snow in January 1881, February put John Couch Adams to bed for a few days with Dr. Latham in attendance for a quinsy on 10 February, which 'had broken on one side which relieved me' on 12 February (Saturday). He was well enough, however, to get to the Senate House on 24 February (Thursday) by fly, 'where we had an immense gathering in support of the Women's Syndicate report. Sat next to Mr. Holland, the Member for Brighton. Grace 1 carried by 398 to 32, Grace 2 by 258 to 26, and Grace 3 not opposed. The Master of St. John's, as well as myself, out for the 1st. time after illness.' Tom Adams, the eldest son of Thomas Adams, had arrived the night before, 23 February (Wednesday) from York 'to support the Woman's Graces tomorrow'.

While the Academic women, with the help of sympathetic men, were skirmishing for recognition in Cambridge in 1881, the Boers and the British were skirmishing for Zulu territory in the Transvaal in Southern Africa. While John Couch Adams on 23 January 1881 in Brighton had sat at the feet of the Bishop of Bloemfontein of the

Orange Free State, a state bordering on the Transvaal, the First Boer War was underway. A month later on 27 February (Sunday) 1881 Adams records 'snow showers – did not go out. We read 2 of Newman's Parochial sermons, and I also read a good deal of Prof. Cooke's book on Religion and Chemistry lent by Mrs. Miller.' Then on 28 February (Monday): 'Did not get up for breakfast as I felt worse. Horrid news from Transvaal.' 1880–81 had seen war between the British and the Boers in the Transvaal, culminating in defeat of the British at Majuba Hill in 1881, after which Great Britain recognized the independence of the Transvaal. Sir George Colley, former private secretary to Lord Lytton when Viceroy of India, and later Governor of Natal in 1880, was killed at Majuba Hill, an event which shocked the British nation in 1881. By 14 March (Monday) 1881, 'News of the assassination of Czar' was recorded in Adams's diary. In a calmer vein just before this event on Ash Wednesday, (2 March) 1881 'E and I came at Jesus Lodge. Found the old Master wonderfully well and bright. We had a talk about former state of manners etc in the University.' On Sunday 6 March, 'St. Mary's where Mr. Bradly of Baliol and Haylebury preached a v. good and temperate sermon on temperance.'

9 March (Wed.): Began Carlyle's Reminiscences. v. interesting.
10 March (Thurs.): Joachim's Concert.
12 March (Sat.): Lunch at Girton. Met Mr. and Mrs. Carr. I think he was war Correspondent in Bulgaria, Montenegro, etc. – also in Turkestan. Saw digging out of several Anglo-Saxon pots with burnt bones. Prof. Hughes came out later, and dug for Anglo-Saxon skeleton that had been found some days ago.
13 March (Sun.): Read Erasmus 'In Praise of Folly'.

At all times, he was acquiring valuable books nearly 1000 of which were eventually bequeathed to the Cambridge

University Library at his death in 1892. He records on 9 May 1881: 'Called at several bookshops [when in London] – v. extravagant – bought a Caxton'. This was no doubt the Ars Moriendi: 'A treatise speakynge of the arte and crafte to know well to dye', translated by W. Caxton (Fascimile Reprint, Fol. London, 1875). About six months before, on Monday 8 November 1880 he states in his diary: 'Found out by referring to Lalande that the CELESTIAL ATLAS I got from Smith at Brighton is by Dr. BEVIS, and is a great rarity.' This is one of three copies bequeathed to St John's College Library, on his death in 1892, and which is still there. Looking back to 1880, briefly the same entry on 8 November concludes with

Started diary again. E to Miss Jebb. To Cambridge to post. A bad account of the Master [Power of Pembroke]. Brought out some books from Pembroke. In the evening we finished Mary Barton [by Mrs Gaskell].

9 November (Tues.): Got a deplorable account of the Master. Had a long argument about the Q of Greek which is to be decided to-morrow.

12 November (Fri.): Our new maid Helen arrived from Scotland. E. went to see Mrs. Power. In evening began Donna Quixote.

14 November (Sun.): St Mary's Dr. Littlejohn, Bishop of Long Island, gave a Capital sermon on Democracy and Individualism. Text was 8th Psalm.

18 November (Thurs.): Wrote to Smith of Brighton re parcel of Ray's works. Went to Cambridge and found the poor Master was released at 11.20 this morning.

19 November (Fri.): After tea to hear the Bishop of Long Island on State of American Church and was much interested.

After the death of the Master of Pembroke on 18 November 1880 arrangements are soon underway to appoint his successor. The day before the funeral he notes:

23 November (Tues.) A raw thaw. In the evening I went in to Burnside's rooms and met the Fellows to consult who should be voted for as the new Master. Budd opened the proceedings and the general feeling was in favour of Searle. We agreed he should be asked to retain the Fellowship. After came home and we finished Donna Quixote.

24 November (Wed.) E and I drove into Cambridge, she to St. Botolph's, I to Lodge to attend the Master's funeral. Searle and Campion read the parts of the lesson in Church. Went in carriage with Venables, Cox and Stokes to Cherry Hinton Church. They told several ancedotes of the Master's School life, and of his friendship with the Bishop of Ely. Heavy rain, especially as we were at the grave. Porter and the Bp. read the service there. Returned in fly with Stokes and Wm. Adams. Stokes and I had lunch with them. Then to College meeting at 2 and unanimously elected Master, and the fellows Porter and Guillemond also.

25 November (Thurs.): Went in Tramcar. E. to call on Mrs. Stokes [née Miss Robinson of Armagh Observatory] and I to call on Mrs. Power. Miss Loraine dined here and we afterwards went to hear 'Israel in Egypt' performed in Guildhall. Enjoyed it very much.

26 November (Fri.) Miss Selwyn to lunch with Alice [Lloyd]. Called at Union, then to Searle's room and soup. Master of Trinity called while I was there. Lunar Theory being worked on.

28 November (Sun.): Gt. St. Mary's. Littlejohn's last sermon. v.gd. lasted 1 and a half hrs. nearly.

30 November (Tues.): Called at Bank. Then we took tramcar to Hobson's corner and made several calls.

1 December (Wed.): Walked in with E and parted at Spalding's. Met with Swan who asked me about valuation of the Master's telescope.

2 December (Thurs.): Mr. Graham brought his calculations relating to 3rd orbit and I gave him the problem of solving the system of linear equations which I had formed some days ago. Went to Senate House to see Bp. of Long Island get his degree of D. D. Sandys made a good speech. Then to

Pembroke Lodge to wish the ladies goodbye and lunched with them and Searle, who was going to walk with them to Cherry Hinton. Then home and afterwards to Girton to call on Miss Davies.

3 December (Fri.): Went to University and called for ladies at Reading room, meeting with Miss Harland there too. Discussion on 'Capital Punishment' to come off to-morrow at Newnham. My joke thereon.

4 December (Sat.): To audit at Pembroke. Called at Swan's about Master's telescope. He told me something about it in confidence.

5 December (Sun.): Ears troublesome.

6 December (Mon.): Called to pay Water works Co.

7 December (Tue.): Called to enquire of Mrs. Cayley who has an attack of something like erisipelis. Talked a little about Master's Wine.

8 December (Wed.): Sort the analysis sent by Pain, which is satisfactory, showing no *sugar*, and only a trace of *albumen*.

9 December (Thurs.): Soames called to see me in reference to the Master's Dallmeyer Telescope. Went to look at the Master's books etc. which are now on view.

10 December (Fri.): Had some broth with Searle before going to the sale, where I remained till end and bought some lots. Harward only got 2 lots for me, including the Hereford 'Mappa Mundi'. Mr. Soames bought the telescope; Orpen the barometer; and I the Chronometer. Later to Brunsides rooms and consulted Budd about wine to be sold to-morrow.

11 December (Sat.) To sale of Master's wine and stayed till 2. Instructed Hodson to buy some Port for me. Then to Syndicate meeting. Only Challis, Darwin, Pearson attended. Later in afternoon went in again after the sale was over and brought home Johnston's British Zooptry tester and the Mappa Mundi.

12 December (Sun.): St. Mary's – Sandys on 'Blessed are poor in spirit' Afts. walked to Scrope Terrace [Miller's] with Liveing and we remarked on want of common sense in the critics with respect to the Gospel narratives. E and I called on Prof. Challis – 77 to-day.

13 December (Mon.): Bad night thinking a good deal of lunar problem. Early to leave instructions to Hodson about wine to be bought. Swan sent out my wine and I put it away in cellar.

15 December (Wed.): Wet day. Drove in with E, who has taken Mrs. E. Foster's place in Local Examn. Syndicate. Walked in again and found Searle who told me of his engagement to Miss F.

Much of these day by day glimpses of Cambridge life, 1880–81, would still be familiar to members of the University today, but there were also more formal afternoon calls being made; there was constant walking to Cambridge, apart from occasional use of trams and carriages and flies as means of transport; trains were frequently used and seemed to run to time, except on certain occasions, which were noted in the diary in a derogatory way.

Gwen Raverat, born 1885, the daughter of George Darwin (1845–1912) (mentioned earlier, in the Diary) and granddaughter of Charles Darwin (1809–1892) describes vividly in *Period Piece* (p. 93, 1952, Faber & Faber) the social customs of her parents in Cambridge, and their contemporary means of transport.

> Then after lunch, Melbourne would go out to Queens' Green, and catch Zoe and harness her to a kind of low, rather shabby, but elegantly built Victoria, squeeze himself into his navy-blue coat, put on his top hat, take up Aunt Cara and my mother, and drive them off to the delightful duty of paying calls. As they bowled gaily along, Glen followed barking behind; and Melbourne drove with his head turned over his shoulder, for he took a principal part in the conversation. He knew all there was to know about the current

events of the Cambridge world, and gave Aunt Cara [Jebb] much valuable information. . . . One of the important duties which ladies had to perform was going to London for the day to shop. They had to catch the 8.30 Great Northern train to King's Cross. In those days no one ever went to St. Pancras by the Great Eastern Railway if they could help it; and Liverpool St. was unknown to the genteel. The early start put a great strain on the whole household. Sometimes the Bull bus came to fetch my mother; it went round the town picking up such people as had bespoken its services. It cost six pence, luggage and all. But sometimes the bus was booked up, and then a fly from the Bull yard was ordered to come at 8 o'clock. . . . In the evening economy often made her come back from the station in the slow old tram, which went swinging and clanking along behind its one ancient horse. What with changing at the Roman Catholic and waiting for the other tram, she could well have walked home in the same time. Racing the tram was a Cambridge sport, a running child could beat it easily.

Professor and Mrs Adams were definitely a part of this scene, and used to make the social call on Darwin's and Jebb's.

The early months of 1883 found J. C. Adams reading *Vice Versa* in the evenings from 19 to 28 February, 'which is very amusing'; Pycroft's book on *Art in Devonshire,* given him by Mr. Mogford; Royston Pigott's book on *Russia;* Platina (Bartolomeo) *De honesta voluptate et valetudine* and to *Bern. Venetus,* Venitiis, 1498 (bought at Toon's 2 March 1883, when in London) which he 'read with Alice [Lloyd] next day in Cambridge on Saturday'. Among some of the booksellers he frequented when in London were Toon's, Quaritch, Ridlers, Wilson's of Bond

Street; and he also ordered books from George's of Bristol and Smith's of Brighton. Many of these antique books and Atlases can be seen in his collection of early printed and other books in the Cambridge University Library. He comments, at times, on his own extravagance, such as the Caxton *Ars Moriendi*, noted earlier.

Apart from wide reading interests, J. C. Adams was a member of 'The Family', a University Dining Club, originally started in Cambridge by Jacobite supporters in 1786, when various members of Cambridge University drank Toasts 'to the family over the water'. It always met on a Friday, but according to *The Life, Letters, and Journals of George Ticknor, American Writer 1876*, mentioned in S. C. Roberts *The Family: The History of a Dining Club* (which was printed for the Club, Cambridge 1963), the club changed its character. Even by 1819, when Ticknor visited it he states:

> Dr. Davy carried me to dine with a club, which originated in attachment to the fallen Stuarts and was therefore called 'The Family'; but has long since become a mere dinner party every fortnight. Six of the 14 masters were there, Smyth, the Professor of Modern History, and two or three other Professors, including Barns (Peterhouse), Davy (Caius), Cory (Emmanuel), Kay (Christ's), Thackeray (King's), Chafy (Sidney). I was amused with the severity of their adherence to ancient customs and manners and was somewhat surprised to find pipes introduced after dinner not so much because smoking was liked, as because it was ancient in the usages of the club.

Romilly, Fellow of Trinity and University Registrary, was a member (1834–60). In 1876 regular records began. J. C. Adams was a member in 1860, and according to *The Family Cycle 1876–7*, the following were assigned evenings when they would be the hosts of the 'The Family': *1876* Rev. T. Brocklebank (20 October), Rev H. Latham (3 November), Mr. J. H. Law (17 November), Rev. A. G. Day. (1 December). *1877* Master of Sidney (2 February), Master of Pembroke (16 February), Dr. Paget (2 March), Rev. H. J. Hotham (16 March), Master of Trinity (13 April), Prof. Birkbeck (17 April), Professor Adams (11 May), Mr. W. G. Clark (25 May). The old custom of the host inviting his wife and other members of his family gradually declined through the years. 'J. J. Thomson was the last exponent of this feature of the ancient regime', though it was still the custom of the period when J. C. Adams fairly regularly attended the meetings. It was always a matter of concern to the host of the evening as to whether the food and wine were approved by the other guests. After conversation, whist occupied much of the evening, with pence involved. S. C. Roberts notes that on 24 April 1936 A. E. Housman dined with 'The Family' for the last time (Toast and Burgundy), and then died six days later: 'His cellar left to "Family".' The last dinner, evidently, was held at Magdalene on 5 June 1942. Thereafter it met, and still meets, for wine and dessert, but the traditions of the club are now mainly maintained in choice of new members. S. C. Roberts in *The Family*, states

> When a vacancy occurs it is customary for a number of names to be mentioned by members when a general agreement has been reached. The sponsor then approaches each member singly and privately. If, and only if, all agree, then they are elected if the invitation is accepted. Election is made at the next meeting of the 'Family'. The Host of this meeting then informs the new member of his election and a copy of 'Family Cycle' is sent to him. At the 1st Meeting he sits on the right of the Host, who proposes his health.

In Romilly's time they dined at 5.30 p.m. 'Good wine, good talk, good fellowship' was the order of the day in this exclusively male club. Between 1860 and 1876, eighty-six names are registered. Up to 1880 the records show the changes in University personnel – four clerics out of fifty-six were elected, forty-six members are in the *Dictionary of National Biography*. In J. C. Adams's diary for 2 March (Friday) 1883 he records: '10 o'clock to London. Lunch at the Atheneum, then to Truefits and had my hair cut. Then called at Troon's and bought Flatina and an Augustine. At King's X met Alice Lloyd and came down together. Dressed at Pembroke, and went to the Family at J. W. Clark's. A good dinner and good wine. Large party. Darwin elected [George Darwin–father of Gwen Raverat].

A few more items in Adam's diary recorded in March 1883, show how Eliza Adams's interests have coincided with her husband's during their twenty years of marriage, and how she had developed some of her own activities on Cambridge committees. The early part of 1883 in the Diary proceeds as follows:

3 March (Sat.): Read some of Platyna with Alice. She showed me some nice photos from Rome. After lunch E and I went to Council meeting at Newnham, discussed opening of Library, and saw some plans for new wing. After dinner had some whist.

4 March (Sun.): Went to Pembroke with E. and had some bread and cheese in my room. Afterwards to St. Mary's where Dr. Barry preached a sermon and had a collection for the Old Schools. Sermon good and well composed but not v. stirring.

6 March (Tues.): High wind and v. cold in the house from draughts. E. went to King Street Committee in aft. [regarding Servant Girls and Girls' Welfare, etc.].

7 March (Wed.): Snow on ground – continued to snow all day.

8 March (Thurs.): Met with Sedley Taylor.

9 March (Fri.): E and I went in to Pembroke to meet an official of the G. E. Railway, who paid us £8 in compensation for the Missing Angels sent from Florence.

11 March (Sun.): Went to St. Mary's and had a good sermon from Dr. Barry on the power of evil in the world and Christ's work in conquering it. Spoke to Liveing about Girton Committee and to Stokes about Denning Mission [Address at Back of Diary reads Rev. Walter Denning c/o Rev. T. R. Tyson No. 51 Isakigi Tokio JAPAN].

Previously on Tuesday 27 February Stokes had called on Adams and 'delivered to me as Treasurer what had been received for Japan Special Mission', and on 1 March 'Recd. £11 cheque for Japanese Mission and card from Roberts'. On the previous Sunday he had listened in St. Mary's to J. M. Wilson answering men's objections to taking orders – a subject which would interest him as he had avoided the issue himself in 1861 when he moved from St John's to Pembroke, where he could hold a Fellowship without taking orders; St John's had required he took orders, if he wished to remain a Fellow there. It was therefore taking decades to break down the traditions of Cambridge University. To conclude the entry for 11 March he finished the day, after entertaining Miss Helen Hutton and Miss Hutton from Girton in the afternoon, by reading 'a good piece of Lord Lawrence's life, and looked at Justice McCarthy's Account of Afghan War.' By Monday 12 March he 'had two men for my last lecture this term' – and he read some of the new number of Macmillan.

The Diary entries for 1883 give glimpses of his interests in human affairs; his critical comments after sermon-tasting, which he indulges in weekly as a constant attender at the University sermon; his apparent enjoyment of female company; his business acumen in College audits, and purchasing of property; his compassion for the sick and dying, of whom there seem to be frequent instances in Cambridge, especially in Heads of Colleges. They also show views of Cambridge life, which does not change overmuch through the centuries, as well as showing the developing scene of his own day; the value of railways, and on the whole their high efficiency and achievements; the beginning of electricity, developments in photography; descriptions of exhibitions, holidays in the Lakes, Yorkshire and the West of England. These hurried glimpses of his life emerge from brief entries in the diaries (and the entries always were brief in the space allowed for each day in the Lett's Pocket Diaries that he regularly used). Yet a hurried run through some of these brief entries recaptures the Cambridge world of a century ago in an effective manner; it reads at times like the contemporary scene, and makes the man and the astronomer come alive as an interested participant in Cambridge life towards the end of the nineteenth century.

In the ten days before Easter 1883 he flashes from one item of interest to another.

16 March (Fri.): Heard that Oxford had won the Boatrace. Pottered all morning.

17 March (Sat): Dined with Latham at Southacre. Met Fawcett who was in good form. Sat next to Mr. Godfray and Mrs. Frank Darwin, Sir H. & Lady Maine and the V.C. also there.

18 March (Palm Sunday): St. Mary's Kirkpatrick on 'Behold the King cometh unto thee'. [Knowing Mrs. Graham, the wife of his Assistant, was dying] I went in to see Mr. Graham, who took me up to see Mrs. G., who knew me and spoke more plainly than she has done to-day. Thos. G arrived soon afterwards. I was much shocked at the change in her.

19 March (Mon.): Sent off large packet of Exam papers to Prof. Söderblom of Upsala. I went in and saw Mrs. G who knew me but was much weaker than yesterday.

20 March (Tues.): Poor Mrs. G died at 8.10 this morning. She was unconscious for last 2 hrs sleeping peacefully away. Went over to speak to Mr. G and Tom. Talked over tides at Pembroke. Called at Jesus Lodge and saw the Master, who was wonderfully better. Soon after returning went to look at Mrs. G's corpse. She looked v. placid and nice.

21 March (Wed.): Went to Cambridge with E. I ordered a new pair of trousers. Signed three petitions at Deighton's. In evening Miss Walker and I collated a good many of Pemberton's letters to Newton, working till rather late.

22 March (Thurs.): V. cold day. Wrote part of Memorial to Gladstone for Miss Challis. At 11 we attended the funeral of Mrs. G. and took Miss Walker with us. It was v. cold. Afts. signed the Memorial. In evening E and I finished collating Pemberton's letters.

25 March (Easter Day): Mr. Leas at Gt. St. Mary's. I could not hear him very well. In evening we read some more of Lord Lawrence, but I did not attend properly, sorting out some papers for waste paper basket at the same time.

For 27, 28 and 29 March, see pp. 000–00. On 27 March he had set off for Eggesford and Lord Porchester and the Newton papers, together with the 'wild dance', and taking Lady Winifred Herbert in to dinner. The visit concluded on 30 March, and he continues home to Cornwall.

30 March (Fri.): Letter from E. who had got to Brighton with B, while he was 'lionizing' in Devon, Mr. Harrison and Lord Porchester left before 10, and Mr. Wood and Lady Agnes by 11.36 train. . . . Mr. Ramsden and I saw them off, and then took a good walk to Chulmleigh and saw the church. In aft. went with young people to see Eggesford Church and its fine monuments. After dinner we had some round games at cards. The young people danced in evening. Lady P. retired with a headache. I went to my room and read Mr. Paddock on Mormon Life.

31 March (Sat.): All guests left this morning by 11.54 train. The rest went to Exeter, and I by Yeoford to Devonport, where I stayed more than an hour and lunched on Lady P's sandwiches. George met me at Saltash. Wm and Mary arrived. After tea George, Wm. and I took a nice walk along the road from top of the town and back by fields.

1 April (Sun.): Met with Grace, Polly with Lizzie and Harry just before Church. [All from Roseveare's Wivelscombe Farm. Grace Adams (sister), Harry Roseveare and Polly Roseveare (sister) (née Adams) and Lizzie Roseveare (eldest daughter of Harry and Polly)]. Grace and Lizzie to lunch – a good chat – showed some Newton Ms. All to St. Stephen's at night.

After a brief stay among familiar family scenes in Cornwall his diary continues

5 and 6 April (Thurs. and Fri.): London. To lectures with Wm. on electric lighting*, and Geikie [geologist] on Cannons [alternative spelling for Canyons] at Hopkinson Institute of Civil Engineering. Money to Grace £10 and Polly £10 and Hy £50 and half sovs. to Wm's children [three].

7 April (Sat.): To Brighton by 11.30 from Victoria. Found that I was hoarse after journey. Polly's voice not good.

9 April (Mon.): Haircut and dentist.

14th April (Sat.): E and I went to Mayall's to be photographed by the electric light.

15 April (Sun.): E and I to Dr. Hamilton's (Presbyterian minister). 'Paul planted', was subject of sermon.

16 April (Mon.): 1.45 Brighton to Victoria. Called at R.A.S. and at Toon's for Book. [He had visited Foster's, Else's and Smith's Bookshops in Brighton.] Left King's X by 5.5 train. Gt crowd at Cambridge Station. Poynter was our Porter. Had chop with tea. Unpacked and looked at Books.

18 April (Wed.): Unpacked large box of books from Ridler.

19 April (Thurs.): Thomas and Maria [his brother, and his

* William specialised on Electricity, lighting as successor to Professor Maxwell, at King's College, London.

eldest niece, daughter of Thomas] arrived and picked me up on road. Ridler sent me 6th Vol. of Blaeu's Atlas for £5. Unpacked it and showed it to the Party. In the evening looked over an extraordinary book about auricular Conf. by Pere Chiniquy, which Thomas brought with him, having recently met the author; and which, [as deafness was beginning to affect John Couch Adams, and his sister Grace even more] Thomas evidently thought would be of interest.

20 April (Fri.): Letter to Tom [his eldest nephew, Thomas's son] enclosing a cheque for £250 advanced to him, and an introduction to the Bishop of Durham.

21 April (Sat.): Looked at Newman's 'Apologia'. T & M left this morning soon after 12. I went with them as far as the Bull, where I called on Miss Simon [Maria's sister-in-law and bridesmaid at 1871 wedding] and Miss Fowler, and took them to see University Library, Caius, Corpus, Old Court, and St. John's Library, Kitchen, and Combination Room. Home to lunch.

22 April (Sun.): New 'Life of Cromwell'.

23 April (Mon.): E. to Brighton. Letter from Tom re. large house for sale and wrote consenting to bid for it. Went in early and called at Library and found out all about Blaeu's Atlas.

24 April (Tues.): Books from Bristol. Audit of St. Giles.

28 April (Sat.): Letter from Tom re. purchasing Ravenshill and wrote in answer. Master of Jesus's 90th birthday. A large gathering and quite a flower show.

29 April (Sun.): Looked a little at St. Augustine's 'City of God'.

30 April (Mon.): Large photograph of me arrived from Mayall, which is v. good indeed.

On 11 May J. C. Adams was visiting A. H. Joy's Studio in London at about 1 p.m. and 'he took the desired measurements for my head'. He had left Cambridge by the 10 a.m. train and found too late that he was in the excursion part, 'and consequently got half an hour late to London.'

A. H. Joy was a sculptor and portrait painter and relative of Eliza Bruce. He did busts for Robinson of Armagh, and Lloyd of Trinity, Dublin, and J. C. Adams, and the medallion of Adams in Westminster Abbey. On 20 May (Sunday) Adams was again at St Mary's, 'where we had a rather transcendental sermon from Westcott. Hear that he has quarrelled with Bishop of Peterborough, and resigned his canonary.' By the end of June on Sunday the 24th 'E and I went to St Clement's, but were not much edified by the service'. The next day, 25 June: 'Got a nice letter from Kingsley. Thunder storm. St Botolph's Church and some other buildings in Cambridge have been struck by lightening [*sic*].' The next day he 'looked at St Botolph's, which had 'lost a figure from the Tower'.

28 June (Thurs.): Looked over Toon's copy of Julius Polinius 1473, and compared it with my later copy. I drove with B. [Lloyd] to top of Gogmagogs. A lovely day. The air was delicious. Waves on Barley field were beautiful.

4 July (Wed.): Took B. for a lovely drive to Fulbourn, and back by Teversham. On returning gave orders to have the hay cut. The Asylum much finer object than I imagined.

5 July (Thurs.): Went off to London by 8.35 train to attend Spottiswoode's funeral in Westminster Abbey. Immense crowd and fine service. Coffin smothered in flowers.

10 July (Tues): Got in all the hay this evening and helped Abraham with it [that is, at the Observatory in Cambridge].

11 July (Wed.): Wrote to Wm. and also to Harveys of Bristol for some wine.

15 July (Sun.): Mr Conybeare at Gt St Mary's 'We have not received the Spirit of bondage but the spirit of adoption.' He had a most disagreeable voice, but the matter was good, and well put together. 'Freedom not anarchy'.

In another entry, that for Tuesday 17 July, disciplinary words were necessary with one of the Observatory servants – 'Found Wm. in a part of the garden where he had no business', but by the afternoon he was 'helping Wm. to draw B. in her chair'.

20 July (Fri.): Sent Abraham for the wine from Harvey, which I find came on Wed. to Pembroke.
21 July (Sat.): E. unpacked Harvey's wine and put it in the new cellar. Letter from Grace to say she would come next week.

Previous to this on 13 July Honorary degrees had been presented at the Senate House: 'King's Garden Party in afternoon and back to dress for dinner with V. C. in Hall to meet new Drs. Talked with Huxley before dinner and sat between Mat. Arnold and Prof. Goodwin.' On 12 May he had already met Mat. Arnold at H. Latham's: 'E and I went to dine at H. Latham to meet Matthew Arnold'. Unfortunately he gives no further comments or recorded conversation. More comments however on Church services appear on Sunday 17 July: 'E and I went to St Giles – some queer movements but Mr Slater gave a good sermon. St Mary's – a queer sermon from Taylor of Peterhouse.' And on another note, on Saturday 23 July: 'E gathered strawberries in evening' in the Observatory grounds. He and his wife presided over these large grounds with the help of two gardeners, while a cook and one servant helped indoors.

On Sunday 22 July he hears Cox at St Mary's with suggestions of the undertones of the Darwin controversy of the century, stemming from the *Origin of Species*: 'A rather interesting sermon. "My father worketh hitherto and I work". He regarded this as our Lord's comment on Genesis 1 and 2, teaching that God was continually working in Nature. Finished reading Macmillan's Life, wh. is very interesting and beautiful. Afts. read Wallace's Essay on Miracles.' Adams's Sunday reading was usually more religious than secular.

24 July (Tues.): Dr Salmon sent me 'The Academy' with

his paper on the date of Polycarp's martyrdom. Prof. Birks' funeral. To see new cottages in Flower Street.

25 July (Wed.): Fine thunderstorm raging to the N. of us.

26 July (Thurs.): Letter from Skeat* about deviation of 'Theodolite'. Examined my old books on surveying etc. to throw light on the point. Read account of Cpt. Webb's death in Niagara.

27 July (Fri.): Had a better night. Thought of a new theory of the word 'Theodolitus'. Wrote to Mary Bruce and Prof. Skeat in part. To University Library in afternoon but could not find Hopton nor Norwood's Architecture. Meet Prof. Cowell and Prof. Skeat and explained my theory to them. Then went down the road and met Grace in the fly with E. She is looking well. She gave an account of George's want of care about his toe. Found my copy of Hopton.

29 July (Sun.): A fine morning, but the glass in going down. Grace, E and I went to St. Giles' Church, and had a front place on Grace's account. A good sermon from Mr. Slater, but Grace was amazed with the motions in part of the service. [Grace's Wesleyan background evidently surprised by High Anglicanism.] Gt. St. Mary's. Judge Day was there.

30 July (Mon.): Mary and Hy. Cayley came out this morning to tell me that Hy. got his Scholarship at Sherborne. Alice L. arrived for lunch. In aftn. Grace and I went to the Assize Courts and got seats on the Bench. Three trials while we were there, and all the prisoners were found Guilty.

31 July (Tues.): Drive with B. and Grace to top of Gogmagogs etc. Looked at new cottages in Flower St. on our way back. Got some ear tubes etc at Orridges for Grace to try. Dined with V.C. to meet the judges. Sat next to Munro and the Judge's Junior Marshal, also near Whiting.

1 August (Wed.): Looked this morning at Dr. Radcliffe's new theory of the Tides sent me by Dr. Lathem. There are

* W. W. Skeat (b. 1835) Professor of Anglo-Saxon (1878) and Chaucer expert in Cambridge (Christ's College), graduated 1858.

some curious facts stated in it. In afternoon took B and Grace for a drive past Fulbourn Asylum and back through Teversham. Got an ear tube for Grace. Tom arrived soon after our return. E and Alice L. to aftn. tea at Miss Clough's. Had a talk with Tom about his house. In evening Tom talked at. gt length about his school matters [near Gateshead].

3 August (Fri.): Tom to Cromer. Walked in with Grace and left papers at Darwin's room.

[The day before, on 2 August, he and Grace had walked home from Cambridge by the Coton footpath, and after dinner went to a fete and ground with fireworks at The Grove, Newnham.] We were v. near the fireworks and balloon. Left about ten. Poynter coming for us. Our Alice went with us.

5 August (Sun.): [Chase was at St. Mary's.] who as I learn from Searle is our Theological lecturer. He gave what Adams described as a thoughtful sermon on Thy will be done, where he evidently affirmed that Scripture was to be regarded from a two-fold pt of view, wh. may be called ideal or prophetic, and actual or evangelical.

6 August (Mon.): In aftn. took Grace to cottage garden show in King's Grounds. She was greatly pleased with everything.

8 August (Wed.): Got a letter from Dr. Dreyer and his 'History of Armagh Observatory', wh. I looked through. Tom called and brought Bovey of Montreal and a Mr. Gordon. He came back from Cromer yesterday. In aftn. called at Wehrle's for Grace's watch. After dinner I went again about Carting Coals.

9 August (Thurs.): In aft. E and Grace and I walked over to Girton and had aftn. tea. Miss Welsh and Miss Woods were v. nice to Grace. After dinner E and I collected some dead wood to G's great surprize. Showed Grace the Moon thro' my little telescope.

11 August (Sat.): Our coals have been brought out to-day.

12 August (Sun.): Grace and I to Presbyterian service at Town Hall, where an Irishman from Co. Armagh gave a v.

gd sermon 'like as a father pitieth his children'. She heard pretty well.

13 August (Mon.): Showed Grace etc the moon through my Rose telescope.

14 August (Tues.): 12 train to King's X. Grace and I drove to London Bridge and left by 2.25 by 3rd Class to Brighton. Took Grace to see the Pier and then the shops in the King's Road and drove back by 6¾. Moon lovely on the water – the wind very high both in aft. and at night. Listened a while to the music on the pier.

15 August (Wed.): Pavilion. Grace much interested in Model of Palestine. Afts. to Aquarium and lunched there. Then we had a ride on the Electric Railway and drove back soon after 4. Had tea and started by 5 o/c for Victoria. Then to S. Kensington and the Fisheries Exhibition, of which we saw a gt deal. Stayed late and afts. went to stay at Charing Cross Hotel.

16 August (Thurs.): Took a complete cold bath. After breakfast found a letter at Club from A. Joy. Then E and Grace went off to Madame Tussaud's and I took our luggage to King's X. Then went to zoo, and was much interested in new reptile house, also with lions, seals and monkeys. Then off to A. Joy's and gave him a sitting of nearly 1 and a half hours. Got to King's X again in good time. E & Grace joined me, tired but much pleased. Arrived at night and had a meat tea.

17 August (Fri.): G and I called at Wehrle's for her watch. Walked home. Had a meat tea. Letters to Bashforth and Darwin. Corrected sheets on Capy. Action of Bashforth, containing 4 pages of my Chapter.

19 August (Sun.): E. Grace and I walked into Cambridge and went to service at Town Hall, where Dr. Wilson from London gave a sermon on 'one of the days of heaven upon earth', wh. I did not care for.

20 August (Mon.) Took several turns about the grounds while working.

25 August (Sat.) Went to lunch at Mrs. Sidgwick's to meet some members of the Psychical Socy. Had some interesting talk. In afts. met with Churchill Babington* who promised to lend me Dr. Bruce on Roman Wall.

26 August (Sun.): Grace walked to Hobson St. [Wesleyan] Chapel. We went to St. Giles where a stranger to us preached on Ezekiel, 'I will put a new spirit within you'. Found Grace at Pembroke and went into the Garden.

30 August (Thurs.): Changed and packed and then had tea and started by 6.40 train to Lincoln. It was v. shaky.

This was the start of a tour of the North, starting at the Great Northern Hotel Lincoln for the night, and next day a visit to Lincoln Cathedral, and then on to York by the 5.47 p.m. from Lincoln. Here their niece Emily Yeld (née Adams) met them but was unable to accommodate them because of the illness of her nurse, so they stopped at the Station Hotel and next day visited the Minster before leaving in the 1 p.m. train to Whitby, and enjoying the Vale of Pickering en route on Saturday 1st September.

A week later they were near Newcastle, according to Eliza's diary, where they met Mr Foxwell, Mr Spencer Watson and Mr Newall, and saw Tom's school at Gateshead and some of the houses, Ravenshill and Musgrave, that Tom was thinking of purchasing with the help of the loan from his Uncle John Couch. They walked from Gateshead to Newcastle, lunched at the Criterion, visited the Castle, and saw the Roman tombs in the Museum. They got an 'excellent tea at Confectioners. Walked about the town and back by low level bridge and got home dead tired at 7.35'. The next day (12 September)

* Churchill Babington (1821–89) Classical scholar, scientist, archaeologist, studied under Chas. W. Goodwin (orientalist and archaeologist). Graduated in 1843, Disney Prof. of Archaeology (1865–80) at Cambridge – lectured chiefly in Greek and Roman Pottery and numismatics, illustrated from his valuable collection of coins and vases, catalogued classical manuscripts in Universal Library, and Greek and Roman coins in Fitzwilliam Museum. Also authority on botany, ornithology, and conchology. A contemporary of J. C. Adams when both undergraduates.

they set off for Hexham and Gilsland, and eventually reached Carlisle on Saturday 15 September. Grace visited the Wesleyan Chapel the next day before going on to Penrith and Keswick. Three days later on 18 September J. C. Adams and Grace went off to Southport until 22 September (Sat) to attend the British Association meeting. He acknowledges proofs received from Bashforth on 24 September from Mrs Taylor's, The Heads, Keswick. On 1 October they climbed Skiddaw and on 2 October visited Ambleside. By 8 October (Monday) they were at Windermere en route for Lancaster, 'a dingy, uninteresting town', and on to Leeds and the Queen's Hotel by 9 p.m. The next day, 9th October (Tuesday) they 'saw Grace off to Sheffield at 8.50 am', and then 'By 10 to G.N. to Doncaster where lunch cost 2/6 and 1.37 to Cambridge via Lincoln and Gainsboro', and Cambridge arr. 5 o/c.'

They are soon back to the Cambridge life of walking to Cambridge.

27 October (Sat.): Fell in with E and Mrs. E. C. Clark and went with them to look at some furniture for reading room. Bulstrode's men bring new bed for B's room, which seems too large.

28 October (Sun.): To St. Mary's where Wilson preached one of his non-dogmatic sermons. He sums up Xy. in the doctrines of the Fatherhood of God and Brotherhood of Man, on the 2 gt commandments of Christ.

29 October (Mon.): Mr. Bulstrode came out about new bed for B's room. To King's X. Then by underground R'y to Victoria to Brighton.

30 October (Tues.): To Smith's for Song Books. E. called at Albion Home and had a satisfactory interview with the girl she sent there.

31 October (Wed.): Into town with E and had haircut. Bought a toothbrush. Then we both called at Mayall's to settle about E's portrait. Afts. called at Dr. Hilton's and were shocked to learn that he is no more! He died last night at 11. Returned to lunch. Then to Oscar Wilde's lecture on America and was amused. [In 1882, Oscar Wilde visited America lecturing on Aesthetic Philosophy.]

Other minor items of interest noted in the diary for November–December 1883 include:

1 November (Thurs.): Found Poynter engaged so took another cab. Had a meat tea. The smell of the new varnish in drawing room etc is v. disagreable.

2 November (Fri.): Dressed for dinner at Dr. Paget's to meet the new Prof. of Anatomy. A pleasant party and I was prudent. Ridgeway, of Caius, whom I had not met before, was v. amusing.

3 November (Sat.): This is E's birthday, though I had forgotten till reminded in the evening.

4 November (Sun.): E. wrote her criticisms on Essays in the 'Hive' on the Crusades. In the evening looked over Spectator and showed Alice Lloyd my Tyndale's 'New Testament'.

5 November (Mon.): We went to dine at H. Latham's to meet Sir Wm. and Lady Thomson. Later (Lord Kelvin) our host was not well. The Cayleys and Prof. Stuart also there. Pleasant evening.

6 November (Tues.): In evening read some of Lloyd's 'Marrow of History', wh. had some queer things in it.

7 November (Wed.): Letter from Tom. Satisfactory news about Ravenshill. Wrote to Tom and to Bashforth. Called on Dr. Kennedy, and had a chat with him. Found him in low spirits. Walked back and dressed for dinner at the Hort's.

9 November (Fri.): E to Brighton by 11.15. Dined with Family at Newton's. Enjoyed the evening, tho' I lost rather heavily at whist.

10 November (Sat.): Found E and B here on my return. B v. well and lively. Likes her new room much.

11 November (Sun.): Being rather late went to St. Giles. A gd sermon from Slater on 'an enemy hath done this', but the usual 'antics'. Lunched at Mrs. Miller's. St. Mary's Canon Holland preached a thoughtful sermon 'No man hath seen God at any time'. Sympathy felt for agnostics.

12 November (Mon.): Had lunch early and went to Wood's to get tickets for the 'Birds'. A gt. crush and finally only tickets for Tues & Wed. were given out. . . . to Council Meeting of Phil Socy. and afts. to Mathl. Board but found it over. Then called at Wood's and made applicn. for tickets for Sat. Dec. 1. In evening went to meeting of Bible Society at Corn Exchange. Lumley made a gd address on Luther. The place was v. cold.

13 November (Tues.): The new carpet was laid down in the drawing room and looks v. well. Took 'Astry Condec'd' to Gray's and called at Pitt Press with amended Proof of Bashforth's plate. In evening read aloud some of Burton's Anatomy.

21 November (Wed.): E. went to meet Evelyn Fraser, who got here about 8.20 looking v. fresh after her journey.

22 November (Thurs.): Read some of translation of Electra. Looked at houses on Honey Hill, and then went to Senate House to see Mr. Graham take his M.A. degree. The orator made a long speech. Drove in to Wisbey's Sale Room and bought 3 houses in Honey Hill and then joined my ladies at A.D.C. The acting was very good. Manning had a cold unfortunately. It was not over till late.

23 November (Fri.): E. had a bad headache this morning. Evelyn went in to Mrs. Miller's to lunch. Pd Mr. Jacob for new greenhouse wh. he had done well. Looked over some more of Electra. In aft. called on Mr. Bell and then went with him to meeting at Ellison & Burrows about Trusts. Took £100 more in subscriptions. Then called at Guise & Matthew and paid £40 deposit on Honey Hill. E. is better and sat up for me.

24 November (Sat.): In afternoon drove through fields to Girton and saw Electra performed and were greatly pleased with it. A first rate Electra and other parts well filled. Music of Antigone adapted cleverly. Had tea after the performance. Walked home by the road. Evelyn got a tumble in the dark.

25 November (Sun.): St. Mary's Bishop of Rochester 'Who hath power over his own will?' Tea with Cayley's. Showed some amusing pictures of Brit. Assoc. and of Prince at Trinity. Showed Evelyn my new purchase. In evening I showed a Vol. of the old 'Weekly Miscellany' wh. I studied as a child.

26 November (Mon.): Up early to breakfast and left by 8.51 for St. Pancras. To Westminster Abbey to funeral service of Sir Wm. Siemens.* Large no. there and good music. Called at Toon's, and bought some books. Lunch at Atheneum. Called at Ridler's and bought a few more books and came down by Gt. N. express at 3. Called at Pembroke and walked home. We all went to evening party at Mrs. Miller's. Wonderful noisy talk.

29 November (Thurs.): Called at Mr. Symons, the Solicitor, and asked him to prepare conveyance of my cottages. In evening went to Alexandra rooms, where we had dissolving views of scenes in Spain and Portugal in illustration of Evang. work there.

1 December (Sat.): Worked at Dr. Kennedy's Translation of the Birds, looking also at the original. In Aftn. E, Evelyn, Alice Lloyd, and I went to see the performance of the Birds and were greatly pleased. The acting was good and the music beautiful. Some passages reminded me of G.O.M. High tea after 6 and saw Evelyn off by train.

2 December (Sun.): St. Mary's Mr. Foxley of St. John's preached a bold and striking sermon 'It is appointed to all men once to die and after that the judgement'. He strongly denounced the popular view of everlasting torment.

3 December (Mon.): Lecture on buried cities of Central America. Heard v. little of the lecture but the illustrns. were most interesting.

* Sir H. Siemens (1823–83) – electrical engineer, born in Hanover, naturalized 1859, Manager of Siemens Bros. Constructed Portrush electric tramway (1883), FRS 1862, President of British Association, 1882.

5 December (Wed.): Just before lunch I took a look at the Central American Antiquities left by Mr. Maundsley at the Museum.

9 December (Sun.): St. Mary's Mr. Foxley preached a striking sermon on 'I will make them one nation' Ezek. 37:22. He spoke of our divisions, political and religious, and their bad results. He also strongly denounced vivisection in a part of the sermon.

11 December (Tues.); Called at Vail's about an Oil Store. After dinner Chapter of Trollope's Autobiography.

14 December (Fri.): 9.45 to L'pool St. Then Metro. to S. Ken. with some delays. Gave Albert Joy a sitting about ¾ hr and then drove to his house where I made the acquaintance of his wife and had lunch. Much pleased with her. Then in bus to Burlington House. Had a long meeting of Council. My report of Stone's paper was read, and the paper rejected. Afts. voted for the Medal. Dined with Club, then attended part of meeting. Stone again brought forward his theme, which I opposed, and read my report.

16 December (Sun.): Sofa from Pembroke newly covered is a gt. success in newly arranged drawing room.

18 December (Tues.): E. had a bad sick headache and could not get up. I to Cambridge. Called at Pitt Press and saw Mr. Clay and left list of persons and institutions to which book was to be presented. Called on Julia Kennedy who agreed to take E's place at examn. (local) this evening. Called at Symonds and give him cheque for – of purchase money £360, and directed for having value partitioned. E. felt better and got some sleep in evening.

19 December (Wed.): E. much better this morning and got up soon after breakfast. Called on Mr. Symonds about insuring houses and brought away title deed. In evening looked at them. They come down from time of Charles 2nd.

20 December (Thurs.): E. got up as usual and is free of headache.

21 December (Fri): Joined E. at lunch at Alexandra Restaurant.

23 December (Sun.): Baby was frightened at me. John Bull's and his Island.

31 December (Mon): Got from Catlin's valuation of cottages and low shed wh. agreed closely with Mr. Death's.

These extracts from the Diary of 1883 give some glimpses of John Couch Adams's interests, occupations, and the day-by-day life of Cambridge. It shows the place of sermons, science, transport, and in some ways the extraordinary opportunities for meeting with celebrities of the day, if a Professor in Cambridge.

1884 was to take him and his wife across the Atlantic for the Meridian Conference in Washington. He writes to his friend Bashforth, on 25 April 1884:

> I have been asked by the Lords of the Cmtee of Council of Educn. to be one of the 2 delegates to represent this country at the International Prime Meridian Conference, which is to meet at Washington, at the beginning of October, and this has decided me to attend the Members' Meeting of the B. Assocn. We shall therefore have to be away from home about 2 mths. My wife looks forward with some dread to the expedition, but I hope it will do us both good.

On Good Friday 11 April 1884 he was at Ventnor, Isle of Wight, when he records in his diary 'Got letter from Christie offering me place of a Delegate to Longitude Conference at Washington, and this morning telegraphed conditional acceptance of it'. By Saturday 12 April came 'Telegram from Christie settling the Washington Business'. He then went on exploring the Isle of Wight: 'Rail to Cowes. Walked about and crossed the Ferry. Then by 7⅓ train to Sandown, home to Miss Grainger's at Bembridge.' On 15 April 'Applied to V.C for leave of absence', and 'Had vouchers for E and self.' On 27 April (Sunday): 'Letter from Mary telling of Wm's arrangements for going to Canada. Wrote to Allan Brothers about passage to America. Wrote to Polly on her birthday.' By 3 May (Saturday) he was at a college meeting for a long time, but failed to mention an application by Mr Reid to allow woman students to attend his lecture in the College Hall. After fifteen years of Girton College, women still did not have the freedom of men undergraduates. However, on 7 May: 'Walked to Girton with E. Called on Miss Morris with whom we had an interesting talk about Theosophy. Then called on Miss Welch who is probably going on August 7th in the 'Circassion'. In evening E. went to Women's Suffrage meeting and I to Ray.' He lunched at the Atheneum on Friday 9 May before attending a meeting of the Royal Astronomical Society (RAS), where he 'had some talk with Christie about Washington Conference'. When he went on to stay the night with William his forgetfulness with letters caught him out: 'Found May did not expect me and discovered letter to her and one to Mr. Chambers had not left my pocket!' On Saturday 10 May: 'Wm. went with me to see ruin of Whiteleys'. On Sunday 11 May he was at the University sermon at St Mary's once more, where the Dean of Manchester preached on the sacramental system 'rather mystically'. On Monday 12 May he got his contract ticket for America from Allan & Co., and next day was looking at 'Henry James's "Portrait of Places" chiefly the American ones'. On 23 May (Friday) he called at the University Library and 'left Bible of 1462 for Mr. Bradshaw to see'. He attends funerals; and 'went to see Cricket match on Fenner's Ground'.

By 4 July the resignation of the Mistress of Girton was received. On 1 July he was in the Chair of the Girton Council in London and had a sitting at A. Joy's: 'I fear he is not getting on v. well'. He was also preparing for the Atlantic voyage on his London visit on 19 July when he visited Holborn and bought a ship's chair as well as slippers and goloshes. Then he went to the Strand and bought trunks for cabin and bag. In the evening: 'to the

"Princess Ida" which amused us but struck us as poor'. On Sunday 20 July they telegraphed to Cambridge at Vere Street saying they are staying on in London. They went to Marylebone Presbyterian Church where they heard Donald Frazer and were disappointed. They went on to William's house at Notting Hill Crescent. However, William was at the North Foreland testing the lights. On 21 July (Monday) he got a hat with an Air Chamber and then called at Toon's and was 'v. extravagant' and finally returned to Cambridge. On 24 July (Thursday) he called on Symonds 'about my will', a draft of which arrived on Sunday. On 29 July 'The tailor came out to try my thin suit'. On Wednesday 30 July he was back in London for the day: 'Called at hat shop about changing new hat. Looked at Air cushions.' Then on to the sale room at Joker House Yard where he was amused by the auctioneer. He was back in London again next day (Thursday 31 July) when he drove to the hatters to 'return my hat for another'. He then bought two 'swimming collars', as well as a small tract of Galileo at Ellis & White's, and then went to a Committee at Lady Stanley's to appoint a new Principal of Girton College: 'Had a long debate. Miss Davies read letters strongly in favour of Miss Welsh. At last decided on delaying the appointment.' A few days before sailing for America he purchased a tin box at Vail's in Cambridge on 1 August. Among his visitors at the Observatory in the afternoon were Mr Lestourgeon's baby grandchild and nurse and 'I made a conquest'. On Saturday 2 August he 'Called at Symonds and read over and signed my will'. On the Sunday he went to the sermon at St Mary's where Mr Drake preached on 'The Authority of the Church in the interpretation of Scripture': 'Not v. conclusive to my mind'. Abraham, after a month's notice left, and 'I gave him a recommendation.' On Monday 4 August: 'To hospital and proposed Dr. MacAlister as Physician and it was carried unanimously. On 5 August: 'Got Symond's bill for making my will, wh. was v. moderate.' He paid it in the afternoon. 'Got Dickens for Latham at Macmillan's. Saw Master of Jesus [aged 91] in garden who gave us his blessing. E. signed her will.'

6 August (Wed.): Cleared rest of study and Sarah helped me to pack and finished only just in time. Met with Miss B and Dr. L. at station. He telegraphed for us to Hotel. Tedious journey to Bletchley, several changes. Met with Mr. Stanley Barnes at Hotel who was v. useful and ordered supper for us.

7 August (Thurs.): SAILED FOR U.S.A. Seen off by Fred and Nelly. Then Tom and Annie and Thomas Laddlie Latham came to call also and changed a £20 cheque for me, as I had come away without money. All the company was too much for E. who got a bad headache. Tried in vain for a lighter hat and a large bag. All the party lunched with us. Gt bustle on leaving but got on board all right. Tom off alone by the Germanic [To Canada]. Had a good dinner at 6 and began to move while having it. Sat in our deck chairs till late. E. better after dinner.

So the die is cast for the Washington Conference on 1 October. He records seven days at sea, but then the diary lapses until Monday 10 November, the day they sail in to Liverpool on their return. On the outward voyage on Friday 8 August he was 'up early and had bath which was v. pleasant. Morn was lovely. Passed near Irish coast and Rathlin Island, but view not v. clear.' They waited off Morville and despatched their last mail, and got the cabin into some order: 'The fog horn sounded before we went to bed', and a number of emigrants 'came on board at Morville'.

9 August (Sat.): Enjoyed my bath. Made rather too heavy a breakfast, esp. on coffee. A gd deal more motion and I had to go to the side. Could not go down to lunch or dinner but had some broth in my cabin. E. also bad.

10 August (Sun.): 'Had my usual bath, but took some breakfast in my berth, where I lay all morning. Afts. heard that there had been a service and sermon. Got up to lunch but had not much appetite. Lay down again afterwards and had some broth (beef) for dinner. In evening went into saloon and joined in some hymns.

11 August (Mon.): Had my bath and went into saloon for b'fast, feeling better. Went on deck, but the sea was rather rough and several times the deck was flooded. Began to read Henry James' 'Roderick Hudson'. The motion being so great I had both lunch and dinner in my cabin. E. still confined to the cabin with a bad headache. Worst motion in the evening than we have had.

12 August (Tues.): Had my bath, and went to b'fast feeling all right again. On deck going on with the reading of Roderick Hudson. E. came up on deck but feeling v. weak.

13 August (Wed.): Had my bath and my appetite had improved much. Went on with 2nd Vol of Roderick Hudson. Finished it in evening, and on going into the saloon found a charade going on wh. was v. well acted. Word – Inconstant. Afts. some singing. Old King Cole was sung with gt. applause by Cpt. Leigh. Later I walked on deck with Dr. Tuke and Mr. Fleet talking about Astronomy till 11 when we had to turn in.

14 August (Thurs.): Found to my disappointment that a fine iceberg was seen in the moonlight last night just as I had gone down, and that another was passed this morning when I was in my bath. We were soon consoled however by another being seen and just before lunch we spied another ahead of us wh. we passed and had a gd. view after lunch. Later a fine one appeared just ahead which we passed at about a mile distance. Afts. saw many others and came in sight of Labrador and Belle Isle Straights. In evening Mr. Dobell took some of us into Chart Room and showed us the course we had made. In saloon had some readings, and songs, and recitations.

15 August (Fri.): Had walk before breakfast with Mrs. Stanley. Had interesting conversation after breakfast with Mr. Dobell who invited us to visit him. He wanted me to give a little lecture and after some hesitation I consented. Thought over November Meteors, and was rather late for lunch. In aft. wrote to George and brought up diary wh. had got sadly into arrears.

The next fortnight must have seen them arrive in New York, and get to Washington in time for the start of the Conference. The diary remains blank.

The purpose of the Conference was to fix a Prime Meridian and a Universal Day. There had been an Act of Congress authorizing the President of the United States to invite the Congress to Washington, and making appropriation for expenses. A circular had been sent to United States' representatives abroad to bring the subject to the attention of foreign governments, and a further circular to United States' Ministers extending an invitation to foreign Governments to attend. Great Britain was one of the countries invited, and Prof. J. C. Adams one of the representatives. Therefore August 1884 saw his arrival in Washington, DC, ready for the Meridian Conference.

7

Meridian Conference: Washington DC October 1884

> Be it enacted by the Senate and House of Representatives of the U.S.A. in Congress assembled, that the President of the United States be authorized and requested to extend to the Governments of all nations in diplomatic relations with our own an invitation to appoint delegates to meet delegates from the United States in the City of Washington, at such time as he may see fit to designate for the purpose of fixing a meridian proper to be employed as a common zero of longitude and standard of time reckoning throughout the globe, and that the President be authorized to appoint delegates, not exceeding three in number, to represent the United States in such International Conference. Approved August 3 1882.

Thus the Edict from Congress went out to the nations. The Prime Meridian was to replace the multiplicity of initial meridians then existing, and a Universal Day was to be established for all.

The Countries represented at the Washington International Meridian Conference of 1884 were: Austria, Brazil, Colombia, Costa Rica, France, Germany, Great Britain, Guatemala, Hawaii, Hungary, Italy, Japan, Mexico, Paraguay, Russia, San Domingo, Salvador, Spain, Sweden, United States, Venezuela. Representatives from Chile, Denmark, Liberia, Netherlands, and Turkey were not present, though invited. Among the delegations were many naval representatives, envoys extraordinary and ministers, plenipotentiaries, directors of observatories, civil engineers, consuls, President of Boundary Commission, first secretaries of legations, Secretary of Railway Time Convention, charge d'affaires. The Great Britain delegation consisted of four members: Captain Sir F. J. O. Evans, Royal Navy; Prof. J. C. Adams, Director of the Cambridge Observatory; Lt Gen. Strachey, Member of Council of India; and Mr Sandford Fleming, Representative Dominion of Canada. France, one of the more contentious members of the Conference, was represented by two members: M. A. Lefaivre, Minister Plenipotentiary and Consul-General, and Professor M. Janssen, Director of the Physical Observatory of Paris. The United States delegates were: Rear-Admiral C. R. P. Rodgers, US Navy; Mr. Lewis M. Rutherford; Mr. W. F. Allen, Secretary of the Railway Times Convention; Cmdr W. T. Sampson, US Navy; Prof. Cleveland Abbe, US Signal Office. No country other than the United States had more than four representatives, and most had one or two. While there was unanimous agreement with Commander Sampson's resolution that it was desirable to adopt a Standard Meridian, the argument eventually developed into mainly an Anglo-French tussle, with the usual French logic versus the British and American practicality battling for results.

The Conference opened on 1 October 1884 in the Diplomatic Hall of the Department of State. The modern need for fixing a Prime Meridian was stated in the Chairman's opening remarks:

> In the absence of a common and accepted standard for the computation of time for other than astronomical purposes, embarrassments are experienced in the ordinary affairs of modern commerce; that this embarrassment is especially felt since the extension of telegraphic and railway communications has joined States and Continents possessing independent and widely separated meridial standards of time; that the subject of a common meridian has been for several years past discussed in this country and in Europe by commercial and scientific bodies, and the need of a general agreement upon a single standard recognized; and that, in recent European conferences, especially, favor was shown to the suggestion that, as the United States possesses the greatest longitudinal extension of any country traversed by railway and telegraph lines the unification measures for such a conference should be taken in U.S.

Once gathered at Washington the arguments began. Janssen of France thought the mission of this conference was to examine the question of *principle* and wished to re-open the whole discussion on the necessity for a Prime Meridian, in spite of the fact, which he acknowledged, that geographers and navigators since the seventeenth century had realized the advantages of a Prime Meridian. Rutherford of the USA countered this by stressing that the Conference had been convened to fix the Meridian, not to discuss the *need for it*. Mr Valera, the Envoy Extraordinary and Minister Plenipotentiary of Spain, the leader of their three-man delegation, said he could not pledge his country to anything fixed at this Conference, and could only recommend whatever other countries agreed. The Rome conference had adjourned, leaving the discussion and final adoption of this or other equivalent unit, and the framing of practical rules for such adoption to the International Conference to be held at Washington, during 1884. The invitations to the countries invited to be present at Washington were to go through 'the Minister of Foreign Affairs' of those countries to be represented by one or more delegates (not exceeding three). Count Lewenhaupt of Sweden was to be in the Chair. The Chairman of the US delegation was to be Admiral C. R. P. Rodgers, who was also to be President of the permanent organization.

It was Admiral Rodgers who made the opening address on 1884, making the points that the Congress came from 'widely separated portions of the globe', and consisted of 'delegates renowned in diplomacy and science', seeking to create a new accord among nations by agreeing upon a meridian proper to be employed as a common zero of longitude and standard of time reckoning throughout the world. In the course of his opening remarks he stated: 'Happy shall we be, if, throwing aside national preferences and inclinations, we seek only the common good of mankind, and gain for science and for commerce a prime meridian acceptable to all countries, secured with the least possible inconvenience.' He abnegated any claim the USA might have had to become this zero in his concluding remarks:

> Broad as is the area of the United States, covering a hundred degrees of longitude, extending from 66°52 west from Greenwich to 166°13 at our extreme limit in Alaska, not including the Aleutian Islands; traversed as it is, by railway and telegraph lines, and dotted with observatories; long as it is its sea-coast of more than twelve thousand miles; vast as must be its foreign and domestic commerce, its delegation to this Congress has no desire to urge that a prime meridian shall be found within its confines.
>
> In my own profession, that of a seaman, the embarrassment arising from the many prime

meridians now in use is very conspicuous, and in the valuable interchange of longitudes by passing ships at sea, often difficult and hurried, sometimes only possible by figures written on a blackboard, much confusion arises, and at times grave danger. In the use of charts, too, this trouble is also annoying, and to us who live upon the sea a common prime meridian will be a great advantage.

Within the last two years we have been given reason to hope that this great desideration may be obtained, and within a year a learned conference, in which many nations were represented, expressed opinions upon it with singular unanimity, and in a very broad and catholic spirit.

So opened the Conference. The Report of the Conference (in English and French), including the Protocols of Proceedings, is among John Couch Adams's Books, bequeathed to Cambridge University on his death in 1892. (Both copies were uncut.)

In October 1883 the Geodetic Conference, held in Rome, very decisively had expressed its opinion that Greenwich should become Prime Meridian, that is the common zero of Time longitude.

In spite of Lefaivre of France declaring that the Washington Conference was in no way bound to the decisions of the Rome Geodetic Conference of 1883, the Washington Conference settled down in earnest to fix finally the Prime Meridian, with the findings of Rome clearly in mind. It was settled that the Conference should be reported in French and English, and that there was no need to elect a Vice-President. Other preliminary questions were dealt with at the start, such as 'Should the Congress be open to the public?' Lefaivre once more raised his voice suggesting that nothing could be gained by this, and stating that proceedings might be embarrassed or delayed as a result. Professor Adams agreed with this, but would agree with the proposition to the extent of including distinguished scientists, who were not members of the Conference, some already in Washington. Paraguay would go further and wished all meetings to be public, and would invite the world to the Capital. Finally, it was decided to publish in full, day-by-day findings of the Conference for the delegates, which could eventually be made public. Mr Hirsch, of Switzerland, not yet arrived, was to be Secretary, as he had been Secretary to the Rome Conference. A committee was appointed to elect secretaries consisting of: Mr C. de Struve (Russia); Mr Juan Valera (Spain); Mr A. Lefaivre (France); and Count Carl Lewenhaupt (Sweden). This committee appointed the following Secretaries: Lt. General Strachey (Great Britain); Professor M. Janssen (France); and Dr L. Cruls (Brazil). It was agreed to have seating for delegates in alphabetical order permanently fixed.

Extra invitations were sent to scientists to express their opinions on all scientific questions discussed, but they were not to be allowed a vote, as the Conference represented governments. There was to be one vote per country, regardless of the numbers of delegates representing a country. The scientists suggested were: Professor Newcomb, Superintendent of the US Nautical Almanac; Professor Hildegard, Superintendent of US Coast Geodetic Survey; Professor A. Hall; Professor D. C. Valentina, Director of Observatory at Karlsruhe; and Sir W. Thomson. Professor Abbe (US) put forward a resolution to allow those who wished to submit 'inventions, devices, systems of universal time' to the Conference should be acknowledged, but the conference would 'abstain from any expression of opinion on their merits.' Professor Adams warned the Conference to be very cautious in admitting the devices and schemes of people who had no connection with 'this body'. He shows his moderation and sense of proportion as he proceeds with this theme: 'there are, no doubt, many inventions and many people who have plans and schemes which they wish to press upon the Conference, and that it was probable that the Conference would be subjected to very great inconvenience, if they took upon themselves even the burden of acknowledging the receipt of these communications.' The President revealed he had received several communications of this character, one proposing that Jerusalem should be taken as the Prime Meridian.

In answer to Rutherford of the U.S., proposing Greenwich as Prime Meridian, Lefaivre's objections were based on the fact that the Rome delegates had possessed no official authority from their governments, and were entirely composed of specialists, and had not meant to examine the question in an international context. He argued that the Washington Conference was composed of various elements, such as 'scientists of the highest standard, but also functionaries of high rank, not familiar with scientific subjects, and who are charged with an examination of this question from a political standpoint.' He concluded: 'It is, moreover, our privilege to be philosophers and cosmopolitans, and to contemplate the interests of mankind, not only for the present but for the most distant future.'

After this preliminary French skirmishing, the session of 6 October was given over to a French resolution, to take the place of the original resolution to make Greenwich the Prime Meridian. The French proposal was: 'That the initial Meridian should have a character of absolute neutrality. It should be chosen exclusively so as to secure to science and to international commerce all possible advantages, and in particular, especially should cut no great continent, – neither Europe nor America.' Captain Sir F. J. O. Evans, Royal Navy (Great Britain) opposed this resolution, arguing that the Rome decisions should not be passed over on these grounds, as twelve of the thirty-eight delegates at Rome were directors of national observatories, and that the Prime Meridian had been discussed without reference to any particular nationality. 'These learned gentlemen' at Rome had agreed on the *need* for the Prime Meridian, and this should pass through an existing astronomical observatory of the first order as modern science demanded such precision. They had, on these grounds, he argued, excluded all ideas of a meridian being established on an island, in a strait, on the summit of a mountain or by a monumental building. The Rome Conference by arriving at these conclusions, had decided unanimously that there were only four great observatories which combined all the conditions – Paris, Berlin, Greenwich, and Washington. Sampson of the United States asserted that no physical feature of our earth commended itself as the best starting point. He thought permanence was necessary once established, and that it should be an observatory under the control of government, and also in telegraphic communication with the whole world. These were imperative conditions, and he thought one of the national meridians, now in use, should be selected, otherwise endless confusion would be introduced into all charts and maps then in use, if mid-Atlantic or mid-Pacific were chosen. Also there would be no scientific or practical advantage if the Pyramid were chosen. For economy's sake it would be best to choose the meridian then in *most* general use, as more than 70 per cent of all the world's shipping used the meridian for purposes of navigation. Charts constructed on this meridian covered the whole navigable globe, and the cost of the plates from which these charts were printed were about 75 per cent of the cost of all plates in the world for printing mariner's charts, and probably not less than ten millions of dollars. It was therefore more economical to let these plates remain. National pride, he showed, had led great nations to establish, by law, their own prime meridian within their own borders, and into this error the United States had been led thirty-five years earlier. If any nation coveted the Meridian for its own nation, when it was once adopted as Prime Meridian, it would lose its identity. Rutherford thought the Paris Observatory might perhaps be moved eventually, as it is in the city, and suffered earth tremors at times. Great Britain had not sought Greenwich to be the Prime Meridian, but it was in a large park, and under government control, and no nuisance could come near it without government consent.

Janssen, of France, countered these arguments by affirming that neutrality was essential, so he was not pushing the merits of Paris compared with Greenwich. He then diverted attention to Marius of Tyre, Ptolemy and Richelieu, who had fixed meridians on the Fortunate Isles and Ferro – the latter had a geographical and neutral character, and Delisle had them simplified, that is Ferro as 20°W of Paris, so no longer impersonal. After further French abstractions and suppositions, he lectured the Conference on the essential distinction between meridians of a geographic or of a hydrographic nature – that is meridians of observation, which were essentially more national and accurate, and meridians of geographic nature, which were more practical. He affirmed that the intervention of astronomy on geography led man away from the object to be attained, and added that economy and established custom should not bias the argument. France had been the first to conceive and execute great geodetic operations for civil and military maps in Europe, America and Africa. Nearly all astronomical tables used by astronomers and the navy were French. He concluded with a further panegyric on France, for it was French hydrographic engineers who were pioneers in Newfoundland, Guiana, Brazil, Japan, China, etc. It was the scientific principle, which should be considered and not the percentage of use. France should not be picked out to bear 'the burden of change and abandonment of a valued and glorious past'. The proposition previously put before the Conference would not be acceptable to France, as it would involve heavy sacrifices to France, *but* 'nevertheless, if we are approached with offers of self-sacrifice, and thus receive proofs of a sincere desire for the general good, France has given sufficient proofs of her love of progress to make her co-operation certain.'

It was Professor Adams, who was called on to follow this Gallic eloquence, and patriotic outburst. He introduced some realism, and common-sense into proceedings, and briefly pricked the romantic bubble. He

> merely desired to refer to one subject touched on by the Delegate of France, Mr. Janssen, whose opinions he thought could hardly be supported, and that was that the question of longitude was purely one of geography. He desired to controvert that and to hold that the question of longitude was purely one of astronomical observation. . . . If an attempt is made to measure the differences of longitude between two points on the earth's surface, especially when they are a considerable distance from each other, it is necessary to depend on astronomical observations – the transit of the star observed in one place connected with the transit in another.

He concluded that so far as he could follow the discourse, it seemed to him to turn almost entirely on sentimental considerations, and that Janssen had overlooked one great point correctly laid down by the President, which was 'how best to secure the aggregate convenience of the world at large', when fixing the Prime Meridian, the zero of longitude, from which all longitude and time would be calculated in future. It appeared to Adams

> that the Question was narrowed to one of fact rather than one of sentiment, which latter would admit of no solution whatever, for it was quite clear that if all the delegates here present were guided by merely sentimental considerations of *amour propre*, the conference would never arrive at any conclusion, because each nation would put its own interests on a level with those of every other.

Professor Newcomb, Superintendant of the U.S. Nautical Almanac, one of the professors permitted to speak but not to vote, agreed with Adams in failing to see what advantage would be gained by a neutral meridian in preference to one fixed by convenience.

Professor Janssen then put to the Conference the advantages of a neutral meridian from a geographical and moral point of view. After this flow of French it was decided to adjourn the Conference for a week in order to find a French stenographer able to report, and to give the Conference time for careful consideration. Meanwhile J. C. Adams was appointed to a Committee to deal with all communications addressed to the President. When the conference reassembled a week later on 13 October to discuss the French proposition for a neutral meridian, Mr Sandford Fleming (Great Britain) urged the conference to consider the French proposition 'in no narrow spirit' but as 'Citizens of the World', and not spokesmen for nationalities, though the question affected every nationality. It should be judged on what would cause least inconvenience, and at the same time promote the general advantage for all future years, at the same time leaving 'nothing undone to avoid offence, now or hereafter, to the sensitiveness of individual nations.' He pointed out that if a neutral meridian were chosen, it would have to be a new one as those already in use were all more or less national. If such a meridian were found would the twenty-six nations represented at the Conference accept it, and if so might it not be in addition to the *eleven* Meridians already in use? In any case, the Conference had been convened to fix a *Prime* Meridian, which would benefit navigation, and also help the regulation of time. A neutral meridian was excellent in theory, but 'entirely beyond the domain of practicality'. He then proved that if the meridian was settled by the number of ships, and their tonnage, which were at present using the eleven meridians, Greenwich, with its 65 per cent ships and 72 per cent Tonnage, easily outstripped its nearest rival

Paris, with 10 per cent ships and 8 per cent tonnage. Cadiz, Naples, and Christiana were the next competitors with 5 per cent ships, 3 per cent tonnage; for Cadiz 4 per cent ships and 4 per cent tonnage; for Naples, 4 per cent ships and 3 per cent tonnage; for Christiana, with Ferro 2 per cent ships and 3 per cent tonnage were a poor sixth in the table. Pulkova 1.5 per cent for both; Stockholm 1.5 per cent, Lisbon 1 per cent (both); Copenhagen 1 per cent and 0.5 per cent; and Rio de Janeiro 0.5 per cent (both) with other miscellaneous meridians 4.5 per cent and 2.5 per cent were negligible in usage.

Unfortunately Greenwich was a national meridian; Stanford Fleming suggested that the only way to get round this difficulty would be to fix zero of longitude in the Pacific on the meridian farthest from Greenwich but calculated from Greenwich, but it should be called just 'longitude' and not 'longitude E or W of Greenwich'. He quoted the Russian astronomer Struve of the Imperial Observatory of Pulkova, as suggesting a meridian 180° from Greenwich should be fixed as the Prime Meridian, as that would not cross any continent, and would not be too near Paris; and would coincide with a date line used by historial maritime discoverers near a number of small Pacific Islands, and make no change to the great majority of navigators except the addition of twelve hours on 180° to all longitudes. The delegate of Brazil, Dr Cruls, then intervened in the battle between France and Great Britain and United States, which he referred to as 'a scientific tournament of the highest interest'. He hoped for a conclusion to the debate, as at present Brazil was subject to its local geodetic charts being based on Rio de Janeiro, its marine charts based on Paris, and its telegraphic determination of the longitude of Rio Observatory on the United States. He would vote for a neutral meridian, to make their decision generally acceptable in the future for all scientific men 'now awaiting our decision'. Professor Janssen after thanking them for considering his proposition then wished to put it to the vote as 'it is not our intention of making this debate eternal' and as 'my honourable colleague, the delegate of Brazil, an astronomer like myself', had recapitulated the question 'with a loftiness of views, and in such happy language, that, in truth, we may take his arguments as our own'.

The Resolution was lost with twenty-one votes against and three in favour (Brazil, France and San Domingo). The Conference then proceeded to fix the Prime Meridian, but not before the President had apologized for circulating copies of resolutions, not yet discussed, in order to allow delegates to have prior consideration before discussion on motions raised at Rome – such as 'that the counting of longitude should take place from the Meridian of Greenwich in the single direction of west to east', a proposition which he discovered did not have universal approval as some counted both ways east to west and west to east. He proposed they stick to the old way and count longitude from the initial meridian in each direction. Another resolution was to make the universal day coincide with the civil day. Rome had suggested it coincided with the astronomical day, an arrangement inconvenient for those near the initial meridian, such as France and England for the morning hours would be one day, and the afternoon hours another day. The President expressed the hope that some day, not far distant, all these conflicting days, local, universal, nautical and astronomical may start from some one point. In order to hasten proceedings he had framed a resolution for discussion: 'That the beginning of the day should be the midnight at the initial meridian, and not the mid-day.'

The Conference then proceeded to discuss the resolution that 'the Conference proposes to the Governments here represented the adoption of the meridian passing through the centre of the transit instrument at the Observatory of Greenwich as the initial meridian for longitude.' The English delegation then split on an amendment by Mr Sandford Fleming who feared the proposition went 'a little too far at a single leap', and who preferred to leave the Greenwich Zero open for further discussion. He wanted the common zero 'to be a great circle passing through the poles and the centre of the transit instrument at Greenwich'. Professor Adams immediately announced his disagreement, and declared that he and the remaining delegates from Britain would vote against it, if it came to a vote. He pointed out that the proposition to count longitude from a point 180° from the Meridian of Greenwich appeared to them not to be accompanied by any advantage whatever. On the contrary it must lead to inconvenience. You do not, by adopting the meridian opposite Greenwich, get rid of the nationality of the meridian. If there was objection to the meridian of Greenwich on account of its nationality, the meridian of 180° from Greenwich would be subject to the same objection. The one half is not as national as the other half. The President pointed out that no specific meridian was mentioned in the amendment. To which Adams replied

> That is true, but at the same time, it should be said that the meridian described is ambiguous. It is the meridian that passes through the poles and the transit instrument of the Observatory of Greenwich. But it is intended to apply to only one-half of the great circle passing through the poles, that is to the distant half of the meridian rather than the nearer half. Unless it defines which half it is intended to take the amendment is ambiguous, and it is not proper to be voted on.

The German delegate, Baron Von Alvensleben, objected that the amendment contained two separate questions, namely that the Prime Meridian, and whether the adoption of the universal day would be desirable and they should be separated for the purpose of voting. At this point, the delegate of Spain, Mr. Valera, threw a further spanner in the works by telling the Conference that his Government had told him to vote for Greenwich as the

Prime Meridian, 'in the hope that England and the United States will accept on their part the metric system' as Spain had done. He thought Italy was also in the same dilemma.

'With great deference' the Chair ruled that 'the question of weights and measures' was 'beyond the scope of this Conference', which was only concerned with selecting a Prime Meridian, and a standard of time-reckoning. Mr. Valera stated it was only 'a hope of his Government', and hopes were not inserted in protocols, which gave the French delegation another opportunity to delay proceedings by suggesting that the Spanish vote in favour of Greenwich would be a conditional one. Mr. Valera repudiated this, but he felt it was necessary for him to mention this 'hope'. General Strachey of Britain went so far as to state that, following instructions from Rome, Britain wished to be allowed to join the Convention du metre, as was the case with the United States. He told the Conference that 'the use of metrical weights and measures is authorized by law' in Britain, but the Government 'does not hold out any expectation that she will adopt the compulsory use of the metric system, either at the present time, or, so far as that goes, at any future time.' He did admit, however, and would be supported by 'the eminent scientific men of my own country, who are here present, that there is a strong feeling among scientific men in England that sooner or later Great Britain would join the very good system, which is already largely in use among scientists.' Before the Fleming Amendment was put to the vote M. Lefaivre, of France, had his final say by asserting that the meridian of Greenwich was 'not a scientific one, and that its adoption implies no progress for astronomy, geodesy, or navigation', therefore if he voted against it he would not be obstructing science. The only merit for the Greenwich meridian was one of 'material superiorities, and commerical preponderances', for did not 'our colleague from GB just now remind us of it by enumerating with complacency the tonnage of British and American shipping.' Mr Hirsch had confirmed this in his Rome report when he stated

> The Greenwich meridian corresponds to an empire that embraces twenty million square kilometres and a population of two hundred and fifty million. Her merchant marine, which counts 40,000 ships of tonnage from six to nine million tons, and crews of 370,000 men, surpasses in importance all the other marines put together. Other states, equally important, make use of the Greenwich meridian.

Mr Hirsch had recognized at Rome that if Greenwich were to be the Prime Meridian, France should be compensated for their loss of the scientific argument to one in favour of the transitory value of power and riches, by the universal acceptance of the metric system in a spirit of justice.

He finished his peroration on a note of self-pity since they had been invited to sacrifice traditions 'dear to our navy, and to national science', without the hope of asserting the metric system, more or less offered at Rome, 'of which France had the glorious initiative'. After all these almost irrelevant emotional arguments the amendment was lost.

Sir William Thomson of Britain, 'one of the most distinguished scientists', was then called on to address the Conference as a guest, on the main proposition 'That the Conference proposes to the Governments here represented the adoption of the meridian passing through the transit instrument at the Observatory of Greenwich as the initial meridian for longitude'. He stressed the fact that it was to be fixed not on scientific arguments but on what would be 'most convenient, on the whole, for the whole world'. He argued that it could be said that one meridian was more scientific than any other, but one could be more convenient, and someone would have to make a sacrifice to achieve this. If a neutral meridian had been adopted all nations would sacrifice; if Greenwich were accepted, few would. He hoped France would be willing. After Sir F. J. O. Evans (Great Britain), a hydrographer at the Admiralty, had stressed that the preponderance of marine charts, sailing directions and nautical almanacs were produced under the authority of the British Government for universal use, the resolution was put to the vote and carried by twenty-one in favour, one against (San Domingo), with two abstaining from voting (Brazil and France).

The following resolution was then put: 'That from this meridian longitude shall be counted in two directions up to 180 degrees, east longitude being plus and west longitude minus'. This was adopted by fourteen to five (Italy, Netherlands, Spain, Sweden, Switzerland) and six abstaining (Austria, Hungary, Brazil, France, Germany, San Domingo, Turkey.) The Rome Conference had suggested 0°–360°.

Adams had made a significant contribution to this decision and was commended by Sampson of the United States and referred to as 'the learned delegate of GB'. 'It is a mere matter of convenience whether we count longitude in one direction only [i.e. 0°–360°] or in two opposite directions [1° up to 180°] [180°–360°] considering longitudes measured in one direction [west to east] as positive and in the opposite direction [east to west] as negative. These methods are nominally different from each other, but in reality there is no contradiction between them', so Adams asserted. 'In comparatively small countries, like Great Britain, it is more convenient when giving the longitude of a place in the West of England to consider it being a few degrees west of Greenwich, rather than 350 and some degrees to the E. of the Meridian'. Common sense and practicality spoke once more through the voice of Adams, and so 'a.m.' and 'p.m.' were born, based on the Greenwich Meridian of 0°.

Another resolution was passed: 'That the Conference proposes the adoption of a universal day for all purposes for which it may be found convenient and which shall not interfere with the use of local or other standard time where desirable.' Passed by twenty-three, with two abstaining (Germany, San Domingo). Adams had been responsible for adding 'which shall not interfere . . . other standard time where desirable'. The original motion had read 'local or other time'. Rutherford had pointed out anomolies of the phrase 'standard of time', which prior to the 1884 conference, could mean local time, national time, railroad time, so had suggested 'local and other time'.

A further resolution was passed: 'That this universal day is to be a mean solar day; is to begin for all the world at the moment of mean [*mean* amended by Adams, as more correct terminology] midnight of the initial meridian, coinciding with the beginning of the civil day and date of that meridian; and is to be counted from zero up to 24 hrs.' The voting was fifteen in favour, three against (Spain, Austria and Hungary), and seven abstaining (France, Germany, Italy, Netherlands, San Domingo, Sweden, Switzerland). Yet another resolution 'That the Conference expresses the hope that as soon as may be practicable the astronomical and nautical days will be arranged everywhere to begin at mean midnight' was passed with twenty-one in favour, with three abstaining (Germany, Guatemala, Sweden). Janseen wished the decimal system to be discussed. Adams would not vote against but regarded it as 'beyond the scope of subjects to be discussed at that Conference'. He would abstain, though he realized that for certain purposes the decimal decision of the circle is very valuable. The voting on this was thirteen in favour, nine against (including Germany, the United States and Britain) with two abstaining (Russia and Sweden).

So the visit to America had achieved its purpose, and Adams had once more made useful contributions to world decisions of lasting importance. And so to England once more, after attending British Association meetings at Montreal. By November he was back in Cambridge again with eight years more of life, and work, and travel ahead.

In a letter to Bashforth, dated 21 November 1884, from the Observatory Cambridge, Adams writes:

> We reached home on Tuesday, 11th. You probably saw my name in the papers as having attended poor Fawcett's funeral on the previous day but this was a mistake, as I only reached Liverpool on that afternoon. We both enjoyed our trip to America very much, and we were greatly pleased with what we saw both of the country and of the people. We everywhere met with the greatest kindness and hospitality, both in Canada and in the United States. We were fortunate, I think, in meeting with a great number of nice and pleasant people. On the other hand, we were not enamoured with the political system of the States, and we were disgusted with most of the newspapers there. The presidential election was pending, and the papers were full of the vilest personal attacks on the candidates of the opposite parties. I have not much respect for some of our own politicians, but I think the standard among them for honesty, truthfulness and respectful treatment of opponents is much higher than in America. For folly, however, in managing the nations affairs I think that Gladstone's will match any government whatever. What a dreadful mess they have made of the Egyptian and of the South African business. I am glad that there is a prospect of a compromise on the new Reform Bill, and hope it will succeed. If so the Irish members will be checkmated in their design of entering into a further bargain with Gladstone, and the agitation which was threatened against the House of Lords will subside.

In March 1880 Disraeli's Government had dissolved after attempting to establish English influence in Afghanistan, with disastrous results, and equal failure to set up a Canadian-type confederation in South Africa, which had led to the annexation of the Transvaal (1877) and the Zulu War (1879). They had also failed to rule sternly at home with a disorderly House of Commons. This gave Gladstone the chance to come from retirement, denounce the threatened alliance in the Middle East with the 'unspeakable Turk' of the 'Bulgarian atrocities' notoriety, and scorn the weak financial policies which paid for useless wars by borrowing, and which hoped to prop up commercial depressions by buying up the London water companies at extravagantly high rates. But as T. F. Tout and York Powell (1903) further comment in their *History of England*, 'there was no such general outcry as that which heralded the fall of Gladstone in 1874. But in democratic England few ministries have much chance of outliving the duration of an ordinary Parliament.' Beaconsfield, in vain, tried to rally the nation by warning that the rule of the Liberals would be dangerous to the empire. At the Election of March the Liberals gained a majority of fifty over the Conservatives and Home Rulers combined. In April Beaconsfield resigned. A year later he died. The second Gladstone Ministry lasted from 1880–85. Gladstone was Chancellor of the Exchequer, and governed together with Forster, Bright, and Fawcett, in addition to the new school of Radicals represented in the Cabinet by Joseph Chamberlain and Sir Charles Dilke. The latter two were unlike the Manchester School of Bright and Cobden, as they believed that vigorous state interference would do more good than the old one of *laissez faire*. 'The dreadful mess' according to Adams that the Government had made by 1884 in Egypt was to lead within the next few months to the death of General Gordon in January 1885 while holding Khartoum against Arabi Pasha, and the fanatical Mahdi, who were fighting to reassert Egyptian nationalism against European domination.

In South Africa a series of disasters led to the restoration of the Transvaal Republic. Ireland had been a hotbed of unrest in 1881 with the passing of the Irish Land Act, which had encouraged peasant proprietorship, and tenants' rents were to be more carefully scrutinized, though English-managed estates were exempt from the Act. Forster's Protection of Life and Property Act was fiercely opposed by Parnell, who was arrested with forty other leaders of the land agitation. They were considered 'an illegal and criminal association' till 1882, when they were released from prison, and Forster resigned in disgust. Immediately after their release on 6 May the 'Invincibles', a Society of Irish conspirators, stabbed to death Lord Frederick Cavendish, (the new Home Secretary replacing Forster) in Phoenix Park, Dublin, together with the permanent under-secretary, Burke. Hopefully, to prevent more trouble, a Prevention of Crimes Bill was hurriedly passed which only led to more fierce Irish hostility to the Government. The Irish question continued as a festering sore. The Third Reform Bill, mentioned by Adams in his letter to Bashforth on 21 November 1884, eventually became law in December 1884. The redistribution of seats was successfully agreed between Liberals and Conservatives. It made the franchise the same in counties and in boroughs, and brought in some new ways of getting a vote. All boroughs with 15,000 inhabitants were disenfranchised, and all with 50,000 were to have one member. The country was cut up into single member districts, each having about 50,000; the only exception being old boroughs returning two representatives, between 50,000 and 165,000 inhabitants, and the City of London cut down to two members. The result was that London got sixty-two instead of twenty-two members; Liverpool nine, Manchester and Salford nine, Glasgow and Birmingham seven each, and so on in proportion. The great towns, mining and manufacturing ones, got representation in proportion to their numbers. Ireland and Wales kept their old number of members, though not really entitled to so many. It was an attempt to make England a thorough-going democracy, dependent on household suffrage, with almost equal electoral districts.

If John Couch Adams were to find himself in England a hundred years on from 1884 the political noises and jargon might still sound familiar to him, with perhaps little progress made, *but* Greenwich is still the Prime Meridian, a fact which was not so until 1884, and as well as fixing the Universal Day from midnight with midday at noon at Greenwich with anti-meridian (a.m.) and post-meridian (p.m.) Greenwich *mean* time. John Couch Adams made no small contribution to this fact.

Fleming (Great Britain) had observed in the discussion on the Universal Day, that 'Time resembles no matter which comes before our senses; it is immaterial, without form, without substance, without spiritual essence. It is not solid, liquid, or gaseous, but capable of measurement with closest precision'. Though in 1884 'it was computed on very erroneous principles', for example solar, astronomical, nautical, civil apparent, and mean time, a great stream flowing onwards in 'one earth, one universe, and one time'. Adams was more in agreement with Rutherford in simplifying calculations of time by taking Greenwich Meridian as the mean noon – all beginning the day at midnight. Atomic time was yet to come.

8

Family Affairs: 1885–86

By 1885 John Couch Adams had revealed his Conservative tendencies in politics. He advocated a stern line with the Irish, in spite of, or because of, his Irish wife. In a previous letter, written to his friend Bashforth on 9 February 1881, at the beginning of Gladstone's Second Ministry and before Phoenix Park and the death of Gordon, he comments on current political affairs:

> What a horrid mess we are getting into in all parts of the world, and I am not much surprised at it. We shall pay dearly for Gladstone's election speeches. I have no faith in the wisdom of any Land Act likely to be brought by his government, which will be merely a sop thrown to the agitators. What Ireland requires is a firm but just despotism, not the encouragement of all the worst elements in the country, which has been the policy for some time past.

In religion he revealed himself in his diary as a moderate Anglican. He had never been drawn to the Wesleyan Commitment of his Cornish background. Though profoundly devout from his youth onwards he seemed to be more at home with the Psalm-singing devotions of the maternal Grylls and Couch side of his family, rather than the hymn-singing, praying paternal Adams. His brother Thomas, and his three sisters, were more Adams; his other two brothers George, and William, were Grylls in their devotions. Had he not presented himself as Anglican, when entering Cambridge University in 1839, he would not have gained admittance, for it was not until 1871 (when the Universities' Test Act abolished religious tests), that dissenters and Roman Catholics were allowed to enter. Thomas Adams always had a great respect for his elder brother, as did all the family. They had all made sacrifices in their youth to allow John's obvious early genius to flourish in Cambridge. Thomas was endowed with a more emotional make-up, together with a larger dose of Celtic gloom, and a consciousness of burdens of sin and guilt, which led to a Methodist conversion, and 'enthusiasm', and eventually to a call to the Ministry, and missionary work of a distinguished order in the Friendly Islands from 1846 to 1861.

Before John had discovered Neptune in 1846, or Thomas had sailed for Tonga later in 1846, the two brothers met in London, while Thomas was at Richmond Wesleyan College, training for the Ministry. In a letter Thomas writes from Richmond to his parents in Cornwall, dated 28 March 1845, he shows the difference between the two brothers in matters religious. He had met his brother unexpectedly in London, and as ever was subservient to him, though delighted to meet him:

> On walking out on Thursday, the 20th inst. I was greatly surprised to meet my brother. I had not heard from him for six weeks. He spent from Friday to Tuesday morning with me here and as it was holyday for a week in Easter I was at leisure with him. Of course I was obliged to be a

> churchman for the time being [that it, an Anglican].

They visited various London churches for the Easter weekend. Another reference to John's almost apologetic approach to the non-conformity of his background and his own inherent Anglicanism, appears in a letter to Bashforth on 8 August 1861, when he is explaining his delay in replying to an invitation:

> I could not come to you when you wished, chiefly in consequence of the arrival at home of a brother of mine, who has been abroad for the last 15 years. He has been – don't be shocked – a Wesleyan Missionary in the Friendly Islands, and I believe has done an immense deal of good there. Of course I wish he had been working in connection with our own Church, but at any rate he has not been interferring with any other body, as the Wesleyans have those islands to themselves. He lost his wife about a year and a half since, and has brought back six children with him.

So speaks the then bachelor brother about one of his brothers, who had contended with pacification of tribal wars, calculated eclipses for the inhabitants of Tonga, as well as translated the scriptures to Tonganuese while away from England and his close-knit Cornish family for fifteen years. John Couch and his brother William Grylls had evidently rallied to meet the arrival in London of the *Duncan Dunbar*, a Blackwall frigate, on 1 June 1861 which had left Sydney on Wednesday 6 February 1861, and passed Cape Horn on Sunday 24 March, according to Lloyds List. A letter from J. C. Adams to W. G. Adams, then teaching at The College, Marlborough, dated 27 May 1861, shows the family in action:

> My dear William, I have made inquiries in the

> Custom House about the 'Duncan Dunbar' and was referred to the office of Messrs. Dunbar, Limehouse, and owners, as the people who would be able to give me the earliest intelligence of her arrival. I have accordingly called at their office and have given instructions for them to telegraph to me and to you immediately on the arrival of the vessel. They tell me she is expected every day. I am just going back to Cambridge having come up on Saturday for the Lord Mayor's dinner, of which you have seen an account in to-day's Times. Believe me, Your affectionate Br. J. C. Adams.

History does not record who was there to greet Thomas when he finally disembarked on 1 June with five of his children.

Apart from not being entirely sympathetic to the Wesleyan aspects of his family, he was equally antagonized by the High Church 'antics' when attending St Giles in Cambridge, though he acknowledges that the sermon was good. He wanders round many Anglican Churches; regularly for the University sermon at Great St Mary's, but also attending periodically St Edward's, the Round Church, St Benedict's and St Botolph's and is even recorded attending on one occasion at Hobson St Wesleyan Chapel, when his sister Grace visited Cambridge, and where his brother Thomas was the minister from 1868 to 1871, and where his niece, Maria, was married in 1871. He gave her away there in 1871, as her father was conducting the service. William and George once took brother John, when in London, to hear a famous popular Cornish Methodist preacher, Rev. Mark Guy Pearce, whom he had never heard. But he was not impressed.

John always kept a fairly even tenor through life, without getting carried away by extremes of emotion, though he was certainly not without much deep feeling. He may have acquired some of this calm from his father, who was rather a shadowy figure, but who was reported on 31 January 1843, by 'Henry Pethick [a Doctor] of Launston' to have called on them when in Launceston 'to inform us of your having obtained Smith's Prize. He takes it very quietly and coolly and seems to enjoy it with settled satisfaction rather than with exultation.' Thomas Adams, Senior, was also reported to be 'a very good reaper' by a Mr Lane, a farmer from Cornwall who Thomas met in Australia, and who 'has not forgotten his reaping'. Thomas Adams, Senior, died in 1859, and Tabitha, his wife, in 1867. John records in his diary his feelings on returning to his mother's house at Badharlick Egloskerry, soon after her death. In his diary for Friday 27 September 1867 he writes, from Badharlick (his mother's home) 'Got my old tea caddy mended. Received note from b. [his wife]. Turned out some of poor mother's stores. In my old college teapot found a letter of mine of Nov. 18, 1837, and one from Aunt Ann. Looked at a little basket of Elizabeth's [his sister, who died aged 16] with a letter from mother. Smoothed old books.' His diary continues

28 September (Sat.) 1867: Looked at old books and papers. George arrived rather early [from his farm at Trewen, where his mother had died while visiting George]. Looked again over bookcase and found 'British Reader'. Packed old parchments and some of my old books up in old carpet bag, which with my coffee pot and spoons Grace placed in chest. Started rather late for Trewen. I rode about 1 mile beyond Camelford, and then drove Grace while George rode off on business. Before starting wrote to Dr. Revelly, to B, and Polly. Dark when we arrived.

29 September (Sun.): Slept in poor Mother's room [at Trewen, George's farm]. Felt very solemn, and sad, yet it was sweet to think of all dear Mother had been to me and all of us. Old watch [George's dog] came into my room in the morning. He seemed very natural. We went to Church in the morning. Mr. Page is absent, and a clergyman with a v. loud voice is taking his duty. He preached shortly on

'Ask and it shall' etc. In aft. we walked over part of farm. A little rain afts.

His mother's death affected him deeply, more perhaps than any other family death, though his comments on the sudden death of his brother Thomas on Saturday 24 October 1885, nearly twenty years later than his mother's, revealed the close-knit nature of the family. He is also constantly in touch with nieces and nephews, who call on him, and make claims on his generosity, especially the children of Thomas as the part of the older end of the family (he was 20 years older than his youngest sister, Mary Ann) and he pays for schooling and other help to his youngest sister's family, still in Cornwall. About a month before the death of his brother Thomas there are glimpses of him back on the old family haunts in Cornwall, in the midst of the family. Prior to this in July he had been in London getting his spectacles 'righted', collecting his Queen's Pension, and visiting Lombard Street, where he 'paid in full for my Brazil debentures' (£1000 of 7 per cent Debentures of the Great Southern Railway of Brazil). By the end of August he was with William and his children at Giggleswick, Settle, Malham Tarn, Clapham visiting Caves, and where he heard the Bishop of Ripon (Boyd-Carpenter) preach 'a capital and clever sermon on Bartimeus, with good remarks on Prayer', at what was apparently a Harvest Service. He notes on 21 August 1885 'the safe arrival of the "Parisian" at Quebec' with his nephew Tom aboard, Thomas's eldest son.

By 4 September 1885 he and his wife had decided to leave the Settle area and desert William and family (who were heading for Scotland), and make for Cornwall: 'Wrote to Mr. Bonnett on my claim to a vote for the County, and also to George to tell him of our intention to come to Cornwall.' After loitering at Ingleton and Ingleborough they journeyed by train to Bristol, and Exeter, and eventually Plymouth, and Saltash. They stayed a night in Exeter, where he 'got hair cut'. The Cathedral 'appeared in excellent condition', he bought some silver buttons, had bread and cheese at their hotel, and so by bus to G. W. Station 'and took tickets for Saltash', where 'George met us and had kept dinner for us', on Friday 11 September. Here they stayed until Tuesday 6 October. On Saturday 12 September they had received a 'letter from Tom from Lennoxville with a cheerful account of his reception'. (His eldest nephew, the eldest son of his brother Thomas, was eventually to become Canon Thomas Adams of Quebec.) Harry Roseveare, husband of Mary Ann (née Adams) and young son Tommy from school called in on them. They met his sisters 'Polly and Grace and most of the children' on Sunday 13 September in Saltash, 'all looking well'. It was Harvest Festival at Saltash Church, and though the 'singing was good' there was 'very little in the sermon, as usual'. The weather was still wet and windy so

> after dinner Harry [Roseveare] came with the trap and we drove to Wivelscombe [Harry's Farm]. E was nervous about my getting a chill. Found all well, baby* particularly lively. George excited her rather too much. Johnny v. silent. Tommy came home from school later. In the evening heavy rain came on and it was agreed that E and I should stay for the night. George walked back in the rain. Gave Polly a cheque for H's schooling.

20 September (Sun.): Met with Wivelscombe folk before going into Church. Mr. Morton gave us a v. splendid ser-

* The baby was six-month-old 'Hilda Alice', later to read History at Newnham College Cambridge, and eventually the last surviving niece of J. C. Adams, and who died as recently as 1981. She possessed many of the family records and letters. 'H' was Harry Roseveare, later Headmaster in Newquay, the eldest of Mary Ann's children. Mary Roseveare, the second daughter, was Senior English Mistress for many years at Streatham Hill High School, after reading English at Newnham College. Johnny reached the Ministry of Fisheries in Whitehall, and Tommy became an Engineer.

mon in condemnation of Spiritualism. Slight rain in the evening prevented us going to St. Stephen's, finally went to Wesleyan Chapel to hear the new preacher. We sat in Henry's pew – Text – 'If I may but touch the hem of his garment', but we were rather disappointed with the sermon.

21 September (Mon.): Master of Jesus died yesterday morning. Saw the account in 'Western Morning News'.

23 September (Wed.): [He and his wife visited Launceston and] 'bought a watch for Harry . . . Met with Miss Grylls afterwards to see the college. [They drove to Badharlick, and had tea with John Grylls, and called on Sam Grylls and had another Harvest Thanksgiving, at Egloskerry this time.]

24 September (Thurs.): Telegraphed to George and got same carriage as yesterday to drive to Laneast. Called at Lidcot on the way, which is greatly changed. Called at Cathern Quoruns, who was very glad to see me. Here we ate our sandwiches, and she made us some tea. Then we walked down to the river. The valley was looking lovely. Then we returned and called on Mr. Haly and his daughter. The latter seems quite well again, and we looked at the Church and school. Got back to Launceston soon after 5. Afts. took a walk on Tavistock Rd. and back by the College.

During the same holiday they took a train to Princetown, via Yelverton, and climbed the Tor, where they sheltered from rain and high winds, but enjoyed a beautiful rainbow and clouds before returning to Plymouth. On their last Sunday but one at Saltash they sat once more under Mr. Morton at Saltash Church on 'one body, and one spirit', in 'the usual style', and a good sermon at St Stephen's, on 'We have not a High Priest', etc. They spent the last week at Wivelscombe with Mary Ann, leaving George's home in Saltash on Monday 28 September. Here he got involved with Mary Ann's young family. On Wednesday 30 September, 'In evening I marked several things for the girls and for Grace'. The next day, Thursday 1 October, 'Received notice of meeting of Greenwich

Visitors on Question of change of Astronomical Time. E. observed and mentioned to me some fine traits in Johnnie. . . . Wrote to Mr. Roberts on my conclusions of Jupiter's Satellites.' On Friday 2 October 'In afternoon Johnny amused himself with the Kaleidescope. In evening I looked at some of Mary's Examn. papers.' On Sunday 4 October 'Henry went off early to preach [a Methodist local preacher].' John and his wife walked to Saltash to St Stephen's, with lovely views of Dartmoor and Tor near Princetown but by the evening he was reading one of Wesley's sermons 'to myself', and one 'On Courtesy' aloud. By Tuesday 6 October they left Saltash, with George, Mary and Tommy to see them off: 'George brought a plant splendidly packed up'. They 'took Third Class tickets to Bath. Mr. Good and his son were fellow passengers. Also a young detective from Manchester and an old gentlemen from N. Devon, and we had some interesting talk. Between Bristol and Bath I had a tussle with an escaped *lunatic*. Stayed at the Royal Hotel and were comfortable. Off to London by 3¾ nearly without adventure. Drove to Wm's.'

Once back in London, after a happy return visit to his native County, and renewed occupation with family matters, by Thursday, 8th October he is reading the papers with 'Lord Salisbury's speech at Newport,' and attending a meeting of the 'Board of Visitors' at Burlington House, where he supported 'Unity of Time Reckoning' – With a large majority in favour. They agreed to epoch 1891. After these decisions he gets a hair cut, and went to see 'The Mikado', 'but could not enjoy it.' The next day 9th October 'E and I went to A. Joy's Studio 11–1.40. Emily and the baby came in to enliven me a little. Very nice baby.' Then train to Cannon St., and dined at Spiers and Pond. E. bought new Specs. Put E. on bus and then went to meeting at Dover St [re Girton College] Heard particulars of Miss Gamble's legacy, and talked of reviewing negotiations for field adjoining the College. . . . Wm and I went to see the managements of the coloured fountains. 10 October (Sat) Early breakfast and off to Cambridge and straight to a Pembroke College meeting, where they discuss 'filling up Framlingham,' Then on to Southacre'; soon after they had sat down Lord John Manners told some anecdotes of old Sir John Gladstone. Also Canning and Liverpool Election. 'Joined a game of billiards just before leaving'. The Cambridge life is once more back in full swing, with books, among which was Knight's Life of Colet and Mandeville's Travels, 'which had come during my absence', and to St. Mary's, where a Mr Billing of Worcester College, Oxford preached an earnest sermon on 'Let not your heart be troubled', which might have been preached in forecast of what was to come, as in two week's time his brother Thomas died suddenly. He maintained a stoical calm throughout but obviously felt the loss deeply. In the week before this event 'Emily Yeld [Thomas's 2nd daughter, eventually married to a Master at St Peter's, York after Wilton's tragic death on Snowdon] and Arthur Lloyd, arrived together about 5 o'clock, on Wed 14th October. The next day 'walked in with Arthur Lloyd and called on Mr. Mallinger at St. John's Library, who showed us the "Liber Memorials" with Bp Lloyd's coat of arms. In the evening read the Bp. of Peterboro's speech on Disestablishment. 16th October (Fri) Gracie had arrived [Thomas's 3rd daughter who eventually married an Anglican cleric – Hyatt Warner], and in the evening he read Macmillan, and also letters on disestablishment.

17th October (Sat) 'Arthur Lloyd left this morning. Afts. walked in and called at Union and then met E. and Gracie, who had gone to a lecture on Education by Dr. Bryant, the first female Dr. Sc. Had a nap after dinner. My new overcoat came out from Neal's.

20th Oct (Tues) Emily and Gracie spent the evening at Mrs. Moultons [Wife of Headmaster of Leys School, Cambridge].

21st. Oct (Wed) Took Emily and Gracie to Girton. Tea with Miss Welsh and saw College.

22nd Oct (Thurs) Called at Gray's, Bonnet's, and at Police Station about trespassers on Sunday.

23rd Oct (Fri) In afternoon to meeting of Henry Martyn Memorial Committee, at Corpus Lodge till five and a half.

Then came Saturday 24th October 1885. 'Did a little more towards testing Hill's method of applying Delaunay's theory. Soon after 2 a telegram arrived from Mr. McCormack at Chatteris telling of Thomas's sudden death. Told Emily. Mr. Graham sent notice to Wesleyan Minister. I went into Cambridge and sent telegrams to George, Wm, and Fred. Then called at Press with corrected proof and went to College meeting where Pilkington was chosen to living at Framlingham. Then went to station and saw Emily and Gracie off to Chatteris and drove back with E. Had some soup and then drove to Church Defence meeting. Good speeches from Professor Creighton, the Master of Selwyn and Mr. Raikes, poor from Beresford Hope. Dr. E. C. Clark made a short but particularly good and firm speech. Drove home though it had became fine.

25 October (Sun) E. read aloud sermon of Philip Brooke. St. Mary's. Bp. of Lichfield on diversity of gifts of different members of Church. Mentioned as examples two Bishops now lying dead. Spoke to Babington and J. W. Clark about my brother's death. Called at Campion's and took the life of Rob and Mary Moffat, my club book. Took some turns about our grounds with E, who was very comforting. Afts. we read together a good deal of Moffat's life which we found v. interesting and well written.

26th October (Mon) Letters from Emily and Polly as E and I were driving to Station for journey to Chatteris at 10.50. Got there at twelve. Fred [Thomas's youngest son] met me. Was struck by the noble appearance of Thomas's head, and the calm dignity of his face. Jane [Thomas's 2nd wife] spoke calmly and lovingly about him. Also Mr. and Mrs. McCormack. Fred and I called on the Vicar – not in – left Fred waiting at the Station. Saw undertaker and returned to dinner or late lunch. Afterwards Emily and I went to cemetery to choose a place for the grave.

Wm. and Maria [Thomas's eldest daughter, aged eleven when her mother died in Tonga] arrived just after five. Post Mortem Examination had just been made. Rupture of heart. Maria was greatly agitated. I went off with Wm. to Stn, but changed my mind, and afterwards telegraphed to E. Returned to New Road. Spent evening talking of old times and my late experiences in Cornwall. Wm and I went to the 'George'.

27th October (Tues) Early breakfast, and then with Wm and Gracie to cemetery and selected the spot for the grave. Then Wm and I took a walk through Chatteris to end of High St. and were caught in a shower. Mr. Moulton, the Circuit Steward, came in with nice letters from the Chairman of the District and the President of the [Wesleyan] Conference. Fred read two Chapters and Mr. M. made a beautiful prayer. Wm. and I started for Cambridge about Twelve and a half.

28th October (Wed) E. drove with us to station for 10.50 and met with George. At Chatteris met with Mr. Alton, the Chairman of the District, who had met me at Richmond in Thomas's time. Funeral a little before one. First part in Wesleyan Chapel. Mr. A. made an excellent address. Spoke of T's translation of N.T. Afterwards returned to lunch. Then took a walk in road. Went to look at grave, which was filled in. Mr. McCormack told us a curious remark of Thos. on the v. spot which we had selected. Went to service in Chapel at 7. Mr. A. preached and spoke warmly of Thomas from 'none of us liveth to himself etc' Heavy rain. Afterwards read a letter of Tom just received. [Thomas's eldest son in Canada].

29 October (Thurs) Did not sleep well. Breakfasted at Globe. Walked with George and William along road. Looked again at cemetery. Left by 12.15 train with George, Mr. Simon [husband of Maria] and Maria. Wm came with us to Cambridge and left for London. Had a late lunch and afterwards a walk round farm. Showed Mr. Simon some of my old books. Mrs. Death drove out and told us they had failed to buy any gas shares yesterday for us.

And so the world of another reality breaks in, and in a day or two Maria and her husband have returned to Bristol, and Gracie to Buckingham and Emily to York. By the end of November comes news of the birth of Tom's son, Lennox, in Canada – so life goes on and another Adams is born. He deals with Thomas's will, gets certificate of Thomas's birth from William, and sent off Tom's succession papers to Somerset House during November and early December. He reports the loss of a glove left in cab at Scotland Yard; turns up too late to vote at Senate House on 14th December; a new post office was opened in Cambridge; and a new maid came to the Observatory; the foundations of the new building of St John's were also appearing. Then comes Christmas 'looked at "Sent to Coventry" – a children's book bought for Tommy – and so to Brighton where on Christmas Day he and E. went to St Michael's Church for "a choral communion, with music, very operatic. I should not have thought it possible so to transform the service". And the year ended by sending cheques of £141 1s 9d, with news of bonds and shares to Tom, Maria, Emily, Gracie, and Fred as their shares in their father's will. On the next day, 27th Dec. (Sun) Dr. Hamilton preached on "So teach us to number our days," and by way of contrast to the human turmoils, he went down to look at the sea "which was very rough. E. could not stand it and had to return. I went on to the Stand past the pier and enjoyed the sight." He received receipts for cheques from his nephews and nieces "The note on the forms was very nice". So ended 1885.

1886 opens with him reading John Ball's "Treatise on Faith," which he calls "an old Puritan work," and which is classified as "a short treatise containing all the principal grounds of Christian religion" in the Cambridge University Library catalogue, where two copies of this book are now among the Adams' Collection (four to London 1657 3rd ed, and eight Vol. 4th Impression Ed by S. Ashe 1654). He found some "striking remarks" among much that "was not good" in a book entitled "Modern Christianity" in civilized Heathenism.' He has a lively discussion on the Irish question with Mr. Hammond, spills his milk on the carpet, has his beard trimmed at Hopgood's, succeeded in making out Thomas's calculations of Income Tax and his return of £117 for last year, and slept in a Jaeger nightdress with a mild attack of bronchitis. He fixes his Lunar Theory lectures for the next term for Tuesdays, Thursdays and Saturdays at 12 pm at the Observatory to begin Tuesday Jan 18. Only three men turned up on February 2, but he 'talked to them for 1 and a quarter hours without difficulty. On Thursday Feb 4 he finished 'my general introduction to the subject and the men seemed interested.' However, by Saturday 27 February he lectured on 'deviation of moon's orbit from elliptic form and change of moderations from disturbing force.' He 'did not get on as well as I wished. Had prepared too much and hardly knew what to give them'. He winds up his brother Thomas's affairs; is 'amused and interested' at the A.D.C; reads Sir H. Main's essays on Democracy 'which are admirable'; and among such domestic details as 'Had to come down and supply water to the cistern, Ernest having forgotten it' on Sunday 7 March. By Monday 15 March 'Ernest gave notice to leave, having quarrelled with Johnson'. On Tuesday 16 March 'Just before dinner Ernest came in with new complaint of Johnson, and I gave him leave to go'. That night 'Slept pretty well, but I hear that I was noisy.' On 17 March he 'began making practical application of Hill's equations but was disgracefully interrupted by Ernest and his mother (Mrs. Metcalfe) coming out, and I confronted them with Johnson, who did not appear to advantage.' After Ernest left for good. 'Did a little more work'. Previously on 9 February Johnson 'tells me the cow is better. Gave my lecture on disturbing forces'. He had also evidently taken 'steps to do away with big nuisance,' and on Thursday 18 March 'had some serious talk with Johnson, particularly spoke to him about his language'. There is never a dull moment in the life of the University Professor of Astronomy, running his estate at the Observatory in Madingley Road, in addition to his family affairs.

He hears a cuckoo on Good Friday (23 April) on way back from Newnham; 'a Trinity freshman was drowned yesterday evening (Saturday 20 March) at Newnham Mill; and Johnson accused Edith of disturbing the cream in the Observatory dairy – but was later acquitted, after E. had gone to look at dairy, but by Monday 10 May 'Edith left to-day'. On the same day he wrote to Secretary of Artizan's Dwellings Coy. to invest £882 in Preferential shares for the three girls in the name of Fred and T. Puddicombe (one of Thomas's in-laws) who married Thomas's wife's sister . . . and wrote to Collector of Taxes at Chatteris enclosing order for 61s income tax. He goes on looking over Newton papers 'but got on slowly', has troubles with his teeth, and a fortnight after the departure of Edith, 'E is still greatly disturbed by the loss of her Mother's antique ring, which has been taken from her desk, I fear by Edith! On Tuesday 6 April he had moved into a different sphere 'To dine at Mrs. Miller's to meet Mrs Fawcett.[1] Took her in and had some political talk. Gladstone no favourite' (Home Rule Bill). He loses one of 'my Icelandic gloves', and read's 'some of Hiawatha,' and when in London 'gave sovereign in mistake for 6d.' Johnson and Fred (of Observatory staff) clear out cesspit, and see to cow giving birth to calf. He also 'looked at young cow which Johnson has just bought' in July, and chooses, with help of George and Grace a Serpentine tombstone for Thomas' grave, looked at Thomson on Tides, and don't like his treatment,' as well as reading Oliver Wendell Holmes 'Breakfast Table',[2] and reads the

1. Mrs Millicent Garrett F/b 1847, Women's Suffrage and Higher Education for Women, Her Husband Henry Fawcett (Politician)
2. American Author, Harvard, M. D. Author of 1858, *'Autocrat at Breakfast Table'*, 1860 *'Professor at Breakfast Table'* 1872, *'Poet at Breakfast Table'*.

'Dilke Case'.[1] In August 'met with Jebb and Hallam Tennyson,[2] and later 'called at the Bull and met with him. Walked out. Read some of Tennyson's Poems, including Clara Vere de Vere, and Locksley Hall'.

He spends 4 September to 9 October on a holiday at Scarborough, and just before leaving 'In a rather thick fog, we then made our way to Bridlington Quay and the Pier. In the afternoon a good deal improved. We had a nice tea and eggs and then took a walk along the shore in direction of Flamboro' Head. Then back to Station for 5.48 train and home to dinner' [in Scarboro']. While in Scarborough they visit Maria Simon (née Adams) and her family of six (Thomas Adams' grandchildren). The baby[3], Grace Elizabeth, was six weeks old, the eldest daughters Sadie thirteen years, Hilda ten years, and the three boys Jack, Tom, Gordon were eight, six and two years. They take them out, give them presents, take meals with them occasionally, and eventually return to Cambridge, where on Sunday 17 October at St Mary's he hears 'a sort of Christian Socialist Sermon from Mr Watson of Trinity. On Thursday 14 October 'Had a very bad night from whorry' (sic). On Thursday 2 December 'Went into Cambridge at 11¼ to the Service before laying the memorial stone of Henry Martyn[4] Memorial Hall'. He grows more deaf and states 'could not hear much of conversation at table' when at a 'Family' gathering at Paget's[5] on Friday 19 December. Mr Turner and a post office official from London called about giving us a 2nd delivery and a pillarbox. 'Got the Mabinogion to-day, and read some of it

1. Dilke 1843–1912 Sir Chas. Wentworth, Radical in Gladstone's Government, Under-Secretary for Foreign Affairs. 1886 Retires to private life because of scandal in which he was innocent.
2. Son of the poet, Tennyson.
3. Author's mother Grace Elizabeth Simon (m. A. W. Harrison) born August 17, 1886.
4. Henry Martyn (1781–1812) b at Truro. Mathematician Classics at Cambridge University. Influenced by Charles Simeon, Cambridge preaching missionary to India.

in evening. Thursday 23 December 'Lord R. Churchill has resigned!' Saturday 25 December Christmas Day – 'St Mary's (Master of Jesus preached) Afternoon Service – Carols at King's.' Finally to the end of 1886, Thursday 30 December 'Bought some socks. On the way thought over the method of finding intersection of two branches of equal decln. line' – So he was still doing much of his valuable calculations in the head and 'perambulando', en route for buying socks.

5. Sir G. E. Paget was Professor of Medicine, from 1872 and physician at Addenbrooke's Hospital 1839–1884 where he advocated open wound healing, and the education of Medical practitioners. He was a fellow of Caius in 1832, and a fellow of the Royal Society in 1855. Adams had attended on 19 June 1885 the Presentation of Paget's bust to Addenbrookes at the end of December.

9

Final Years: (1887–92)

1887 was the year of Queen Victoria's Golden Jubilee, and John Couch Adams was to celebrate this at Cowes, and in Westminster Abbey, forty years after he had refused a knighthood. He begins the year in January with Knight's 'Life of Erasmus', and once more hearing 'Mrs Fawcett on Women's Suffrage, who was very good'. This was soon followed by a Transit of Venus Committee, and the A.G.M. of the R.A.S. with a good address by Glaisher, followed by a Girton meeting and a night at Notting Hill Square with William, where he gets 'a fit of aphasia in the evening. Felt v. tired'. Five days later he is visiting an Exhibition of Vandyck's at the Grosvenor Gallery and Old Masters at Burlington House, combined with Turner water colours. No one came to his Cambridge lectures on January 20th and 22nd, so he 'cleared away preparations.' At the end of January he started for church with E. and Connie 'but meeting some loafers I turned back to take care of the house. Looked round the place.' He reads Ruskin 'King of the Golden River', and some Dorothy Wordsworth. Mr Foxley at Great St Mary's was proposing great changes in the Prayer Book, and 'strong in condemnation of War'. He meets Trade Union

Representatives, Mr Burnett and Mr Hay, at Trinity College and in the evening goes to a meeting of the Social Questions Society, and had an interesting account of Trade Unionism from the two representatives. 'The Master of Trinity presided judiciously.' He votes for the Hughes' proposition about the Sedgwick Memorial which was carried 90–71. He thinks of 'a new way of applying Hill's equations to Lunar Problem'. On 27 May 'Had my Family dinner from the Downing cook, which was a success. Both dinner and wine much commended. J. W. Clark seemed not so lively as usual. Drew lots for next year's cycle'. On Whit Sunday he goes to St Giles, and is amazed at *Cross used in procession.* On the Whit Monday he 'put a stop to Smith's proposition for a Cross on the altar at Pembroke College.' He had already registered dismay at the Cross at Ely, which 'many laity would find offensive.' In May he was looking over some of Newton's papers relating to dispute with Leibnitz and 'put titles to them'. At the end of May he attends an organ recital at Trinity, and the Jesus Garden Party where 'unfortunately rain came on. Wore new hat'. He attends a meeting at Greenwich of the Nautical Almanac Committee, travelling from Cannon Street to Greenwich in the same carriage as Lord Rayleigh and Sir William Thomson, 'getting out at Maze Hill', and 'in time for lunch in Octagon Room. Took in Miss Clerk. Afts. went through Observatory'. On Wednesday 8 June he goes to 'a meeting at Caius Lodge to consider admission of women to degrees.' Ten days later 'Classical Tripos list came out. Girton highly distinguished itself.' He dines at the Mansion House on the same day and sat between the President of the Linear Society and Dr Westcott, but the 'speeches not striking'. On 20 June he visits, while in London, Mr Cooper, the aurist, and had a long interview: 'He tried to show me how to touch the back of my throat, and to plug my nostrils'. On Tuesday 21 June he was in Westminster Abbey with William for Golden Jubilee Celebrations. 'Had an early breakfast and were off by train about 8 o/c.

Great crush in train. Walked from St James' Station across Park and left E. at Waterloo Place, and Mary at Atheneum. Then Wm and I went by Whitehall to the Abbey. Got a good airy place in East Sacrarium and had a perfect view of Coront Chair. Whitting was next to me. The Queen arrived about half past 12. Scene v. impressive. Homage of the princes and princesses very touching. Left quickly and saw the Queen pass just after leaving the Abbey and again as she passed the Atheneum. Afts. found E and went with her to Bolton Gardens and had tea. Then returned to Notting Hill Square [William's house] and related our adventures. Had a long nap and afts. went to see the illuminations at High St Kensington.'

The next day he went to Victoria Station 'after writing a short notice of Darwin's paper, walked to Westminster and met with procn. of schoolchildren and accompanied them to Buckingham Palace. Then across Green Park and to Burlington House and gave paper to Lord Rayleigh. . . . Then left cards at Mansion House and lunched at Restaurant. Afts. called at Mr Nettleship who cheered me about my eyes. Got a bus at Marble Arch, but were blocked a long time on account of the Queen being in the park. At length she left for Windsor and we were able to get on'. They saw more illuminations with William's children, and the American Exhibition with Buffalo Bill and the Wild West, and so to Cambridge again where the hay at the Observatory was being mown, then 'looked at the calf, which is a very nice one, but the cow gives her milk very grudgingly'. And 'the watering hose is out of order. Spoke to Goff about his engaging a labourer without leave'. He has a correspondence with Skeat about Chaucer's passages on Venus and Mars.

And so to Cowes. They only just caught the 'Triton' owing to delays en route but once aboard 'everyone was most kind', and they 'sailed down on side of shore squadron and returned between the 2 lines, and finally took up position near Hydra gunboat. Had nice lunch about 1. The Queen left Cowes about 3 and after some time we saw the yacht pass. Returned to Southhampton and landed some of our visitors. Then returned to see the illuminations, which were grand. Got in time for mail train which was v. late. They gave us dinner and tea also on board. Found Mrs Inge waiting for us at Lyndhurst and got back about 2 and to bed about 2½. Not so tired as might have been expected.' While in the New Forest they visit the Rufus stone and write a letter of thanks to Cmdr Izzard. On Wednesday 17 August the entry in the diary reads 'In evening to party of Miss Clough's for schoolmistresses and miners. Talked to several and enjoyed the evening.' In December he went with his wife to a Presbyterian Service in Cambridge to hear Rev. James Stuart on Exodus 23rd 'Behold I send an Angel before you'. 'He was rather too good for his audience, speaking of poetry of life'. On Monday 12 December 'Goff sold the red cow for £10.14.6,' and they also went to 'The Comedy of Errors'.

He is beginning to be more conscious of his health, his indigestion, and his sleeplessness. This obsession with health develops to the time of his death in 1892, and his wife worries about him, and she herself suffers from headaches, and sickness rather reminiscent of migraine. However, January 1888 sees them in London, trying a pantomime but failing to get in, so they opt for 'She Stoops to Conquer' at Strand Theatre, and the Natural History Museum.

In early January 1888 J. W. Myers 'called early to ask me to be President of Psychical research,' but he refuses; and Dr Grossart wrote to him asking him 'to solve the problem of the origin of evil'. Evidently he refused this challenge too; Neptune might prove more easy to trace. He goes to a performance of 'Dandy Dick' which was 'most amusing' and goes to St Giles with his wife 'but forgot to take any money with me'. Then on 27 February came the death of his youngest sister, Polly [Mary Ann Roseveare], who had been ill with bronchitis for only a few days. 'Got a cheerful letter from George,' which proved deceptive for 'a telegram came later to tell us dear Polly had passed away at 9 last night. Wrote a letter to Hy and also to George. My wine came from Whitmore's and E packed it in cellar and repacked some of the old wine. Wrote short report on Newton Ms.' So one more family funeral faced him, but he seemed to hesitate before going to Cornwall.

28 Feb (Tues) 'Had a rather disturbed night. Got letter from George and made up my mind to go down. Wrote to French Association to decline invitation to Algeria . . . Started by 4.00 train. E seeing me off. Read some of Abel's life on the war. Mary [William's wife] very kind. Wm. left at 9 this morning. Helped Willie [Wm's son] in his Trigonometry. Wrote a letter to E. by night post.' [He spent that night at William's London home].

29 Feb (Wed) [Leap Year] 'Had a fair night. Breakfasted at 8 and started by 9. Well wrapped up in overcoat and Ulster and had a comfortable journey. George and Wm. met me at Saltash. Telegraphed to E. on arrival and afts. wrote. Had a good deal of talk in evening about Polly's illness and state of her spirits of late. Fred [Thomas's son] came from Wivelscombe later in evening.

1st March (Thurs) Had a v. disturbed night. Slept little. Cd. not keep my hands warm and felt nervous. Did not take bath in morning fearing there wd not be reaction. Got letter from E. telling me of H. Armstrong's death. Drove to Wivelscombe, leaving 8¾. Saw poor Polly's remains wh. looked lovely. Funeral was well performed, partly by Mr Fraser, and at grave by Wesleyan minister. Returned to dinner and spent aft. and part of evening at Wivelscombe. Had long talk with Grace. A cold day with wind but fine. We walked back in the evening. Stayed up rather late, having a long talk with George about Grace etc.

2 *March (Fri)* Had a good night feeling much letter. Had a letter from E and wrote to her telling of yesterday and walked to Wivelscombe and had an early dinner there. Had a long talk with Henry and Grace and arranged for the boys to return to school with us to-morrow.

A v. fine day. Johnnie and Hilda [Mary Ann's two youngest children] playing in the field. We stayed to tea and then walked back. Wm's cold better.

3 March (Sat) Had a v. fair night. Tea before getting up. George and I settled accounts yesterday morng. Started with boys at 9.58 and left them at Bristol. Came on with Wm. to Paddington. Much snow about Swindon. Drove to King's Cross and had to wait half an hour for 7½ train. Poynter met me, and I found all well at Observatory and was very glad to get back again all right. E. had made all necessary arrangements about Ray etc. Much kind feeling shewn by all.'

By 14 March he was back again in the swing of Cambridge life. 'In evening went to *very noisy meeting* of Liberal Unionists. Duke of Argyle and Warden of Merton spoke' [These were the Liberals who had broken with Gladstone over Home Rule].

27 March (Tues) 'Looked at Mr Goschen's [A Liberal Unionist, serving under Lord Salisbury's Conservative Government as Chancellor of the Exchequer, after the fall of Gladstone's Home Rule Bill. In 1888 he carried out a conversion of the National Debt. He took a keen interest in Universities.] Budget speech, which is excellent.'

19 April (Thurs) 'Dressed and went in with E. to hear Glaisher's address, which was very good, though too laudatory for me'.

On Saturday 21 April he read Glaisher's address in 'Chronicle'. He was also sitting to Wiles, and later to Herkomer for portraits. On 30 April he went to see Newton Autograph at Sotheby's and read it carefully. He also went to hear Canon Ainger read Shakespeare and Dickens at St Mark's parish room and enjoyed it v. much. On Thursday 3 May He voted at the Senate House to oppose Grace about Free School and was defeated. On Monday 7 May he heard Dr Hudson Taylor and others at a meeting of China Mission at Town Hall, and the next day Professor Middleton gave him some information about going to Italy; he finished a letter to Lady Portsmouth; and 'Goff showed me the young pig which is dying of swine fever. Gave orders for it to be killed and buried.' He played at whist in the evening. The next day, Wednesday 9 May he spoke to Goff about what he had done with the pig. The policeman came out about it. In the meantime Mr H. Lloyd arrived, the son of Professor H. Lloyd of Dublin. On Monday 14 May Stokes could not attend a dinner at Pembroke as a four line whip was on in Parliament and he had been sent for as M.P. for Cambridge University. On 15 May he went to Squire's in Savile Row and ordered a coat – [Neal's of Cambridge are evidently superceded]. 'Then we went to Jay's where E. spent a long time buying a mantle.' They visited the New Gallery and saw the Kendalls in 'Ironmaster' at St James' Theatre. They enjoyed London Theatres, and had seen Benson as Othello a few years earlier. Towards the end of May he decided to withdraw his offer to go to Bologna in consequence of a conversation with the Master of Peterhouse. In June he hears from Hydrographer of a coral island in the Red Sea, and approves a gd. sermon at St Edward's by Mr Finch on Dives and Lazarus and Christian Socialism, and listened to the Bishop of Minnesota speak on Red Indians at Divinity School, though E. was not admitted. He dines at St John's Lodge to meet two American Bishops on 12 June. Reads 'Renan's 1st Vol. on "History of Israel" and finished in evening; and on Saturday 16 June is at a dinner at Greenwich meeting French scientists, Lafford and Bossute, 'found my French very deficient'. News of the Emperor's death was announced on 15 June, and on Sunday 17 June the Dead March was played in Lancaster Gate Church, where he worshipped with Mary and May [Wm's wife and daughter]. On 20 June he attends a service with William and his wife Mary, at the Society of Antiquaries 'with a wonderful collection of Antiquities. Maces of more than 100 corporations, including Saltash.' In July he is discussing the Bishops and the Athanasian Creed with the Master of Balliol, whom he meets at the Jebbs, and later is reading 'Robert Elsmere.' On 11 June he writes to Baron

Von Hügel, whom he met previously, and got a telegram from Herkomer 'asking me to come up to-morrow'. This is the beginning of many sittings for the rather unattractive portrait, now at Pembroke, showing his increasing age – a great contrast with the young Adams in St John's. He got Herkomer's address from London Directors at Hotel, and drove to it, and then sat for one hour. Later, back in Cambridge he went to Senate House in a red gown and dines between Bishop of S. Dakota and Bishop of Waiapa at St John's. On Tuesday 24 July he is back with Herkomer. This time with E, but he vexes Herkomer by getting his hair cut en route. 'H. confined himself to "tailoring" to-day.' The next day 'we went to Herkomer's at 10.30 by bus and were punctual'. Yesterday they had gone by bus to Bond St and Victoria, but had 'called to get a haircut and to order a new hat,' and were probably late again in consequence; 'He worked on my ear' on Wednesday 25 July. On 26 July 'We went again to Herkomer's at 10½ and got there a little before time'. On 27 July they were 'too early for Herkomer at 2'. On 28 July the sitting was postponed because of the death of Herkomer's father, about whom they had previously had conversation. So back to Cambridge, and on Sunday 29 July they go to the Presbyterian service where they get a young man who did not please them very much on the 'hope' of being like Christ. 1 John 3^3. They go on to Mrs Jebb's to lunch, where he entertains them with a number of anecdotes of his childhood and how George detected Kniver, the sheep killer. The next day he gets a letter from Tom 'asking me to lend him £100', which he sends immediately. On Thursday 2 August 'My new hat arrived from Scott's.' On 4 August he dines at Downing in honour of the new Professor of Laws, Maitland. 'Sat next Perkins, who carved well' Professor Cayley opposite. 'Walked part of the way home with him. Got home soon after 11.' On Wednesday 8 August 'Prof. and Mrs Mary Cayley drove out and brought my Diploma, which had arrived from Bologna. It is very handsome.'

In August 1888, they have a holiday at Cromer, leaving Cambridge on Wednesday 15 August on the 4.8, 'a rather shaky train', and arriving at Cromer at 7.30, 'with a most brilliant display at sunset in the N.E.', they make for the Bath Hotel for the night, before looking for lodgings next day. 'At length found a little set of rooms in West Street. Afts. nice walk along cliffs to Runton and back by sands. Then short turn towards the lighthouse before dinner.' On Friday 17 August 'Pd. bill at Bath Hotel – which was rather heavy, and afts. moved to our lodgings. Dined at Tucker's Hotel. Table d'Hote. Bought bread and butter and made ourselves at home.' After a good night 'got on well with the portable bath. E. bought some sandwiches and cherries and we went off for a lovely walk through country lanes to W. Runton and Beeston. Chops and tea at lodgings. In evening read The Times, wh. arrived direct from office.' From these extracts we get a brief glimpse of Victorian summer holidays towards the end of the century. On Sunday they get 'a poor sermon' at the parish church, but capture more interest at the jetty, where they 'heard a rather striking discourse from an open air preacher on the conversion of St Paul,' who also knew the road to Damascus, and told 'some anecdotes of a revival in Ireland very well'. They walk to Overstrand, and Sidestrand, armed with 'a capital supply of sandwiches' from Burton's, and in the evening settle in with Forster's 'life', and 'an early dinner on a nice duck'. They visit Runton Gap – get up an hour earlier than they intended, so visit Norwich, having gained this advantage. Here they visit the Cathedral, 'first with party and guide, afts. leisurely with guidebook'. They lunch on steaks at the Temperance Hotel, visit St Peter's Mancroft, the Castle Keep, esp. the fine Norman Arch, and on to the Nun's Hospital; buy a basket and some books at Jarrold's, and then return by train to Cromer'.

He deals with Calculations and a table of Magnetic Charts from Admiralty Charts for N. Polar regions. Beeston Priory, and Sherringham claim their attention, as well as a thunderstorm, and they meet Dr Besant, 'who comes here regularly'. He also picked up at the P.O. 'Ridler's parcel of books' on 30 August, 'which had been there sometime', and they go on walking and picnicing – 'meat pie and buns', and 'dined on Irish Stew'. He sleeps very well, till he starts 'thinking in a confused way about Hill's problem'. He finds 'cornelians' on the beach. They visit an old college friend, Brummel, at Holt, who shows them Registers of 1588, referring to the Spanish Armada, as well as talk of Newton. A few days later they visit N. Walsham Church, returning to Cromer to dine on 'our own chicken'. Another day they visit Wroxham Broad, where they hire a boat (+ boatman) for 1s. an hour, and on their return to Cromer that day they go 'down to watch the incoming tide from the pier. It blew quite a gale and the sea was very fine.' Having been rained off a visit to Yarmouth, he later reads some of the proceedings of the British Association and 'did a little to put equations of motion of Hyperion disturbed by Titan into a simple form', and read Bradly on 'Job'; after which on the Sunday they get a sermon on 'what will you do in the swellings of Jordan? Jer.12^{5},' having listened to the Bishop of Norwich at Cromer the week before on 'walk in the spirit and ye shall not fulfil the lust of the flesh'. When they went to Church again at 3 p.m. on the Sunday of 'the swellings of Jordan' they were not so lucky as they 'had a "typical" sermon of "Joseph is a fruitful bough", from the curate – I suppose.' These are a few revelations of Victorian Sabbaths, and the food provided for the faithful. They chance to meet Mr and Mrs Stewart at the Post Office, and talk about the 'Government system of Education'. This is not such a remarkable turn of conversation for a summer's day in a Norfolk sea-side Post Office as might appear, as he had been reading Forster's 'Life'. It was W. E. Forster (1818–1886) who had revolutionised education organization in England in 1870, by his Education Act in Gladstone's first Ministry. Forster was of a Yorkshire Quaker family, and had married a sister of Matthew Arnold (who had spent some of his time as an Inspector of Schools – mainly of the Nonconformist Primary type). Forster was friendly with the reforming figures of his day: Cooper (1805–97) the Chartist, Owen (1771–1858) the socialist co-operative, F. D. Maurice (1805–1872) the Christian Socialist, – all contemporaries also of J. C. Adams. The 1870 Education Act had divided the whole of England and Wales into School Districts. School Boards were to be appointed in Districts where there were not sufficient church or other schools to provide Education for 5–12 year olds. Education was to be cheap but not free. One-third of expenses was to come from a Government grant, one-third from a local rate levied by School Board, one-third to come from School fees. It was not until 1876 that Education became compulsory, and not until 1891 that it became free. Church Schools got the Government grant, but nothing from the rates, but they could give religious instruction according to their denomination, but not the catechism or dogmatic teaching according to the Cowper-Temple amendment to the 1870 act. By 1889 Councils were allowed to spend money on technical education. It would be interesting to know what the conversation in the Cromer Post Office was all about on Tuesday 11 September 1888. Finally, on this last evening, after a last walk on the sands to Runton Gap, when 'I returned by cliffs and E. by sands', they are 'sorry to leave' Cromer next day for Cambridge.

They leave Cromer on the 11.10 train, stop off at Lynn, where they get 'a good lunch at Restaurant after seeing St Margaret's Church under guidance of the old clerk, and the Red Mount Chapel, and finally reach Cambridge by 4 'and were met by Fly'. On Sunday he is back to St Edward's and Mr Lias 'on raising of widow's son at Nain', and articles in the 'Quiver' on the Jewish Day of Atonement; and on 24 September has another sitting with Herkomer at Bushey.

He and Eliza stay at Bushey from Monday 24 September to Thursday 27 September while Herkomer works at the portrait, and Mrs Herkomer entertains Eliza. A new theatre is being built at the house but the portrait is not 'making satisfactory progress' until he made 'a complete change in the light', and soon 'a complete transformation took place in the picture'. Some music for Herkomer's play for his theatre is played while he paints. 'Mr and Mrs H. most kind and genial'. At intervals the Adams explore Bushey and Watford and get beautiful sunsets. His brother William with his daughter May, visit them at the Herkomers. On Thursday 27 September Herkomer 'worked till 11.30 and finished the portrait very satisfactorily. Wrote my name on Mrs H's fan, but very badly. We left by 12.30 train, drove at once to King's.'

By Sunday 30 September they lunch with Mrs Miller, as usual, and 'called on Mrs Jebb, who is being painted by Richmond and is pleased with him,' and on 1 October, he registers 'two more horrible murders' in London. In spite of all this he 'cleaned up some points about Newton's treatment of the solid of least resistance which had puzzled me'. On Saturday 13 October he and Eliza dined at Trinity Lodge. 'Took in Mrs Cayley and sat next the bride. The Master was v. polite as usual, and his bride looked very young.' On Sunday 14 October 'E. and I to Presbyterian. Good sermon though the voice was unpleasant. Text was "No man speaketh like this man".' On Saturday 20 November 'Mr Royston Piggott called with his wife, who is wonderfully recovered. He is full of ballooning.' In November Eliza attends Gosse's lecture on Pope. William asks for a loan of £100 and 'I sent him a cheque'. He also reads the Proceedings of the Parnell Commission, and talks about Krakatoa at Ray. On Sunday 11 November he hears a good sermon from the Bishop of North China – 'sensible and hopeful without being enthusiastic' – 'the maid is not dead but sleepeth'. On Monday 12 November Eliza attended a meeting at Newnham and got 'rather snubbed by Mrs Sidgwick and Miss Gladstone. Was lazy and read a good deal more of "Black Arrow".' By now R.L.S. has appeared on the reading list. On Friday 16 November he dined with The Family where J. J. Thomson – a new member – appeared and we had a full party. Was a slight winner at whist'. On Monday 19 November "A v. fine sunrise. In aft. we all (including B) drove into meeting at Clare Combination to hear Bishop of Falkland Isles'. By the end of November Tom's wife, Annie, returns from Canada with the baby, and he also writes to thank Maria for a lovely photo of Tonga, as well as attending the funeral of the Provost of King's, and dines with 'Family' at Latham's. 'One visitor joined us. The port was bad. Had some talk of Parnell's Trial.' On Thursday 6 December he goes to the Senate House 'after lunch with Master and saw Wm. take his D.Sc. On Tuesday 11 December 'In evening to immense party at Christ's Lodge to meet the contributors to Encyclopedia Britannica, after a dinner given to Robertson'. On Thursday 13 December 'Annie came when we had nearly given her up and brought little Tom, who is a very engaging child. He showed much intelligence over Lear's 'Book of Nonsense'. Called at Dr Donald's, where we found Wm. Dr D. gave us a satisfactory account of the child'. By the end of 1888 'Edwin Drood' is the novel in hand for his light reading. On Boxing Day, 'Had some poached eggs and cocoa in evening.' On 27 December, after a disturbed night, 'we were both late in getting up and had no prayers'. He attends the Johnian dinner and has a 'long talk about Tonga with Dr Moulton.' [Headmaster of Leys School.] Next term he is to lecture on the Lunar Theory, 'with special reference to Newton's treatment of the subject.' At sixty-nine years of age he is still mentally active.

John Couch Adams reached the age of seventy in June 1889; then the last two and a half years of his life showed a slowing down of energy; his two students came to the observatory for lectures not he to them; and a growing obsession with health develops. In the diaries there is constant reference to insomnia, and discomfort, with some pain.

His first serious illness began on 26 October 1889 at the Observatory, when he fainted at dinner in the presence of his wife and two brothers, George and William, who happened to be visiting for a few days. After vomiting he lay on the sofa for some time, but eventually was able to walk upstairs to bed that night. The next day however, according to Eliza's diary, while still in bed he had 'a stomach haemorrhage', and 'blood poured from his mouth' after what had looked like a convulsion. Dr Donald MacAlister attended him through this serious illness, which lasted into 1890. In early November 1889 he was still suffering 'a great deal of pain from which I could get no relief', according to his own diary, until Dr Donald MacAlister 'came out early' on Sunday 10 November, and 'was v. re-assuring about the pain and gave me some relief'. He then 'sat up while the new mattress was put on my bed. Afts. slept a good deal under the influence of morphia', so that by Monday morning (11 November) he 'awoke from pain and bright and made a good breakfast. In the afternoon Dr Bradbury and Dr Donald came and overhauled me and planned a dietary for future guidance. After they had gone, I sat up for fifty mins. and had my tea while up. Walked from my bed to the fireplace without help.' By 1890 he has recovered, and was at work again on Saturn's satellites; was reading J. M. Barrie's *Window in Thrums,* and writing to the booksellers, Quaritch, for Crabbe's *Tales of the Hall.* In March 1890 he visited 'The Family' at Newton's and 'was unlucky at cards'; he signed an address to Pasteur (1822–95) on 17 March 1889, who by that time had explored a whole world of preventative medicine, and antibiotics. On 29 March 'J. W. Clark sent me a proof of a sheet of Sedgwick's life, and my letter to S. on my engagement to E.' He was also walking 'with E. by the fields to Coton, and returned by windmill and the road. Afts. did some cutting of hedges.' On Saturday 29 March, the day before Palm Sunday, he was reading Thomas à Kempis. On Good Friday (28 March), 'After lunch E. and

I walked in to St Mary's, and the Master of Trinity preached to a nearly empty Church on "Looking unto Jesus".' By Wednesday 23 April 'Began to have regular prayers again'. He is also reading *Woolman's Journal*.* By 9 May (Friday) John Couch Adams 'went to the "Family" at Latham's, but was v. dull. Sat next Latham but was not conversible. Did not play whist. J. Prior was rather noisy. Left soon after half past ten.' Evelyn and Grace Darby arrive for May Week, and by 22 May (Thursday) 'was rather brighter to-day. In aft. went with B. and the girls to Mr Latham's Garden Party. I walked about with Evelyn. E. and I. had first gone to lunch at the Town Hall on the laying the Foundation Stone of the New Presbyterian Church.'

Soon after he was complaining of a cough and insomnia, and by 1891 was a frail old man taking at times to a Bath Chair, until on 29 October 1891 he finally took to his bed, after visiting Honey Hill with Mr Death on 28 October in a 'brutal E. wind', according to Eliza Adams's Diary. He had a sore throat, and was hoarse on the evening of 28 October and Dr Donald MacAlister was telegraphed, and advised inhaling terraline, but he took to his bed next day. On 3 November, Eliza Adams's birthday, her closest friend B. Lloyd died at the Observatory, after having been seriously ill with heart trouble since the end of October – and over many years before. A week after B's death Eliza records 'Hans had a v. poor night', but nevertheless she 'took him to get his hair cut, etc. home by one ¼. His niece Mary Roseveare called and also the Cayley's, Mrs Prothero, Lady Stokes, Mrs Marshall, Mrs Todhunter, Mrs Potts, Mrs Peile, Mrs Darwin, Miss Welsh.' By 12 November he returned to bed, and on

* Published 1775, edited with Whittier's Introduction 1821. Woolman was an American Quaker, essay (1720–72) about whom Charles Lamb wrote 'Get the writings of John Woolman by heart and love the early Quakers.' He preached against slavery and worked for African Slaves and Indians.

the same day 'an enlargement of prostate' was diagnosed, and relieved by Mr Wherry, and he was reported to be 'low and depressed'. On 31 December 1891 Eliza's diary reads 'I am reading Dante in his room; the only thing that interests me – and so ends this detestable year. The one gone who was the light of my life, and Hans going – soon there will be no one to love – and oh what a brute I shall become. Hans and B have been for *years* the two objects of my life.'

John Couch Adams never rallied and on 20 January 1892 Eliza wrote in her diary:

> He was quite unconscious. Nothing could rouse him. George and William Adams both came. Dr Donald came at three and a half and again at ten and three quarter pm. Hans never regained consciousness and at five mins past twelve he left this world and me with no one and nothing left to care for – without *even a sigh* to say he was going – happy for him. I sat all night in the drawing room.
>
> *21 January (Thurs.)*: Alone in the world now and for ever. The first dark day of Nothingness. I, Wm. and George went early to Cambridge on business. Nurse Malet left and was really touching in her farewell to me.
>
> *26 January (Tues.)*: Fine early and showers later. Mary Adams (Wm's. Wife) came about eleven a.m. and Maria Simon and her husband just before one. At 2.30 we went (he and I for the last time together) to Pembroke Chapel – a *very* nice service. Dear good Dr Donald stood by me and was a tower of strength for me.

John Couch Adams was buried in St Giles' Cemetery; and as his widow comments in her diary 'there we left His servant sleeping next to good Dr Luard. In the evening everyone but myself went to a beautiful memorial service at St John's. All came back here to meat tea.' (Eliza's own funeral service took place in St John's College Chapel in 1919.)

The next few months were spent by Eliza Adams trying to find a suitable house for herself in Cambridge, when she had to move from the Observatory. On 1 February 1892 the entry in her diary was 'Wm. left by 8.30 am train this morning. Gracie and Elizabeth went in a Fly to look at the late Dr Wright's house for me. Mrs Sidgwick paid me a very nice kind visit. Dr Donald tele. in the evening on *no* account to think of that house – drains *hopelessly* bad.' Dr Wright, no doubt, was of 'Anglo-Saxon' fame. No. 4 Brookside was eventually chosen, where Eliza Adams lived until 1919, when she died in Cambridge, as a result of the prevailing devastating flu epidemic of that year. She was buried with her busband in St Giles' Cemetery, on the Huntingdon Road, Cambridge. Many friends had visited her at 4 Brookside, where she had moved on 8 July 1892. A revealing entry in her diary on 10 July 1892 (Sunday) read 'fine but gloomy. Mrs Miller – Emma and Edith called – It is awfully lonely here. Dear M & J Kennedy came to see me.'

Perhaps it is more suitable to end this account of the end of John Couch Adams's life, not with the lonely widow, but with an entry from the Cambridge Philosophical Society:

> Mon Jan 25 1892 at 4.30 o'clock. Professor G. H. Darwin, President in the chair. The following resolutions were proposed by Prof. Cayley, seconded by Dr Lea and passed unanimously.
> 1. That the Cambridge Philosophical Society desires to express its sense of the great loss sustained by the University and the Society by the death of Professor Adams, who shed lustre on the Society by the brilliancy of his scientific career, and set an example to its members by the earnestness and simplicity of his life.

2. That the Society do now adjourn without transacting the business of the meeting as a mark of respect for the memory of Professor Adams, one of the benefactors of the Society.
3. That the president be instructed to convey the foregoing resolutions to Mrs Adams.

So the final act of an active and vigorous life ended in words – resolutions and an inscription on a granite Celtic cross in a Cambridge cemetery.

In a corner of St Giles' Cemetery, Cambridge, bordered by the wide acres of the University Farm, and the busy Huntingdon Road, the seven foot high granite cross records in stark simplicity two names, their dates and places of birth and death.

JOHN COUCH ADAMS AND ALSO HIS WIFE
ELIZA ADAMS

ON THE LEFT PLINTH	*ON THE RIGHT PLINTH*
BORN AT LIDCOT, CORNWALL	DIED AT THE OBSERVATORY
JUNE 5 1819	JAN 21st 1892
BORN IN DUBLIN	DIED AT CAMBRIDGE
NOV 3 1827	MARCH 4 1919

St Giles' Cemetery abounds in names of world-wide Fame, whose achievements were once well-known. John Couch Adams achieved some world-wide fame in his day, but much of the man is forgotten.

An attempt has been made in these pages to revive a little of his background and his times. The names of Marx and Freud have had more lasting repercussions on mankind than that of Adams, though who can decide whether the realm of mathematics is nearer to the truth for mankind than the realms of economics and psychology. There is little doubt that Neptune and the planets were in space long before the theories of Marx or Freud were mooted on earth, and no doubt the planets will remain, together with new theories of space and time, long after the realms of Marx and Freud have been superseded by other mortal ideas. Man will continue to analyse his ills and shortcomings, as he always has throughout the ages; possibly in the twenty-first century it will be the turn of the theologians and the scientists to dominate once more, as in the Copernican Age. Man's many needs remain; his saviours, or revealers and discoverers of truth, are few.

Postscript

As a postscript to the Neptune Controversy a letter from Dr Allen Chapman of the Centre for Medieval and Renaissance Studies, Oxford, dated 6 February 1981, refers to a lecture he gave on this subject in Cambridge on November 1979, which took an unusual line, which probably needs exploring further. His researches on Sir George Biddell Airy, the Astronomer Royal at the time of the Neptune controversy, led him to argue that:

> Airy, who failed to give credence to Adams' work until too late, was none the less acting correctly, within the basic presuppositions of the science of his time.
>
> Airy was a pragmatic, experimentally-minded scientist who believed that mathematics could only explain planetary phenomenon, *after* observation and measurement had been made. He regarded it as impossible to predict a planet's place – an unknown, such as Neptune – merely from the data obtained by observing others. Adams, I believe had a different concept of what mathematics could do; he saw it as a means of abstraction and truth in its own right. Airy instinctively thought of application, brilliant first Wrangler as he had been in his time. The whole of Airy's work at the Royal Observatory shows this

> cast of mind, inventions, engineering, mechanisation and data analysis. In a nutshell, I don't think that he appreciated what Adams was trying to do, or more exactly regarded it as futile. To launch a planetary search, moreover, would have taken thousands of observing hours, at a time when Airy's resources at Greenwich were already stretched to the limit.
>
> What is also important, is that Adams and Le Verrier were only right by good fortune. Though both of their calculations were basically the same, their respective 'predictions' applied to a part of Neptune's orbit where, quite by chance, their theory fitted. It is possible that had they been using the same approach in 1900, nothing would have been found.

Mathematicians and astronomers may wish to dispute this theory – yet another theory propounded in defence of Airy. 'But where is wisdom to be found, where is the source of understanding?' Job's question might be put equally well in relation to scientific truth.

Tributes to the memory of J. C. Adams from his contempories flowed in after his death at the Observatory in January 1892. Dr J. W. L. Glaisher, in his Memoir, published in *The Scientific Papers of John Couch Adams, M. A., ScD., D.C.L., LLD, F.R.S.*, published by the Cambridge University Press in 1896 (which also contains a Preface by William Grylls Adams, Sc.D., F.R.S.) refers to him 'an omnivorous reader, and his memory was exact and retentive, there were few subjects upon which he was not possessed of accurate information – Botany, Geology, History and Divinity, all had their share of his eager attention.' His enjoyment gained from novels, as well as from early printed books, is mentioned as well as his simple and unaffected manner. He was regarded as 'a delightful companion, always cheerful and genial, showing in society few traces of his really shy and retiring disposition. He was sympathetic and generous, and his moral and intellectual qualities were evenly balanced.'

At the conclusion of his address to commemorate the discovery of Neptune in 1946, Professor W. M. Smart adds further information and praise; and part of Sir Donald MacAlister's more contemporary tribute, concluded the words used, to praise this modest, yet illustrious scientist some years after his death. An international committee was formed to perpetuate his memory by means of a memorial in Westminster Abbey, and there, in 1895, close to the grave of Newton, was placed a medallion executed by A. B. Joy. Portraits of Adams are to be found in St. John's College and in Pembroke College – the first painted by Mogford during the Christmas vacation of 1850 – one at the request of the Master and Fellows, and the second by Herkomer in 1888 – and busts in St John's College, the Royal Astronomical Society's apartments (this bust, executed in his youth, was not regarded by Adams with very great approval) and in the library buildings at Launceston which were erected as a memorial to Adams by Passmore Edwards; a memorial tablet, with an inscription by Archbishop Benson, was placed in Truro Cathedral. The *Scientific Papers* in two large quarto volumes, edited by his brother, Professor W. G. Adams, and Professor R. A. Sampson, with a biographical memoir (already referred to) by Dr J. W. L. Glaisher, were published by the Cambridge University Press, the first volume in 1896 and the second in 1900. In a letter dated 16 February 1892, to the Cambridge Vice-Chancellor, Mrs Adams wrote: 'It is my wish to have a memorial of Professor Adams's connection with the Observatory and with the Science of Astronomy that shall be commemorative and lasting. I wish that the holder of this office to be known as the "John Couch Adams Astronomer".' This benefaction was gratefully accepted by the University and became available shortly after the First World War when the writer W. M. Smart had the honour of the first appointment. Professor W. M. Smart concludes his tribute as follows:

> It would be presumptuous of me to attempt to assess the character of one who was a shining example of a noble and simple Christian life, the kindest of friends, modest in all his intercourse and gently considerate to all with whom he came in contact. Let Sir Donald MacAlister's noble tribute terminate this brief biography of a great leader in Science.
>
> His earnest devotion to duty, his simplicity, his perfect selflessness, were to all who knew his life at Cambridge a perpetual lesson, more eloquent than speech. From the time of his first great discovery scientific honours were showered upon him, but they left him as they found him – modest, gentle and sincere. Controversies raged for a time around his name, national and scientific rivalries were stirred up concerning his work and its reception, but he took no part in them, and would generously have yielded to others' claims more than his greatest contemporaries would allow to be just. With a single mind for pure knowledge he pursued his studies, here bringing a whole chaos into cosmic order, there vindicating the supremacy of a natural law beyond the marginal limits of its operation; now tracing and abolishing errors that had crept into the calculations of the acknowledged masters of his craft, and now giving time and strength to resolving the self-made difficulties of a mere beginner, and all the time with little thought of winning recognition or applause.

Others referred to him as 'no bookworm – life interested him more than literature', and added 'Happily he never lost his sweetness of manner or his keen sense of humour; to the end he enjoyed a good joke. Like other great men he always kept the heart of his childhood; he loved children and took great delight in their games.' Another said 'he was not only a great mathematician and astronomer; he was also a great christian and a great churchman'. A woman who visited him in his old age wrote:

> What struck me most was the extraordinary humility, almost self-effacement, of this intellectual giant, who was regarded as the greatest astronomer England has had since Newton. He was singularly gentle, simple and most deeply religious. He seemed to project about him an atmosphere of purity, and elevated thought. There were family prayers every morning at the Observatory. It was Professor Adams who read the Bible, and said the prayers. His singularly reverential attitude, earnestness, and almost childlike belief were striking in those days of agnosticism and atheism.

Prior to the International Committee being formed with reference to the Westminster Abbey Memorial, a meeting had been held on 20 February 1892 at St John's College, Cambridge, with a view to placing a bust, or other memorials to his memory in Westminster Abbey. (A report of this meeting was published in a special issue of the *Cambridge University Reporter*, dated 10 March 1892.) Glaisher, in the Monthly Notices of the RAS (Vol. LIII No. 4, 1893) also refers to this meeting as bearing

> eloquent testimony to the admiration and affection in which he was held by his friends, and to the widespread wish throughout the country for such a memorial to one, who was not only a great but a good man. No suitable site for a bust could be found in the Abbey, but a medallion will be placed in an admirable position close to the grave

of Newton. This medallion is being executed by Mr Bruce Joy, who is also engaged upon a bust for presentation to St John's College.

It was not until 1895 that the medallion was unveiled in the Abbey – fifty years after Adams had first handed in his calculations on the planet Neptune. The scene of the unveiling of the Medallion in the Abbey was reported as follows:

A meeting was held yesterday, in connection with the memorial to the late Professor Adams, in the Jerusalem Chamber, Westminster Abbey, the Dean of Westminster in the Chair. After a few words from the Dean, the Duke of Devonshire said he wished to tender his sincere thanks to the Dean and Chapter for the way in which the request of Cambridge University had been met. In the opinion of men well competent to judge, Professor Adams was the greatest of the successors of the illustrious Newton, and it was his honour and his glory to give the most striking development of all those principles and theories which Isaac Newton discovered. In the name of the University of which he was Chancellor he thanked the Dean and Chapter for the honour they had conferred upon the late Professor. The Master of St John's College, Cambridge, referred to the studies of Adams, which gave to the world a fuller idea of the irregularities of the planet Uranus.

Lord Kelvin, Sir William Thomson LLD president of the Royal Society, who as a fellow undergraduate of Professor Adams knew him intimately, alluded to the pride the University felt in Adams even in his undergraduate days. He spoke of the discoveries of Adams as to the earth not being a correct time-keeper, and that the earth was becoming less and less rapid from century to century, and the consequent necessity of looking to the moon as a correct time-keeper.

Professor Stokes said he was there as one of the most intimate friends of Professor Adams, and so, perhaps, he might be allowed to say something of his character as a man. Every one who came to know him was charmed by his simplicity and perfect modesty, and it was not only as an astronomer that his medallion was worthy of a place in Westminster Abbey.

The Master of Pembroke College, Oxford, wished to testify to the interest the University took in the proceedings, and, as bearing out what Professor Stokes had said as to the modesty of Professor Adams, he referred to the abstaining of Adams from the controversy which raged and in which the French astronomer Le Verrier had played so prominent a part as to who was the first to discover the planet Neptune. Mr Courtney referred to the funeral of Newton 170 years ago. He said his remains had been carried to rest in Westminster Abbey by the most noble and distinguished people of the time. Yet he thought even Newton himself would be proud to have had placed near him the memorial to a man who had done so much to develop his discoveries.

Professor Jebb Litt D, Regius Professor Greek followed, and alluded to the modest attitude of Adams to Le Verrier; and after Sir John Gorst had briefly proposed a vote of thanks to the Dean of Westminster and to the Duke of Devonshire, and they had as briefly replied, the meeting adjourned to the Abbey, where the Duke of Devonshire unveiled a memorial tablet to the late Professor Adams. Those present included the Duchess of Devonshire, Lord Kelvin, Sir Robert Ball, Professor Adams of King's College, brother of the late Professor Adams, Professor Jebb, M.P. Professor Sir. G. G. Stokes Bart, LLD, M.P., Principal Fairbairn, Mr Courtney, M.P., Sir John Gorst, Q.C., M.P., and Professor Price (Master of Pembroke College Oxford). The tablet has been placed in the north aisle, close to the graves of Newton, Herschel, and Darwin. It is the work of Mr Bruce Joy, and bears the following inscription:-

JOHANNES COUCH ADAMS, Planetam Neptunum
Calculo Monstravit MDCCCXLV.

The following account by Nellie Adams, written to her husband, Fred Adams, the youngest son of J. C. Adams's brother Thomas, and an Anglican cleric in Shropshire who was unable to be present at Westminster Abbey on 9 May 1895 when the Medallion was unveiled before the distinguished gathering, throws a more human and family atmosphere on the occasion.

Dear Fred

We have come back from the Abbey very tired but all agreed that we have seen the most interesting ceremony we shall ever witness. I wish you had been there. Hilda had your Ticket [Hilda Adams Simon, aged 18 years, was Maria's second daughter and was J. C. Adams's great niece]. We arrived about 1.15 and went across Dean's Yard and were ushered into the Jerusalem Chamber. A small room, considering its reputation, so it seemed to me, with beautiful tapestry round two sides, old small paned windows, some old carving. A few people there already, Mary Roseveare [another niece of J. C. Adams] with Miss Kennedy, Millers, and Mrs Cayley. They had just come from Cambridge. We watched everybody arrive: Sir W. Ball, etc., Glaisher, D. MacAlister and bride, Mr Graham – all Cambridge nearly, room was full. The Dean in a purple skull cap, with chain and medallion round neck leading in the Duke and Duchess of Devonshire. Last of all Uncle Wm. [Adams] and Aunt Mary looking heated, as if they had just missed a train. The Dean spoke first rather feebly, but his speech and all that followed was a chorus of praise, then the Duke spoke on behalf of Cambridge. Then Lord Kelvin, we could tell he was a master before we knew who he was. He told us of what had been done by your uncle in correcting Laplace's calculations (?) of the accelerating of the moon's mean motion, which he said was even finer work than the Neptune discovery. (I may be talking nonsense but that is what I can remember). He said that the triad – Kepler, Newton, *Adams* were immortal. The Master of John's gave a sort of resumé of his whole work at Cambridge. Sir G. Stokes spoke on behalf of Pembroke and of their personal friendship – that they used to go for walking tours with their knapsacks; and that he never saw his temper ruffled. Master of Pembroke next spoke on behalf of Oxford. Sir John Gorst, Prof. Jebb, Clonary Courtney one of the nicest speeches as a Cornishman. Some others whose names we could not find out spoke and said that as a man he was also worthy a place in that sanctuary. The Master of John's said that the delay owing to the accident the artist met with had brought this year to the *jubilee* of the Neptune discovery 1845–1895. The Duke was very good in his closing remarks. Then after one hour or more of this we trooped off to the Abbey the Dean leading the way with the Duke & Duchess. The organ was playing for us and we went just near the organ where the medallion was veiled in red silk – north of the choir. The Dean said a collect, and the Duke pulled off the curtain. There was a big crowd, it was a very white round medallion and though there was a strong gaslight thrown on it hidden under curtains, we could not see it very well. At last I said to Maria 'I don't see the likeness yet,' and the gentleman in front of me who I am afraid was Bruce Joy, said with some feeling – 'You must go round in front to see it.' It is a very beautiful work, but we all here can't see it is a good likeness. It is like a youngish handsome man with beard and much hair – a little bit like Uncle Wm. There is no trace of the overhanging brow or the large head. We just spoke to Uncle and Aunt Wm.

> but we wanted to look longer at it, and by that time the crowd had melted away. Inscription round the head 'JOHANNES COUCH ADAMS NEPTUUM CALCULO MONSTRAVIT 1845.' The Daily News had the best account.

In a letter to Professor Smart, dated 28 November 1947 Mary Roseveare refers to the Abbey Ceremony with a little more 'awe and wonder' than her cousin-in-law Nellie Adams. She thanks Professor Smart for his Memoir to Adams and adds

> I did not know that J.C.A. wished for delay in the writing of his life by Dr MacAlister (as we remember him). My eldest brother [Harry], who died in 1941, was at St John's while he [Professor Smart] was still tutor there – so that we know something of his heavy responsibilities even before he went to Glasgow. I was in the Abbey just before the Royal Wedding to see the Battle of Britain window, and felt as I did in 1918, the wonder of its escape from destruction. I shall not forget being a guest in the Jerusalem Chamber when the Memorial was unveiled in 1895.

And so the Medallion and the Abbey still remain into the Nuclear Age; as no doubt Neptune, and the moon, and the tides, will remain through ages to come; though meridians may be more at the mercy of the future whims of men. 1989 revealed more of the face of Neptune at close quarters when Voyager II passed by en route for Mars, and though the Meridian line may be subject to further future calculations of men serving their present age (though this is thought to be highly unlikely among modern navigators), the basic fact of the existence of Neptune remains. Yet every discoverer of new truth, if he is worth his salt, would agree with Newton's conclusion – 'After all I have only been like a little child, picking up a few pebbles on the sea-shore of the great Ocean of Truth'. John Couch Adams was one of these children among humankind, and he would claim no more.

A Cornish man by birth and family background, much of his life was spent in Cambridge and its University. These were his earthly bases in Victorian England. Mentally, however, he frequently lived beyond this earth, at home with the elements of sky and sea, and moon and tides, 'Voyaging through strange seas of thought alone' (Wordsworth, *The Prelude*, Book III, line 61, referring to Newton). Though much concerned with human events on earth, nevertheless, he really resembled Wordsworth's skylark, the 'Ethereal Minstrel':

> Type of the wise, who soar, but never roam;
> True to the kindred points of Heaven and Home!

Appendix

Date	(Obs.– Hypoth. I.	Theory) Hypoth. II	Date	(Obs.– Hypoth. I.	Theory) Hypoth. II.
		Ancient Observations			
1712	+6.7	+6.3	1756	−4.0	−4.0
1715	−6.8	−6.6	1764	−5.1	−4.1
1750	−1.6	−2.6	1769	+0.6	+1.8
1753	+5.7	+5.2	1771	+11.8	+12.8
		Modern Observations			
1780	+0.27	+0.54	1810	+0.56	+0.61
1783	−0.23	−0.21	1813	−0.94	−1.00
1786	−0.96	−1.10	1816	−0.31	−0.46
1789	+1.82	+1.63	1819	−2.00	−2.19
1792	−0.91	−1.06	1822	+0.30	+0.14
1795	+0.09	+0.04	1825	+1.92	+1.87
1798	−0.99	−0.93	1828	+2.25	+2.35
1801	−0.04	+0.11	1831	−1.06	−0.82
1804	+1.76	+1.94	1834	−1.44	−1.17
1807	−0.21	−0.08	1837	−1.62	−1.53
1810	+0.56	+0.61	1840	+1.73	+1.31

To quote Adams: 'The greatest difference in the above table, viz. that for 1771, is deduced from a single observation, whereas the difference immediately preceding, which is deduced from the mean of several observations, is much smaller. The error of the tables for 1780 is found by interpolating between the errors given by the observations of 1781, 1782 and 1783, and those of 1769 and 1771. The differences between the results of the two hypotheses are exceedingly small till we come to the last years of the series, and become sensible precisely at the point where both sets of results begin to diverge from the observations; the errors corresponding to the second hypothesis being, however, uniformly smaller. The errors given by the *Greenwich Observations* of 1843 are very sensible, being for the first hypothesis +6".84, and for the second +5".50. By comparing these errors, it may be inferred that the agreement of theory and observation, would be rendered very close by assuming $\alpha/\alpha' = 0.57$, and the corresponding mean longitude on the 1st October, 1846, would be about 315° 20′, which I am inclined to think is not far from the truth. It is plain also that the eccentricity corresponding to this value of α/α' would be very small. In consequence of the divergence of the results of the two hypotheses, still later observations would be most valuable for correcting the distances, and I should feel exceedingly obliged if you would kindly communicate to me two normal places near the oppositions of 1844 and 1845.

'As Flamsteed's first observation of *Uranus* (in 1690) is a single one, and the interval between it and the rest is so large, I thought it unsafe to employ this observation in forming the equations of condition. On comparing it with the theory, I find the difference to be rather large, and greater for the second hypothesis than for the first, the errors being +44".5 and +50".0 respectively. If the error be supposed to change in proportion to the change of mean distance, its value corresponding to $\alpha/\alpha' = 0.57$, will be about +70", and the error in the time of transit will be between 4^s and 5^s. It would be desirable to ascertain whether Flamsteed's manuscripts throw any light on this point.

'The corrections of the tabular radius vector of *Uranus*, given by the theory for some late years, are as follows:-

Date	Hypoth.I.	Hypoth.II.
1834	+0.005051	+0.004923
1840	+0.007219	+0.006962
1846	+0.008676	+0.008250

'The correction for 1834 is very nearly the same as that which you have deduced from observation, in the *Astronomische Nachrichten*; but the increase in later years is more rapid than the observations appear to give it: the second hypothesis, however, still having the advantage.

'I am at present employed in discussing the errors in latitude, with the view of obtaining an approximate value of the inclination and position of the node of the new planet's orbit; but the perturbations in latitude are so very small that I am afraid the result will not have great weight. According to a rough calculation made some time since, the inclination appeared to be rather large, and the longitude of the ascending node to be about 300°; but I am now treating the subject much more completely, and hope to obtain the result in a few days.

'I have been thinking of drawing up a brief account of my investigation to present to the British Association.

Mr Main, acting for the Astronomer Royal in his absence, answered this letter as follows:

No. 21. The Rev. R. Main to J. C. Adams, Esq.

Royal Observatory, Greenwich, 1846, Sept. 5.

The Astronomer Royal is not at home, and he will be absent for some time; but it appears to me of so much importance that you should have immediately the normal errors of *Uranus* for 1844 and 1845, that I herewith send you the former (the volume for 1844 has been published for some time), and I shall probably be able to send you those for 1845 on Tuesday next, as I have given directions to have the computations finished immediately. If a place (geocentric) for the present year should be of value to you, I could probably send one in a few days.'

In acknowledging this letter, Mr Adams used the following expression:

No. 22. J. C. Adams, Esq. to the Rev. R. Main.

[Extract.]

St. John's College, Cambridge, 7th Sept. 1846.

I hope by to-morrow to have obtained approximate values of the inclination and longitude of the node.

On the same day Mr Main transmitted to Mr Adams the normal places for 1845, to which allusion was made in the letter of 5 September.

On 31 August, M. Le Verrier's second paper on the place of the disturbing planet (the third paper on the motion of *Uranus*) was communicated to the French Academy. I place the notice of this paper after those of 2 September, etc., because, in the usual course of transmission to this country, the number of the *Comptes Rendus* containing this paper would not arrive here, at the earliest, before the third or fourth week in September; and it does not appear that any earlier notice of its contents was received in England.

It is not my design here to give a complete analysis of this remarkable paper; but I may advert to some of its principal points. M. Le Verrier states that, considering the extreme difficulty of attempting to solve the problem in all its generality, and considering that the mean distance and the epoch of the disturbing planet were determined approximately by his former investigations, he adopted the corrections to these elements as two of the unknown quantities to be investigated. Besides these, there are the planet's mass, and two quantities from which the eccentricity and the longitude of perihelion may be inferred; making, in all, five unknown quantities depending solely on the orbit and mass of the disturbing planet. Then there are the possible corrections to the mean distance of *Uranus*, to its epoch of longitude, to its longitude of perihelion, and to its eccentricity; making, in all, nine unknown quantities. To obtain these, M. Le Verrier groups all the observations into thirty-three equations. He then explains the peculiar method by which he derives the values of the unknown quantities from these equations. The elements obtained are:

Semi-axis Major	36.154 (or $\alpha/\alpha' = 0.531$.)
Periodic Time	$217^{Y}.387$
Excentricity	0.10761
Longitude of Perihelion	284° 45′
Mean Longitude, 1 Jan. 1847	318 47
Mass 1/9300 = 0.0001075	
True Heliocentric Longitude 1 Jan. 1847	326° 32′
Distance from the Sun	33.06

It is interesting to compare these elements with those obtained by Mr Adams. The difference between each of these and the corresponding element obtained by Mr Adams in his second hypothesis, is, in every instance, of that kind which corresponds to the further change in the assumed mean distance recommended by Mr Adams. The agreement with observations does not appear to be better than that obtained from Mr Adams's elements, with the exception of Flamsteed's first observation of 1690, for which (contrary to Mr Adams's expectation) the discordance is considerably diminished.

M. Le Verrier then enters into a most ingenious computation of the limits between which the planet must be sought. The principle is this: assuming a time of revolution, all the other unknown quantities may be varied in such a manner, that though the observations will not be so well represented as before, yet the errors of observation will be tolerable. At last, on continuing the variation of elements, one error of observation will be intolerably great. Then, by varying the elements in another way, we may at length make another error of observation intolerably great; and so on. If we compute, for all these different varieties of elements, the place of the planet for 1847, its *locus* will evidently be a discontinuous curve or curvilinear polygon. If we do the same thing with different periodic times, we shall get different polygons; and the extreme periodic times that can be allowed will be indicated by the polygons becoming points. These extreme periodic times are 207 and 233 years. If now we draw one grand curve, circumscribing all the polygons, it is certain that the planet must be within that curve. In one direction, M. Le Verrier found no difficulty in assigning a limit; in the other he was obliged to restrict it, by assuming a limit to the eccentricity. Thus he found that the longitude of the planet was certainly not less than 321°, and not greater than 335° or 345°, according as we limit the eccentricity to 0.125 or 0.2. And if we adopt 0.125 as the limit, then the mass will be included between the limits 0.00007 and 0.00021; either of which exceeds that of *Uranus*. From this circumstance, combined with a probable hypothesis as to the density, M. Le Verrier concluded that the planet would have a visible disk, and sufficient light to make it conspicuous in ordinary telescopes.

M. Le Verrier then remarks, as one of the strong proofs of the correctness of the general theory, that the error of radius vector is explained as accurately as the error of longitude. And finally, he gives his opinion that the latitude of the disturbing planet must be small.

My analysis of this paper has necessarily been exceedingly imperfect, as regards the astronomical and mathematical parts of it; but I am sensible that, in regard to another part, it fails totally. I cannot attempt to convey to you the impression which was made on me by the author's undoubting confidence in the general truth of his theory, by the calmness and clearness with which he limited the field of observation, and by the firmness with which he proclaimed to observing astronomers, 'Look in the place which I have indicated, and you will see the planet well'. Since Copernicus* declared that, when means

* I borrow this history from Smith's *Optics*, sect. 1050. Since reading this Memoir, I have, however, been informed by Professor De Morgan, that the printed works of Copernicus do not at all support this history, and that Copernicus appears to have believed that the planets are self-luminous.

should be discovered for improving the vision, it would be found that *Venus* had phases like the moon, nothing (in my opinion) so bold, and so justifiably bold, has been uttered in astronomical prediction. It is here, if I mistake not, that we see a character far superior to that of the able, or enterprising, or industrious mathematician; it is here that we see the philosopher. The mathematical investigations will doubtless be published in detail; and they will, as mathematical studies, be highly instructive: but no details published after the planet's discovery can ever have for me the charm which I have found in this abstract which preceded the discovery.

I understand that M. Le Verrier communicated his principal conclusions to the astronomers of the Berlin Observatory on 23 September, and that, guided by them, and comparing their observations with a star-map, they found the planet on the same evening. And I am warranted by the verbal assurances of Professor Challis in stating that, having received the paper on 29 September, he was so much impressed with the sagacity and clearness of M. Le Verrier's limitations of the field of observation, that he instantly changed his plan of observing, and noted the planet, as an object having a visible disk, on the evening of the same day.

My account, as a documentary history, supported by letters written during the events, is properly terminated; but I think it advisable, for the sake of clearness, to annex extracts from a letter which I have received from Professor Challis since the beginning of October, when I returned to England.

No. 23. Professor Challis to G. B. Airy.

[Extract.]

Cambridge Observatory, October 12, 1846.

I had heard of the discovery [of the new planet] on October 1. I find that my observations would have shewn me the planet in the early part of August, if I had only discussed them. I commenced observing on July 29, attacking first of all, as it was prudent to do, the position which Mr. Adams's calculations assigned as the most probable place of the planet. On July 30, I adopted the method of observing which I spoke of to you. *****In this way I took all the stars to the 11th magnitude in a zone of 9′ in breadth, and was sure that none brighter than the 11th escaped me. My next observations were on August 4. On this day **** I took stars here and there in a zone of about 70′ in breadth, purposely selecting the brighter, as I intended to make them reference-points for the observations in zones of 9′ breadth. Among these stars was the planet. A comparison of this day's observations with a good star-map would most probably have detected it. On account of moonlight I did not observe again till August 12. On that day I went over again the zone of 9′ breadth which I examined on July 30. **** The space gone over on August 12, exceeded in length that of July 30, but included the whole of it. On comparing [at a later time] the observations of these two days, I found that the zone of July 30 contained *every* star in the corresponding portion of the zone of August 12, *except one star of the 8th magnitude*. This, according to the principle of search, which in the want of a good star-map I had adopted, must have been a planet. It had wandered into the latter zone in the interval between July 30 and August 12. By this statement you will see, that, after four days of observing, the planet was in my grasp, if only I had examined or mapped the observations. I delayed doing this, partly because I thought the probability of discovery was small till a much larger portion of the heavens was scrutinised, but chiefly because I was making a grand effort to reduce the vast number of comet observations which I have accumulated; and this occupied the whole of my time when I was not engaged in observing. I actually compared to a certain extent the observations of July 30 and August 12, soon after taking them, more for the sake of testing the two methods of observing adopted on those days than for any other purpose; and I stopped short within a very few stars of the planet. After August 12, I continued my observations with great diligence, recording the positions of, I believe, some thousands of stars: but I did not again fall in with the planet, as I took positions too early in right ascension. **** On Sept. 29, however, I saw, for the first time, Le Verrier's last results, and on the evening of that day I observed strictly according to his suggestions, and within the limits he recommended; and I was also on the look-out for a disk. Among 300 stars which I took that night, I singled out one, against which I directed my assistant to note 'seems to have a disk,' which proved to be the planet. I used on this, as on all other occasions, a power of 160. This was the third time I obtained an approximate place of the planet before I heard of its discovery.

This letter was written to me purely as a private communication, but I have received permission from Professor Challis to publish it with the rest.

Before terminating this account, I beg leave to present the following remarks:

First. It would not be just to institute a comparison between papers which at this time exist only in manuscript, and papers which have been printed by their authors; the latter being in all cases more complete and more elaborately worked out than the former.

Second. I trust that I am amply supported, by the documentary history which I have produced, in the view which I first took, namely, that the discovery of this new planet is the effect of a movement of the age. It is shewn, not merely by the circumstance that different mathematicians have simultaneously but independently been carrying on the same investigations, and that different astronomers, acting without concert, have at the same time been looking for the planet in the same part of the heavens; but also by the circumstance that the minds of these philosophers, and of the persons about them, had long been influenced by the knowledge of what had been done by others, and of what had yet been left untried; and that in all parts of the work the mathematician and the astronomer were supported by the exhortations and the sympathy of these whose opinions they valued most. I do not consider this as detracting in the smallest degree from the merits of the persons who have been actually engaged in these investigations.

Third. This history presents a remarkable instance of the importance, in doubtful cases, of using any received theory as far as it will go, even if that theory can claim no higher merit than that of being plausible. If the mathematicians whose labours I have described had not adopted Bode's law of distances (a law for which no physical theory of the rudest kind has ever been suggested), they would never have arrived at the elements of the orbit. At the same time, this assumption of the law is only an aid to calculation, and does not at all compel the computer to confine himself perpetually to the condition assigned by this law, as will have been remarked in the ultimate change of mean distance made by both the mathematicians, who have used Bode's law to give the first approximation to mean distance.

Fourth. The history of this discovery shews that, in certain cases, it is advantageous for the progress of science that the publication of theories, when so far matured as to leave no doubt of their general accuracy, should not be delayed till they are worked to the highest imaginable perfection. It appears to be quite within probability, that a publication of the elements obtained in October 1845 might have led to the discovery of the planet in November 1845.

I have now only to request the indulgence of my hearers for the apparently egoistical character of the account which I have here given; a character which it is extremely difficult to remove from a history that is almost strictly confined to transactions with which I have myself been concerned.

II. Account of Observations at the Cambridge Observatory for detecting the Planet exterior to *Uranus*. By Professor Challis.*

After some preliminary remarks, Professor Challis says – 'In September, 1845, Mr. Adams, Fellow of St. John's College, Cambridge, placed in my hands a paper containing the results of computations he had made to account for irregularities in the motion of *Uranus*, on the hypothesis of disturbances caused by a more distant planet. These results embraced the mass, mean distance, mean longitude at a given epoch, longitude of perihelion, and excentricity, of the orbit of the disturbing body, with its probable geocentric longitude at the end of September.' The time was unfavourable for looking after the planet, on account of its angular distance from opposition; but the main reason which deterred the Professor from the search was, that it was 'so novel a thing to undertake observations in reliance upon merely theoretical deductions, and that while much labour was certain, success appeared very doubtful.'†

The publication of M. Le Verrier's first memoir, and the close agreement of his deductions with those of Mr. Adams, together with the recommendation of the Astronomer Royal, induced Professor Challis to undertake the search of the predicted planet.‡ The observations were commenced 29 July 1846, three weeks before the expected opposition of the planet.

In suggesting a plan for finding the planet, Mr. Airy advised the close scrutiny of a zodiacal zone, having its centre in the ecliptic at 325° of longitude (the point marked out by Mr. Adams and M. Le Verrier) extending

* This paper was presented on the evening of 13 November 1846.

† M. Le Verrier published his first determination of the probable longitude of the exterior planet in June 1846, yet it does not appear that any systematic attempt was made elsewhere to detect it by observation for nearly four months, nor until he had published his second determination.

‡ Mr Airy's suggestion was made in a note dated 9 July 1846.

each way 15° of longitude and 5° of latitude. A power not lower than 120 was advised, with which a zone of 15′ would be well seen; also that the transits should be taken at one wire; and the north polar distances estimated in parts of intervals of 3′, marked by horizontal wires. It was calculated that 80 sweeps, each averaging one hour, repeated three times, would occupy about 300 hours of observing weather. In this mode of observing, the telescope is supposed to be 'fixed' during the whole, or at least during the consecutive portions of each sweep.

Professor Challis adopted this plan with the following modifications – he used a power of 166, having found experimentally this to be the power most comfortable for vision. This gave a field of 9′. The transits were taken at the edge of the micrometer, ascertained to be quite straight, and the declination from the teeth of the comb, noting by estimation the fourth or even tenth of a tooth, each tooth or revolution of the micrometer screw being equal to 17″. All stars were observed which were well visible in a moderately illuminated field, i.e. all stars to the 11th magnitude inclusive. But as such stars are very numerous, and frequently would have interfered with each other, another mode of observing was sometimes followed, which can only be successfully practised with an instrument of a similar construction with that employed.

The Northumberland equatoreal has, at its lower end, a complete hour circle, divided to 24 hours and moved uniformly by clockwork. This circle is wholly detached from the frame of the equatoreal, turning freely on the lower pivot, but the two can be attached at pleasure, when their relative positions can be altered at the will of the observer by a tangent screw, and measured by vernier readings or microscopes. If the hour circle and the clock be properly adjusted, the apparent right ascension of any object is read off at once upon the circle; and the error, either of the hour circle or clock, can be ascertained and eliminated by the observation of known stars. By the handle which governs the tangent screw, the observer is enabled to bring each star in order of right ascension to the meridian wire, and to give out the relative declination, magnitude, &c. to one assistant, who writes this down with the corresponding time by chronometer, while a second assistant reads off the apparent right ascension on the hour circle. The *known* stars thus observed furnish the correction of the declination wire, of the hour circle, and of the rate. Professor Challis distinguishes this from the ordinary method by the words 'telescope moving.'

On making trial of both methods, it was found that *more* stars were noted in the same *space*, but *fewer* stars in the same *time* when the observations were made 'telescope moving'. Hence, the Professor determined to go over the required space as carefully as possible, first in the ordinary method, and then a second time with the 'telescope moving'; if the planet were not then discovered by its motion, it would, most probably, be found among the stars of the second operation which were not found in the first.

'The only reason I can give', says Professor Challis, 'why I did not use hour XXI. of the Berlin star-maps is, that I was ignorant of its existence, as that hour was not to be found in the University Library, and consequently, as I believed, unpublished. If I had had this map a *first* sweep would have been unnecessary, I should have compared by field of view with the map at once.'

The first observations were made on 29 July, chiefly as a trial, but still carefully, and with the telescope turned to the most probable place of the expected planet. This place was taken from a paper by Mr. Adams, in which he had calculated the right ascension and declination of the planet for every twentieth day between 20 July and 8 October, and for every fifth degree of heliocentric longitude, from 315° to 335° inclusive. The places are deduced from theory, only assuming the planet to move in the ecliptic. The following is a specimen:

For 325° of Heliocentric Longitude.

Date	R.A. Planet	Decl. Planet
	h m	°
July 20	21 51.3	−13 0
Aug. 9	21 49.5	−13 9
29	21 47.9	−13 18
Sep. 18	21 46.5	−13 26
Oct. 8	21 45.1	−13 33

As the observations of 29 July, with the telescope fixed, did not include all the stars which it seemed desirable to observe, the following observations on 30 July were made 'telescope moving'. For the next set, 4 August, the telescope was moved in declination by the milled head of the differential sector through 70′ and all the *brighter* stars were *carefully* observed in declination as well as in right ascension, to obtain places for correcting the partial zones of 9′. These declinations are probably correct to about 3′.

Moonlight and bad weather stopped proceedings till 12 August. On this day the observations were made 'telescope fixed', and the zone of 30 July repeated, taking in a larger extent in right ascension. Soon after, and probably next day (but there is no note of the exact time), the two series of 30 July and 12 August were partly compared, and so far as the comparison extended, every star taken on 12 August *was included* in the series of 30 July, 'telescope moving'. Being thus practically convinced of the adequacy of the method, the Professor observed earlier in right ascension, so as to secure a scrutiny of the largest possible space this year. The observations were thus carried on for two months at every available opportunity, chiefly with the telescope fixed. On 29 September, Professor Challis first read M. Le Verrier's communication of 31 August, *in which he expressly recommends the endeavour to detect the planet by the appearance of a disk*. Mr. Adams had found the mass to be about three times that of *Uranus*, and had thence inferred that the brightness would not be below that of a star of the ninth magnitude.

He had mentioned this to Professor Challis, who preferred, nevertheless, proceeding on his original plan, as less liable to ultimate disappointment.

The general agreement of M. Le Verrier's results respecting the mass and orbit of the unseen planet with those of Mr. Adams, as it gave greater confidence, induced Professor Challis again to modify his mode of observing. The evening of 29 September was favourable, and a considerable breadth in declination was swept over within the limits of longitude pointed out by M. Le Verrier, paying particular attention to the physical appearance of the brighter stars, in accordance with his suggestion. Out of the 300 stars thus observed only one attracted particular attention, and to this the assistant was directed to add the note, 'It seems to have a disk.' The observations could not be repeated the next night, and on 1 October information arrived that Dr Galle had found the planet on 23 September. Up to this time Professor Challis had noted 3000 positions of stars.

It was then found that the star selected for its appearance on 29 September was the planet, thus verifying M. Le Verrier's remarkable prediction, 'that the planet would be discoverable in a good telescope by its physical appearance'.

On looking back at his earlier observations, Professor Challis had the vexation of finding that if he had compared *all* the observations of 30 July and 12 August, the planet would then have been detected. The stars up to No. 39 of the series of 12 August, 'telescope fixed', were all found in the series taken 30 July, 'telescope moving'. If this comparison had gone on a little further, it would have been found that No. 49 in the former series, *a star of the eighth magnitude, was wanting in the latter series.* From the principle of the search this must have been a planet. (It had, in fact, wandered into the zone between July 30 and August 12.) The comparison was really undertaken for another purpose, and probably was discontinued at that time after No. 39, as a cloud then interrupted the observations, after which a line of separation was drawn in the memorandum-book, and the clock was set going.

On a further examination, it was found that the planet was observed on 4 August, when, as has been mentioned above, brighter stars were taken to serve hereafter as points of reference.

Professor Challis remarks that his oversight was partly caused by the pressure of comet reductions, but principally from an impression that a long search was required to ensure success. He was also anxious to secure the greatest number of observations, and so postponed the comparison till he had greater leisure. He admits, moreover, that he had too little confidence in the indications of theory, though perhaps as much as others might have felt in similar circumstances, and with similar engagements.

The observations, when carefully reduced, give the following places of the planet with considerable certainty:

	Greenwich M.T.			Planet's R.A.			Planet's N.P.D.		
	h	m	s	h	m	s	°	′	″
Aug. 4	13	36	25	21	58	14.70	102	57	32.2
12	13	3	26	21	57	26.13	103	2	0.2

The errors of right ascension are probably not greater than those which belong to single transits. In north polar distance they are scarcely greater than 3" on 4 August and 4" on 12 August.

Employing the foregoing observations, and others which extend to 13 October, Mr. Adams finds the following elements of the planet's orbit:

Heliocentric Longitude	326° 39′ August 4, 1846.
Longitude of the Descending Node	309 43
Inclination of the Orbit	1 45
Distance of the Planet from the Sun	30.05

The other elements do not admit, as yet, of any accurate determination. In remarking on the advantages of the mode of observing 'telescope moving', Professor Challis says, 'in the course of these observations [he] could not help noticing that the stars are more generally disposed in groups than scattered equally over the celestial spaces'. To secure a complete survey of any portion of the heavens, this or some similar method seems almost necessary.

III. An Explanation of the observed Irregularities in the Motion of *Uranus*, on the Hypothesis of Disturbance caused by a more distant Planet; with a Determination of the Mass, Orbit, and Position of the disturbing Body. By J. C. Adams, Esq., M.A. F.R.A.S. Fellow of St. John's College, Cambridge.*

The author introduces the subject by remarking, that when Bouvard constructed his *Tables of Uranus* (those now commonly in use), he found it impossible to reconcile the ancient observations, made before the discovery of *Uranus* as a planet, with the modern observations, and that, therefore, in the formation of his tables, he relied solely upon the latter; but that, in a very few years, the still more modern observations exhibited a departure from the tables nearly as great as the ancient ones, and, therefore, there seemed now to be no sufficient reason for rejecting the ancient observations. The author then states, that his attention was first directed to this subject by reading the Report on the recent progress of astronomy made to the British Association, at their meeting in Oxford; and that in July, 1841, he formed a design of investigating the yet unaccounted-for motions of *Uranus*, in order to discover whether they could be explained by an exterior disturbing planet. In 1843 he made a first attempt, supposing the orbit of the disturbing planet to be a circle, and its mean distance twice that of *Uranus*. This investigation was founded

* This paper was presented to the Society on the evening of 13 November 1846.

exclusively on the modern observations, using, as far as 1821, the errors given in the equations of condition in Bouvard's tables, and for subsequent years the errors given in the *Astronomische Nachrichten*, and the Cambridge and Greenwich Observations. The result shewed a good general agreement of the observed disturbance with the disturbance which would be produced by the action of such a planet. In February, 1844, the author received from the Astronomer Royal the results of the general reduction of the Greenwich Planetary Observations.

In the meantime the Göttingen Academy had proposed for the subject of a prize the theory of *Uranus*, and though the author had no hope of being able to complete an essay in time to compete for the prize, he was stimulated by the publication of this proposal again to enter on the investigation. He now took into account the possible eccentricity of the disturbing planet to the first order, retaining the same assumption for mean distance. For the modern observations, the tabular errors used, as far as 1830, were exclusively those of the Greenwich Observations, except one by Bessel in 1823; after 1830, the Cambridge and Greenwich determinations and those in the *Astronomische Nachrichten*, were used. Those for the observations anterior to the discovery of the planet were taken from Bouvard.

Results for the elements of the disturbing planet were obtained, which were communicated, in September 1845, to Professor Challis, and in October 1845 (slightly altered) to the Astronomer Royal. Afterwards the investigation was repeated, supposing the mean distance diminished by about 1/30th part. The results were communicated to the Astronomer Royal in September 1846. They seemed to shew that the mean distance ought to be still further diminished.

The author after adverting to the dates of M. Le Verrier's papers, and showing that his own calculations were earlier in date, says,

'I mention these dates merely to shew that my results were arrived at independently and previously to the publication of M. Le Verrier, and not with the intention of interfering with his just claims to the honours of the discovery, for there is no doubt that his researches were first published to the world, and led to the actual discovery of the planet by Dr. Galle, so that the facts stated above cannot detract, in the slightest degree, from the credit due to M. Le Verrier.'

The investigations proceeded as follows: First, to diminish the number of equations, the results were collected in groups of three years each; and these were so arranged as to present results nearly independent of the error of radius vector. Thus twenty-one equations were obtained; and these, without extension for the two or three last years (which might subsequently have been included, but which would have disturbed the similarity of the calculations) were also used in the subsequent calculations for a different assumed mean distance. Then all the principal inequalities in the recognised theory of *Uranus* were verified, and corrections for an error pointed out by Bessel, and for the altered mass of Jupiter, were applied, as well as for some terms of the second order of masses pointed out by Hansen. Other inequalities of higher orders were neglected; as their effects may be represented, either by a very slow alteration of the epoch and mean motion, or by a very slow alteration of the perihelion and eccentricity; both which may, without sensible error, be assumed as constant, during the comparatively short period through which *Uranus* has been observed. The author then gives a table of the differences between the theoretical longitudes (thus corrected), and the observed longitudes; the maximum values are as follows:

In 1712	+ 92.7"	In 1804	+ 24.2"
1750	− 47.6	1840	− 66.6

These are then converted into corresponding errors of mean longitude, which the author finds more convenient.

Then, formulae are investigated for the effects of small corrections of the elements of the orbit of *Uranus*, and for the perturbations of mean longitude produced by a disturbing planet, expressed in the notation of Pontécoulant. These are expanded as far as the second order of eccentricities (involving only the first power of the eccentricity of the unknown planet), and the whole is reduced to numbers, with no symbols remaining, except for functions of the corrections of the elements of *Uranus*, and functions of the epoch, longitude of perihelion, eccentricity, and mass, of the disturbing planet. All the numerical quantities are computed on the supposition that the mean distance is double that of *Uranus*. Any one of these expressions, adapted to a certain time, being made equal to the error in the tabular place of *Uranus* for the same time, furnishes an equation of condition.

These equations of condition are treated by the method of least squares; and the successive steps of elimination are given. The author considers that the modern observations are scarcely sufficient to give the eccentricity and longitude of perihelion of the disturbing planet; but when the ancient observations (always omitting that of 1690, as uncertain) are combined, there are ample means for determining these elements. The equations, after the elimination had proceeded to a certain degree, were solved by successive substitution. The results thus obtained were:

Hypothesis I

Assumed Mean Distance = 2 × that of *Uranus*.

Mean Longitude, 6 October, 1846	325° 7′
Longitude of Perihelion	315 57
Eccentricity of the Orbit	0.16103
Mass (that of the Sun being 1)	0.0001656

Which were communicated to the Astronomer Royal in October, 1845.

The author then states that he made a second investigation, on the supposition that the mean distance of the disturbing planet = mean distance of *Uranus* $\times$ 1/0.515. The process, with very little difference, is the same as that for the former assumption of mean distance. The formulae, the equations, &c., are given in the same manner as before. The elements obtained thus are as follows:

Hypothesis II

Assumed mean distance = 1.942 $\times$ that of *Uranus*

Mean Longitude, 6 October, 1846	323° 2′
Longitude of Perihelion	299 11
Eccentricity of the Orbit	0.12 0615
Mass (that of the Sun being 1)	0.00 015003

The corrections to the elements of the orbit of *Uranus* are investigated on both hypotheses. Then on substituting the effects of the corrections, and the effects of the perturbations, the residual errors are obtained, of which the following are the maximum values:

	Hypoth. I.	Hypoth. II.
	"	"
1712	+6.7	+6.3
1715	−6.8	−6.6
1753	+5.7	+5.2
1764	−5.1	−4.1
1771	+11.8	+12.8 Single Observation

After this time, to the year 1840, the largest error is 2" .35.

After 1840, the errors increase on both hypotheses. They are,

	Hypoth. I.	Hypoth. II.
	"	"
1843	+7.11	+5.77
1844	+8.79	+7.05
1845	+12.40	+10.18

It appears from this extremely probable that the mean distance of the disturbing planet ought to be assumed nearly = mean distance of *Uranus* × 1/0.574.

The residual errors for the single observation of 1690 are,

Hypoth. I.	Hypoth. II.
$+ 44.''5$	$+ 50.''0$

It seems probable that these errors would be increased by still further diminishing the mean distance.

Expressions are then investigated for the correction of radius vector produced by the correction of elliptic elements, and by the effects of perturbation. The numerical values are as follows:

	Hypoth. I.	Hypoth. II.
1834	+0.00505	+0.00492
1840	+0.00722	+0.00696
1846	+0.00868	+0.00825

The author states that no satisfactory results could be found for the node and inclination of the planet's orbit, as deduced from the irregularities in the latitude of *Uranus*.

The author then remarks that the perturbations of *Saturn* produced by the new planet will be undoubtedly sensible; and he suggests that it would be interesting to examine anew the theory of *Saturn*, and to ascertain whether the masses of *Jupiter* and *Uranus* deduced from it are consistent with those obtained by other methods. He remarks that the published Reductions of the Greenwich Observations now make such an inquiry comparatively easy.

INDEX

The entry under John Couch Adams (JCA) is arranged under the following headings: Life; Career; Astronomy; Correspondence; Books and Papers

Index compiled by Jill Ford